The Art Collection of The First National Bank of Chicago

THE ART COLLECTION OF THE FIRST NATIONAL BANK OF CHICAGO

CHICAGO, ILLINOIS, 1974

On the front cover:
Richard LaBarre Goodwin
Hunting Cabin Door, ca. 1880–90

On the end-leaves:
Herbert Bayer
Chromatic A, Tapestry
in the employee's cafeteria.
Photograph by Hans Namuth

Library of Congress Catalogue Card Number 74-15702
Designed by Everett McNear
Composition, printing and binding
by R. R. Donnelley & Sons Company

INTRODUCTION

It may seem inappropriate for an aggressive, profit-oriented corporation to collect works of art. However, as we at The First National Bank of Chicago planned our new headquarters' building, we devoted much thought to making it pleasant and attractive as well as an efficient center for banking services. We sought to design a structure that would be both handsome and functional. We further sought to make its Plaza an ingratiating place for people, scaled to offset the sweep of our towering architecture.

Though acutely conscious of our own limitations, we also wanted something more. We wanted a distinguished collection of art. We even aspired to acquire representative works from a wide range of periods and places covering the centuries of man's development.

Doubtless, this would have proved little more than an exercise in corporate vanity if we had not been fortunate in finding a friend and advisor in Katharine Kuh. She has, we believe, not only achieved our purposes, but has given them meaning. Thanks to her, we have a collection of paintings, drawings, sculpture, tapestries and other art that is worthy of a small museum. It has been augmented with hundreds of original modern prints to provide interest in virtually every working area of our Bank and has been gradually extended with works of art for our dozens of offices across the country and around the world.

In presenting this catalogue, we seek only to encourage greater interest on the part of our employees and customers and perhaps to stimulate the interest of those few scholars who might care to know more about this corporate collection.

If our art is interesting to our customers and both pleasing and stimulating to our employees, we will feel that our commitment has been worthwhile.

Gaylord Freeman

FOREWORD

The art collection of The First National Bank of Chicago has been assembled to provide pleasure and enlightenment for visitors, clients and the several thousand men and women who work at the Bank and in its many branches and offices throughout the world. Because this is an international institution, the works acquired since the art program was started in 1968 have come from diverse places and periods, ranging from the sixth century B.C. until today, and including art from Asia, the Near East, Africa, Latin America, the South Seas, Australia, the Caribbean basin, Europe and America.

Our aim was to accumulate objects of high quality before their prices became unduly inflated. In a word, we have tried to buy fine works that were not necessarily in fashion. As a rule we have avoided thinking in corporate terms and have been suspicious of offers proposing "just the right thing for a bank." Whether in a bank, home or museum, art has the same mission—to enrich life and widen horizons.

Works at the First National have not been bought as investments, as decorations merely to humanize stark modern walls, nor as a thesis for any single movement or period. The main body of the collection is intended as a permanent extension of daily life.

Though the Bank has acquired some fifteen hundred original, signed and numbered prints, chiefly by twentieth-century artists from all parts of the world, these works are not included in the catalogue. On request, however, a check list is available. Famous as well as lesser-known printmakers are represented.

In branches and offices as widely separated as Tokyo and São Paulo, London and Singapore, Panama City and Athens, Beirut and Jakarta, the Bank has installed works of art with emphasis on objects indigenous to each country. As this catalogue goes to press the collection, the major part of it in Chicago, is still growing.

Research for the catalogue was shared by Judith Shamberg and Patricia Farmer, to both of whom I am indebted, and also to those many scholars who have generously supplied helpful opinions about individual works. Without the imaginative support of Gaylord Freeman, Chairman of the Bank's board of directors, neither the collection nor the catalogue would have been possible. Indeed, it is difficult to acknowledge adequately how much his exuberance, patience, unfailing cooperation and determination have contributed.

Katharine Kuh—June 1974

TABLE OF CONTENTS

Giuseppe Recco, *Still Life with Watermelons*, ca. 1670–75

Attributed to Frans Snyders, *Still Life with Hare, Dove and Artichokes*, ca. 1625

Louis Michel Van Loo, *Portrait of M. de la Croix van Crucius*, 1767

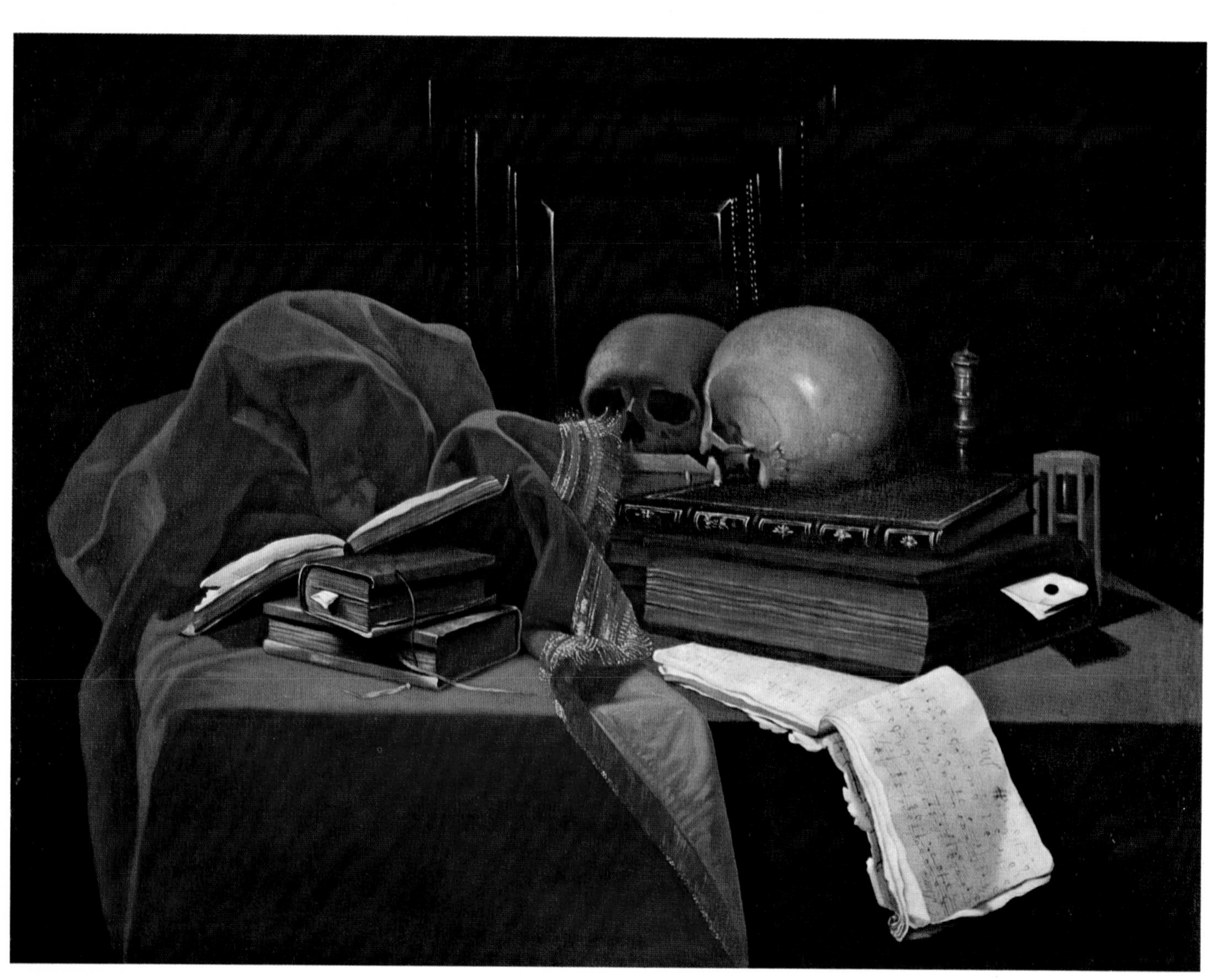

Madeleine de Boullogne, *Still Life*, 1674

Gilbert Stuart, *Colonel Hugh Nugent*, ca. 1787–1792

Eugène Isabey, *The Cove*, 1827

Thomas Lawrence, *Frederick, Duke of York*, 1815

Severin Roesen, *Still Life with Peaches*, after 1850

James B. Sullivan, *The Conflagration of 1871*

Alfred Stevens, *Sailing Vessels on a Choppy Sea*, ca. 1885

C.H. Chapin, *Lower Falls, Grand Canyon of the Yellowstone River*, 1886

Edward Lear, *Roman Campagna, Alexandrian Acqueduct*, 1864

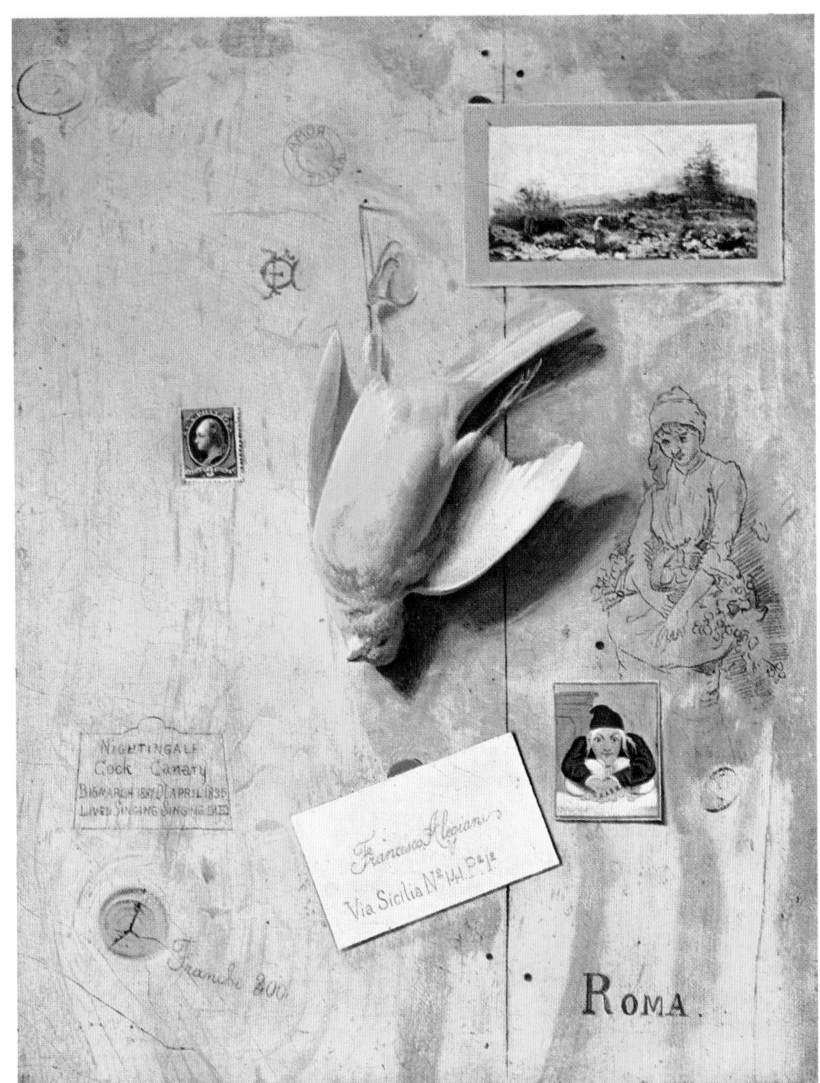

American/Anonymous, *Still Life with Canary*, ca. 1880

Richard LaBarre Goodwin,
Hunting Cabin Door, ca. 1880–90

Claude Raquet Hirst, *Still Life with Books and Vase*, late 19th c.

Richard Anuszkiewicz, *Volumes*, 1970

Michelangelo Pistoletto,
Self-Portrait with Plant, 1965

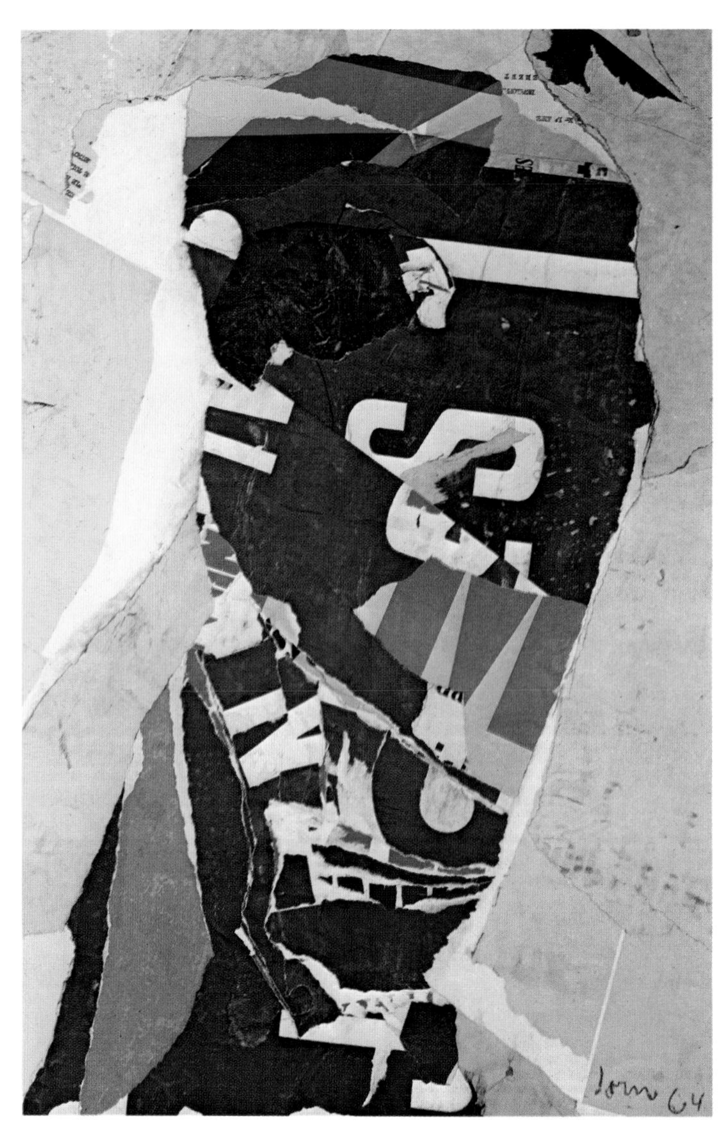

Asger Jorn, *Who is Hamlet?* 1964

Romare Bearden, *Interior with Profiles*, 1969

David Smith, *Circle: Black, White and Tan*, 1963

Jagannatha Pilgrim Painting, India, 19th c.

Buddhist Guardian Figure, Japan, 11th c.

Jambudvipa (*Tantric Cosmogram*), India, late 19th c.

PAINTINGS

Key to abbreviations for The First National Bank of Chicago's branches and offices

Abbreviations accompanying accession numbers indicate locations of works of art. Unless otherwise indicated, works are in Chicago.

Abb.	*Location*
AM	Amsterdam
AT	Athens
BE	Beirut
BS	Brussels
CA	Caracas
DS	Düsseldorf
FR	Frankfurt
GN	Geneva
GU	Guatemala City
JA	Jakarta
KI	Kingston, Jamaica
LA	Los Angeles
LN	London
MA	Madrid
MC	Mexico City
ML	Milan
NA	New York (6th Ave.)
NW	New York (Wall St.)
PN	Panama City
PR	Paris
RO	Rome
SP	São Paulo
SI	Singapore
TK	Tokyo

For measurements of paintings, drawings and hangings, height precedes width; for sculpture the order is height, width, depth.

Carl Abrahams

Born 1914 in St. Andrew, Jamaica. Abrahams attended Calabar College in Jamaica where he studied art. He began to work in 1938 as a free-lance cartoonist for newspapers and periodicals, but under the influence of the English artist, Augustus John, soon became one of the first native Jamaicans to paint professionally. Recently his work, *Quod Erat Demonstrandum*, a statement on the first moon landing, was accepted by the American government to hang in the Space Center at Houston. Abrahams' style is both naive and painterly.

WATERFALL
Oil on board, 21¾x27½ in., ca. 1970
No. KI1467

A partly imaginary scene where textural contrasts are basic to the composition.

John White Alexander

Born 1856 in Allegheny, Pennsylvania; died 1915 in New York. Alexander left Pittsburgh, his boyhood home, in 1874 for New York where he made illustrations in the art department of Harper and Brothers. Working there at the same time was the great cartoonist Thomas Nast. In 1877 Alexander studied art in Munich and later worked with a colony of American artists in northern Bavaria. In 1879 he accompanied the American painter Frank Duveneck to Italy where he stayed for two years. During this period he sent drawings back to *Harper's*. In Venice he met Whistler whose work subsequently influenced him. Dividing his time between Europe and America, Alexander exhibited in the Paris Salons and in 1894 became a member of the Société Nationale des Beaux-Arts. Chiefly a portrait painter, he made likenesses of such notables as Thomas Hardy, Walt Whitman, Robert Louis Stevenson, Mark Twain, Grover Cleveland and Oliver Wendell Holmes.

AUGUSTE RODIN
Oil on canvas, 66x48 in., 1899
No. 287

Alexander's portraits were often thinly painted on coarse canvas. He depended on a limited, almost monochromatic palette that showed the influence of Whistler. He was also impressed by Japanese woodcuts, popular in Paris at the end of the nineteenth century. In his portrait of Rodin the stark setting recalls the economy of Japanese design. Alexander exhibited the painting, done when the French sculptor was fifty-nine, at the Exposition Universelle in Paris during 1900 and received a gold medal for it. The canvas is signed and dated lower left, "J. W. Alexander/Paris '99."

J. Herbert Allchin

Dates of birth and death unknown. An English painter and engraver in the second half of the nineteenth century, Allchin was a member of the Royal Academy in London from 1877 to 1881. His still-life paintings are typical of Victorian taste.

WHO KILLED COCK ROBIN?
Watercolor, 4x7½ in., 1878
No. 252

Victorian sentiment was strong in this juxtaposition of blossoms and dead bird. Ruskin's plea for an "earnest study of nature" produced a flurry of animal compositions in nineteenth-century England. The trend laid a foundation for the later fancies of the English "fairy painters." It is with their work that Allchin's little picture shares a delicacy of detail and technique, though lacking the element of fantasy. The watercolor is signed and dated.

America/Anonymous

A RIVER VIEW
Oil on canvas, 30x40 in., ca. 1840
No. 542

This scene of a winding river bound by steep hills and giant elms reflects the romanticism of the Hudson River School. The concern for detail suggests that the artist has described a particular setting although perhaps one which he had not seen in person. The source might have been the pages of an illustrated travel book, popular in the nineteenth century with those who were curious about the world but could not afford to take trips. Because it resembles his style, the picture could well have been inspired by a work of William Henry Bartlett, an Englishman well known in America. He traveled twice to the United States to record its landmarks and scenery in carefully rendered watercolors, which were then engraved for books. It is unlikely this canvas is by Bartlett himself who seems to have remained a watercolorist always, but rather by an artist who admired Bartlett's composition and used it for guidance in his own painting.

John White Alexander
Auguste Rodin

Karel Appel, *Child*

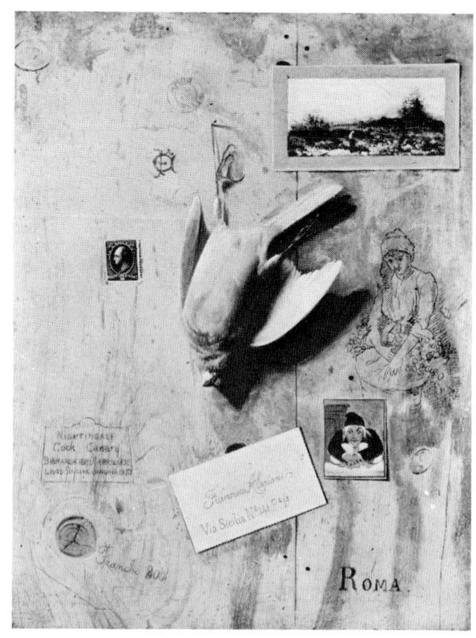

America/Anonymous

STILL LIFE WITH CANARY
Oil on canvas, 16x12¼ in., ca. 1880
No. 1839

At first glance this small composition seems to belong with American *trompe l'oeil* painting of the nineteenth century. However, closer observation has suggested that the picture might be the work of an Italian or Italian-American named Francesco Alegiani, since a letter addressed to that name is part of the composition. A monogram with the entwined letters "F" and "A" and the phrase "Franchi 200" also appears on the simulated wooden panel of the painting, yet no record of an artist named Alegiani has been found. The Italian ambience of the work is strengthened by the use of the word "Roma," written out in one place and used in the print of a postal stamp in another where it has been reversed to read "amor." This conundrum is not the only peculiarity of the picture; an epitaph for the dead bird reverses birth and death dates and proclaims he "Lived, Singing—Singing, Died." As this catalogue goes to press, Alfred V. Frankenstein writes he has just seen a *trompe l'oeil* still life painted in much the same style as the Bank's and formally signed Francesco Alegiani. The picture also includes references to Italy and presently belongs to Oscar Saltzer of Los Angeles.
See colorplate, page 19.

Karel Appel

Born 1921 in Amsterdam, Holland. Appel attended the Royal Academy of Art in Amsterdam during 1940–43, and in 1946 had his first one-man show at the Beerenhuis in Groningen, Holland. In Paris in 1948 he was a founder of COBRA, a group that reacted against the geometric abstraction so popular at the time. COBRA was an acronym for the native cities (Copenhagen, Brussels and Amsterdam) of the founding artists who included the Danish and Belgian painters Asger Jorn and Corneille. The group, which lasted three years, held several exhibitions and published a series of monographs on its members as well as a review, *Le Petit Cobra*. COBRA artists specialized in highly spontaneous, emotional expression. Color was hot and vibrant, line free and powerful. Appel's paintings and sculpture invariably include human or animal figures with emphasis on mask-like faces. The artist who lives in Auxerre, France has made several large murals for public buildings in Holland and one for UNESCO headquarters in Paris. His polychrome sculpture deals with the same exuberant images.

CHILD
Oil on paper, 25¾x19¾ in., 1953
No. PR1619

Using only three strong colors, black, red and yellow, Appel gave this early painting a pulsating vigor. The picture is signed and dated.

Alberto Arboleda

Born 1925 in Popayán, Colombia. Arboleda studied with the Spanish painter Jorge Oteiza. From 1945 to 1952 he was director of the Colombia School of Ceramics in Bogotá. In 1954 he went to Paris where he studied with the Italian painter, Gino Severini. Arboleda's work, recalling patterns found in Pre-Columbian art, is filled with a sense of ancient ritualistic mysteries. He lives in Rome.

WHITE BIRDS III
Paper collage, 27x33½ in., 1966
No. RO2037

Romare Bearden

Born 1914 in Charlotte, North Carolina. Bearden, who spent his youth in New York and Pittsburgh, graduated from New York University in 1925. The next year he studied with George Grosz at the Art Students League. Considered one of the outstanding black painters of America, he was intermittently engaged as a caseworker for the New York City Department of Social Services from 1938 to 1966 and also as a songwriter with several published works to his credit. The life of the southern Negro usually provided subject matter for him during the forties. During the 1960's Bearden turned to collages dealing with the daily life of American blacks, often in urban settings.

INTERIOR WITH PROFILES
Collage on composition board, 39¾x49⅞ in., 1969
No. 732

With juxtaposed areas of paper and paint, Bearden portrayed the household of a black family. Both structural and psychological break-up suggest the influence of Cubism. *See colorplate, page 27.*

OUR BACKYARD
Collage, 21x17 in., 1969
No. NA1582

A smaller collage that again depicts Negro life in America.

Stefan Bergmann

Born 1946 in Radeberg, Germany. From 1964 to 1971 Bergmann studied at the State Academy of Fine Arts in Karlsruhe where he was a student of Horst Antes. During his student years, he also traveled extensively in the Middle and Far East and practiced Za-Zen in a monastery in Kyoto. Receiving a scholarship from the German Academic Exchange Service, he studied at the Royal College of Art in London during 1969–70. His paintings usually consist of everyday objects with forms simplified and enlarged. The artist lives in the Black Forest.

THE 24TH OF FEBRUARY 1970 (OPUS 40)
Acrylic on canvas, 16x19¾ in., 1970
No. LN1484

This painting, entirely in tones of blue, was done in London. Its title refers to the date it was painted.

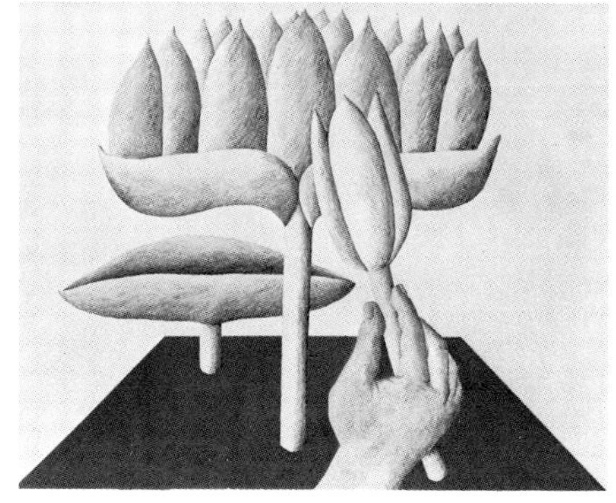

Albert Bierstadt, *Mountain Landscape*

Albert Bierstadt

Born 1830 in Solingen, Germany; died 1902 in New York. As a small child Bierstadt came with his family to New Bedford, Massachusetts. He returned to Germany in 1853 where he studied at the Düsseldorf Academy of Art, subsequently traveling—sketchbook in hand—along the Rhine, through the Alps and into Italy. Soon after returning to the United States in 1857 he accompanied a military expedition to the Pacific Coast. His first painting of the Rocky Mountains was exhibited in 1860, the same year he became a member of the National Academy. He specialized in dramatically lighted panoramic scenes of America's natural wonders. Bierstadt maintained his studio in New York but made numerous trips throughout the United States, also to Europe, Canada and the Bahamas.

MOUNTAIN LANDSCAPE
Oil on paper, 12¾x17⅝ in., date unknown
No. 553

Bierstadt's interest in grandiose aspects of nature is clear, even in this small painting; two fishermen are deliberately dwarfed by towering mountains. The picture was a sketch done on the spot for later transfer to canvas in the studio. The scenery may be either the White Mountains or the Rockies.

Robert Birmelin

Born 1933 in Newark, New Jersey. Birmelin received his BA in 1956 and his MFA in 1960 from the Yale School of Art and Architecture. He also studied at Cooper Union and the Skowhegan School of Painting and Sculpture. Later, in 1960 a Fulbright grant enabled him to work at the Slade School of Art in London. The following year he earned the *Prix de Rome* in Painting which took him to the American Academy in Rome where he remained until 1964. He is now a professor of fine arts at Queens College, New York. Birmelin magnifies the realism of nature.

SHORELINE I
Oil on canvas, 24x24 in., 1969
No. 660

SPLIT ROCKS I
Oil on canvas, 24x24 in., 1969
No. 661

Both paintings are characteristic of Birmelin's preoccupation with the texture of landscape, seen in close-up.

Robert G. Bobrowski

Born 1944 in Chicago. Following a period of study at Pratt Institute, Bobrowski completed his training at the School of the Art Institute of Chicago in 1968. He worked under a fellowship and financial grant from the Fine Arts Work Center in Provincetown, Massachusetts in 1969 and in 1970.

THIRD DUNE SERIES, No. 8
Gouache, 24x20 in., 1970
No. 832

A work done in Provincetown.

Varujan Boghosian

Born 1926 in New Britain, Connecticut. After serving in the United States Navy, Boghosian attended Central Connecticut Teachers College and the Vesper George School of Art in Boston. In 1953 he was awarded a Fulbright grant to paint in Italy. From 1956 to 1959 he worked under Josef Albers at Yale University where he earned both his BFA and MFA. Boghosian is known chiefly for his assemblages in which he employs a variety of objects—parts of weathered barn doors, antique dolls' heads, old leather, marbles, ping-pong balls. He combines seemingly incongruous yet evocative three-dimensional material. The starting point for much of his work is the Orpheus legend which he endows with multiple associations, both literary and visual. In 1948 after the war Boghosian became fascinated with the Orpheus myth through his own writing of poetry. He had specialized at this point in literature and only later turned to watercolor, sculpture and drawing. The medieval theme of the Knight, Death and the Devil also interests him. He is presently a professor of sculpture at Dartmouth College.

VARIATION ON HERMES
Watercolor, 30x22 in., 1969
No. NA1583

Boghosian thinks of Hermes as a carrier of souls and messages. This watercolor is the result of his early interest in poetry.

Madeleine de Boullogne

Born 1646 in Paris; died 1710 in Paris. A member of the important Boullogne family of painters, Madeleine specialized in still lifes. She studied with her father, Louis de Boullogne the Elder, who was Painter to the King and a founder of the French Academy where Madeleine and her sister Geneviève were admitted in 1669, the second and third women to achieve this distinction. Madeleine and other members of her family were employed by French royalty and by upper-class Parisians. From 1673 to 1675 she painted a series of eight still lifes representing trophies of war for the Salon of the Queen at Versailles, four of which still remain there.

STILL LIFE
Oil on canvas, 39½x52½ in., 1674
No. 307

This still life with skull, smoldering candle, musical score and other symbols of life's transience is a characteristic *vanitas* painting, a Catholic theme also popular in Calvinist Holland due to its moralizing attitude. Madeleine de Boullogne may have painted other similar still lifes, for we know that at the 1704 Salon she exhibited a canvas called *Pensée de Mort*. Along the spine of the book on which the skull rests, the picture is signed and dated, "MBO/LLO/GNE/1674."
For colorplate see page 12.

Claudio Bravo

Born 1936 in Valparaiso, Chile. Since 1961 Bravo has lived in Madrid. A meticulous technician, his favorite subject is the wrapped and tied paper parcel painted with *trompe l'oeil* proficiency. Bravo claims his art is influenced by experiences with hallucinatory drugs and also by the "luminous whites" of the seventeenth-century Spanish painter Zurbarán.

ONE POTATO TWO POTATOES
Ink, pencil and sepia, 24x18 in., 1970
No. LN1005

Bravo turns commonplace objects into precious icons. By isolating the potatoes and making them the entire focus of a composition, he gives them new importance.

Beatrix Briceño

Born 1911 in London. Beatrix Briceño moved to Panama where she became a naturalized citizen in 1943. In 1956, after raising her family, she began to study art at the University of Panama in Panama City where she now lives. Her compositions are related to magic realism.

HEADS
Oil on canvas, 45x29 in., 1970
No. PN1601

Wig dummies are clustered on the hooks of a wooden stand against a multicolored, striped background. The principal interest here is in pattern and color.

Alfred Thompson Bricher

Born 1837 in Portsmouth, New Hampshire; died 1908 in New Dorp, Staten Island. Chiefly a painter of marine landscapes, Bricher started on a commercial career in Boston before becoming a professional artist. He began to study art in 1851 and sketched along his native New England coast during leisure hours. In 1858 painting became his career. He moved to New York in 1868, joining the American Society of Painters in Watercolors in 1873. He was made an associate member of the National Academy in 1879. His seashore scenes were romantically conceived but naturalistic in style.

COAST OFF GRAND MANAN
Oil on canvas, 16x33 in., 1885
No. 1941

Here Bricher captures the mood of the coastal environment on the north Atlantic. Grand Manan is an island located at the entrance to the Bay of Fundy in New Brunswick, Canada. The artist painted Grand Manan subjects repeatedly, starting in 1876 and continuing for many years.

William Brooker

Born 1918 in Croydon, Surrey, England. The artist attended the Croyden School of Art until 1939. After serving in the second World War he resumed his art studied at the Chelsea School of Art during 1947–48. Brooker's paintings deal with themes drawn from daily life, with quiet interiors, gentle landscapes and familiar still lifes. The latter, usually painted in muted color, are influenced by Morandi. The artist lives in London.

STILL LIFE WITH TRESTLE TABLE
Oil on canvas, 39½x35 in., 1968
No. 248

Still lifes in tones of white and pearly grey have interested Brooker throughout his career. He returns repeatedly to the same objects, finding numerous compositional possibilities in their interrelationships.

Alfred Bricher, *Coast Off Grand Manan*

Daniel Brustlein, *Self-Portrait*

Bruno Bruni

Born 1935 in Gradara, Italy. From 1953 to 1959 Bruni was a student at the Pesaro Institute of Art, specializing in ceramics. He spent the following year on a scholarship at the state art school in Hamburg, and has remained in that city since completing his studies. Bruni, who began his career as an etcher and later turned to lithography, also paints. At times his graphic work shows the influence of twentieth-century German Expressionism. In 1967 Bruni's adopted city awarded him the Hamburg Lichtwark prize for art.

THE HATS
Oil on canvas, 58½ in. diameter, 1972
No. RO2023

This tondo, composed entirely of men's fedora hats, suggests the influence of pop art with its emphasis on everyday objects. However, the picture has been painted with a tenderness reminiscent of the Italian Renaissance and quite opposed to the billboard advertising techniques of Pop.

Daniel Brustlein

Born 1904 in Mulhouse, France. Brustlein graduated from the Geneva School of Fine Arts in 1925. For a time he was a well-known cartoonist whose work, under the name "Alain," often appeared in *The New Yorker*. In 1954 he decided to devote full time to painting, and since then has specialized in figure studies, frequently using his own image as a point of departure.

SELF-PORTRAIT
Oil on canvas, 32¼x26 in., ca. 1965–70
No. PR1620

Typical of Brustlein's many self-portraits, this likeness depends more on generalized characteristics than on realistic details.

Constancia Calderon

Born 1938 in Panama City. The artist graduated from Rosemont College in Pennsylvania and then pursued her studies in art for a year in Paris at the Académie Julian, the Académie de la Grand Chaumière and the Sorbonne. She now lives in Panama City.

HANDS
Tempera, 16½x23 in., 1971
No. PN1602

Eugenio Carmi

Born 1920 in Genoa, Italy. Carmi, who first specialized in chemistry, later turned to art. Not only a painter, he is also an advertising designer. As graphic consultant to various Italian industrial organizations he has become interested in mass produced art and has sponsored reasonably priced multiples sold by mail order. Carmi has also made fabric designs, maintaining that a work of art can be utilitarian as well as esthetically valid. Since the sixties, his paintings have dealt with only one theme—imaginary traffic signs. During 1965 he lectured at Southern Illinois University in Carbondale and at the University of Southern California. He lives in Genoa-Bocadasse, Italy.

IMAGINARY SIGN
Oil on canvas, 25⅝x25⅝ in., 1970
No. ML1526

Alfredo Castañeda, *A Telephone Call*

Laurent Casimir

Born 1924 in Haiti. At the age of twenty-two, Casimir moved to Port-au-Prince where he studied at the Centre d'Art and the School of Plastic Arts. He is known for his market scenes and crowds of people painted in the vigorous primary colors used by many of Haiti's artists.

UNTITLED
Oil on pressboard, 18x59 in., 1970
No. PN1603

Casimir crowds his space with rows of human figures, using them as devices in decorative patterns. The painting is signed.

Alfredo Castañeda

Born 1938 in Mexico City. Castañeda received his introduction to art through his uncle, artist Ignacio Iturbide. A graduate architect from the National University of Mexico, Castañeda, who lives in Mexico City, divides his time between architecture and painting. His meticulous drawings are influenced by Surrealism and emphasize the isolation of human beings.

A TELEPHONE CALL
Mixed media, 22½x30½ in., 1970
No. MC1668

Robert Cato

Born in New Orleans, Louisiana. Cato, a student of Moholy-Nagy, works in a nonobjective style. He is a graphic designer in New York where he lives.

UNTITLED
Red ink, 30x23½ in., 1968
No. 546

The artist has allowed an apparently accidental flow of ink to dictate the form of his painting.

Jean Charles Cazin

Born 1841 near Samer, France; died 1901 in Lavandou, France. Active as both painter and ceramicist, the artist studied at the School of Design in Paris with one of the most important teachers of the time, Lecoq de Boisbaudran. Cazin's work was first exhibited publicly at the Salon des Refusés of 1863, an exhibition that helped launch the impressionist movement. Rather than join the renegade painters, Cazin sought approval from the established Salon, exhibiting there throughout most of his life. For a brief period in 1870 he was the director of the Ecole des Beaux-Arts and the Musée des Beaux-Arts at Tours. In 1871, because of the Franco-Prussian War, he went to London where he taught drawing at the South Kensington Museum (now the Victoria and Albert Museum). In 1893 he visited New York during an exhibition of his paintings there. Like many of the Impressionists he used broad brush strokes and was interested in momentary effects of light. His work also showed the influence of the Barbizon painters.

HAGAR AND THE ANGEL
Oil on canvas, 27⅞x31⅞ in., ca. 1890
No. 767

Scenes from the story of Hagar occupied Cazin throughout most of his life, probably because they afforded an excellent opportunity for representations of landscape. Here, the angel reflected in a pool of water miraculously appears before Hagar who had feared that she and her son Ishmael would perish in the desert. Cazin's treatment of the subject is unusual. His figures seem more like French peasants than biblical characters. The pool is a Cazin invention which does not appear in traditional representations of the story. The painting is signed in the lower left corner.

LANDSCAPE
Oil on canvas, 58½x65½ in., ca. 1895
No. 772

As he grew older Cazin became interested in pure landscape without benefit of figure or narrative. Light, the dominant element in this picture, is dramatized by sun rays breaking through storm clouds. Rich color and heavy pigment characterize Cazin's later works, of which this spacious, freely painted landscape is an outstanding example. Signed in the lower right corner.

C. H. Chapin

Although the Bank's painting is signed "C. H. Chapin, N.Y." and dated 1886, no other biographical material clearly referring to this artist has been discovered. In an issue of *Harper's Weekly* for October, 1864 there are sketches of Union battle troops signed C. H. Chapin. More Civil War drawings appear in November issues of the same year bearing the name Charles H. Chapin. One other painting, entitled "Adirondack Mountains" but undated, also carries the signature C. H. Chapin. It belongs to the collection of the Butler Institute of American Art in Ohio. A history of the Brooklyn Art Association also mentions five paintings by a C. H. Chapin.

LOWER FALLS, GRAND CANYON OF THE YELLOWSTONE RIVER
Watercolor and tempera, 40x60 in., 1886
No. 565

This painting exemplifies the drama that marked American landscape painting in the nineteenth century. In an age of exploration and discovery on a new continent, the country's natural wonders provided an inexhaustible supply of subjects. Here, the artist has used sharp contrasts in light, texture and color to express the majesty of a mountainous and wild terrain. *For colorplate see page 19.*

Jean Charles Cazin, *Landscape*

Serge Chermayeff

Born in 1900 in Grozny, U.S.S.R. When only a child, Chermayeff began his studies in England at the Royal Drawing Society. The first World War interfered with his acceptance of an honors entrance to Cambridge University following graduation from Harrow in 1917. Important as a pioneer modern designer and architect, he came to Chicago in 1946 as director of the Illinois Institute of Design. He has taught at Brooklyn College, Harvard, Yale and the Massachusetts Institute of Technology. He is the author of many articles and several books on contemporary design and its influence on society. Chermayeff's work grows out of the uncluttered geometric principles associated with Bauhaus design. He eliminates details and stresses the tensions of carefully organized spatial relationships. The artist lives in Wellfleet, Massachusetts.

PROFILE
Collage, oil and crayon 14½x21½ in., 1962
No. 1878

A work inspired by a trip to Greece.

Eleanor Coen

Born 1916 in Normal, Illinois. Eleanor Coen has been both student and teacher at the School of the Art Institute of Chicago. While attending classes there she studied painting with Boris Anisfeld and lithography with Max Kahn. From 1939 to 1940 she was part of a Federal Art Project team in Chicago, and in 1942 won a travelling fellowship from the School of the Art Institute to study at the School of Fine Arts in San Miguel de Allende in Mexico, where she executed a fresco. Her subject is almost invariably landscape—both urban and rural. Her expressionistic style is invigorated by swift brush strokes and intricate overlays of color.

YELLOW SUN—LANDSCAPE
Oil on canvas, 24x30 in., 1972
No. 1293

Using a heavy impasto of green and yellow pigment, Coen has created a countryside in the glowing color typical of her rural paintings.

Edwaert Colyer

Born about 1640 in Breda, the Netherlands; died during first decade of eighteenth century probably in the Netherlands. Colyer, a member of the Painters' Guild in both Leyden and Haarlem, specialized in still lifes. When he worked in England during the 1690's he signed his canvases, "Edward Collier." He stressed *vanitas* compositions and also did several still lifes featuring letter racks which were forerunners of similar scenes by such American artists as Charles Willson Peale, Harnett and Peto.

THE CARTOGRAPHER'S TABLE
Oil on canvas, 19½x24 in., ca. 1695–99
No. 240

A casual glance reveals the instruments of a cartographer but after more careful study one is aware of another theme—the passage of time—a typical *vanitas* subject. The hourglass, the names of the months written around the globe and the book open to a page on "dialling" (a method for measuring time) are intended to remind the viewer of time's ephemeracy. The use of English for the months and for the text of the open book indicates that the Dutch artist probably painted this work in England where he lived during the 1690's. The painting was previously in the London collection of James Pope-Hennessy.

Edwaert Colyer, *The Cartographer's Table*

Thomas Couture,
Young Boy in White Collar

Edward Corbett

Born 1919 in Chicago; died 1971 in Provincetown, Massachusetts. The son of an army officer, Corbett spent his youth in the southwestern part of the United States, also in the Philippines and Ohio. He began his art studies at the California School of Fine Arts in San Francisco in 1937. After spending World War II in the army and merchant marine, and after a year in New York, he returned to California to teach at San Francisco State College and later at the California School of Fine Arts. He moved to Taos, New Mexico in 1951 and two years later took a teaching position at Mt. Holyoke College which he held for nine years. During this period he divided his summers between Taos and Provincetown and later had a home in Washington, D.C. Chiefly an abstract artist who painted poetic equivalents of landscapes inspired by the various environments in which he lived, Corbett was capable of producing the most subtle changes in color and surface.

TAOS NO. 3
Charcoal and pastel, 21x13½ in., 1951
No. 439

Though he often titled his paintings and drawings with the names of places where they were done, Corbett never tried to portray specific locations. In his Taos series he suggested an eroded mysterious landscape where the earth is cut by arid gullies.

Thomas Couture

Born 1815 in Senlis, France; died 1879 in Villiers-le-Bel, France. Couture came to Paris in 1826 where he first studied with the painter Baron Gros in 1830 and later with Paul Delaroche. While still in his early twenties he received the *Prix de Rome*, after which he began exhibiting at the Salon where in 1847 his canvas, *The Romans of the Decadence*, aroused special interest. Known as a teacher of importance, his most famous pupil was Manet. Students flocked to his studio, among them the Americans William Morris Hunt and John La Farge. Couture felt the processes of painting could be readily analyzed and taught, a theory which is expounded in his book, *Méthode et entretiens d'atelier*.

YOUNG BOY IN WHITE COLLAR
Oil on canvas, 17x14 in., date unknown
No. LN982

The young boy of the portrait is unknown. Here Couture followed his own advice: "Refrain," he wrote, "from giving theatrical poses to your portraits; be simple and modest in your poses as well as in your expressions . . ." This portrait, tenderly and freely painted, was probably done in the late 1850's or early 1860's. It is a far cry from the artificiality of Couture's official works. The artist's monogram appears in the lower right corner.

Keith Curwin

Born 1937 in Kingston, Jamaica. Curwin, who is now a commercial artist for an advertising agency in Kingston, took courses at the Jamaica School of Art and the Central School of Arts and Crafts in London. His style is based on the flat, broad surfaces often seen in commercial art.

NAHDJILA
Oil on canvas, 46⅞x15¼ in., 1971
No. KI1472

A portrait of a woman whose face and hands are done in black silhouette which contrasts with vivid areas of color in her clothing.

José Daroca

Born 1932 in Játiva, Spain. After finishing his studies in Spain, Daroca moved to Paris where he stayed for six years. Since 1967 he has been living in Valencia, Spain. His work consists entirely of landscapes: desolate beaches, sparsely-wooded rocky plains—in short, the countryside of Spain. Although he is not a "naive" painter, his work suggests an ingenuous simplicity.

SPRING
Gouache, 12½x19½ in., 1973
No. MA2045

DUNES
Gouache, 12½x19½ in., 1973
No. MA2046

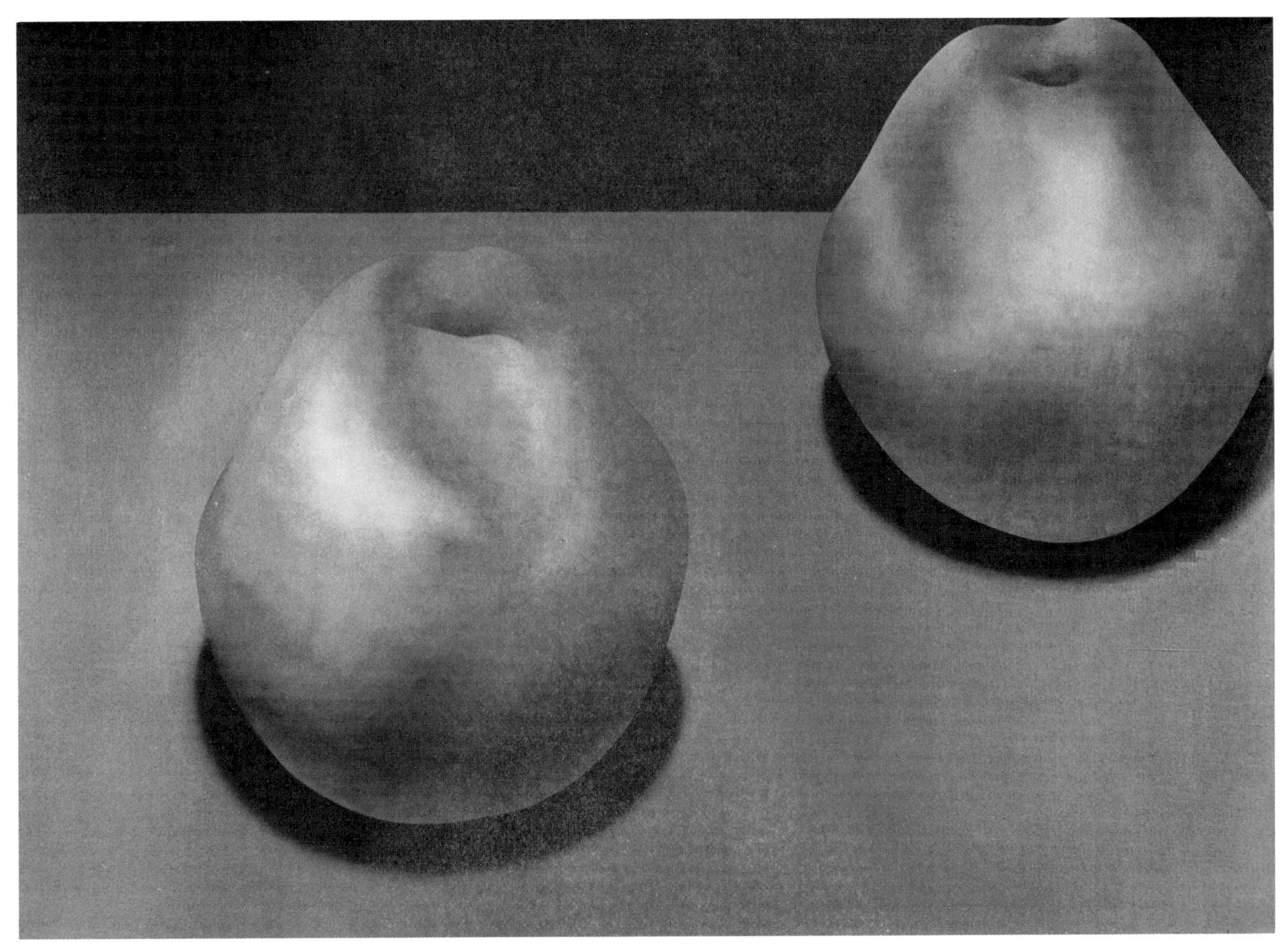

Peter Dechar, *Pears,* No. 226

Arthur B. Davies

Born 1862 in Utica, New York; died 1928 in Florence, Italy. In 1878 Davies' family moved to Chicago where he studied at the Academy of Design. After a brief stint in Mexico as a drafting engineer, he returned to Chicago in 1882 and enrolled at the School of the Art Institute. Four years later he left for New York where he worked at the Gotham Art Students School and at the Art Students League. Davies was one of "The Eight," a group of independent artists who were opposed to the doctrinaire conservatism of the National Academy. Other members were Robert Henri, William Glackens, George Luks, Everett Shinn, Ernest Lawson, John Sloan and Maurice Prendergast. Though Davies' style was quite different from that of the other members, he was sympathetic to nonacademic thinking and was one of the prime instigators of the Armory show. He traveled widely in Europe where he became familiar with the most important contemporary art movements. His own work, however, tended toward poetic stylizations with special emphasis on slender female nudes.

ITALIAN SEASCAPE
Watercolor, 10x21 in., ca. 1920–30
No. 168

WAVES
Watercolor, 10x25 in., ca. 1920–30
No. 169

Two lyrical landscapes where parallel bands of land, sea and sky stress light and space. Both drawings are signed in the lower right corners.

Evelyn De Morgan, *Medusa*

Peter Dechar

Born 1942 in New York. Dechar first studied electrical engineering but soon turned to art at Pratt Institute in 1960–61. He then spent two years working on a chartered schooner, returning to painting in 1963 in Cologne, Germany where he lived for a short time. Two years later he settled in New York. Dechar's favorite subject is the pear which he paints both at close range and from a distance, singly or in groups. His fruit at times recalls the curves of human bodies.

PEARS
Oil on canvas, 32x52 in., 1968
No. 224

PEARS
Oil on canvas, 52x72 in., 1968
No. 226

Evelyn De Morgan

Born 1855 in London; died 1919 in London. Mary Evelyn Pickering, the daughter of a distinguished English family, first studied under her uncle, R. Spencer Stanhope, who was a member of the Royal Academy. His influence remained a key factor in her artistic style, especially during the time she spent at his villa in Florence where she began to study early Renaissance painting, an interest basic to her own personal Pre-Raphaelite style. After she married William De Morgan, a skilled ceramicist in the Pre-Raphaelite movement and a well-known novelist, her career was overshadowed by his. When her husband died, he left two unfinished novels which Mrs. De Morgan successfully completed. The similarity of her drawings to those of Burne-Jones has often been noted.

MEDUSA
Pastel, 19½ in. diameter, 1855
No. LN2027

This tondo of Medusa is signed with a monogram and dated. The romantic, sensuous head is typical of the Pre-Raphaelite movement.

Erwin DeVries

Born 1929 in Surinam. DeVries, who lives in Amsterdam, began exhibiting in Jamaica in 1956. In 1971 he was commissioned by one of Jamaica's largest companies to create a nine-foot high bronze sculpture entitled "Hope," which now stands in the downtown area of Kingston. DeVries' work is nonobjective in style.

COMPOSITION
Watercolor, 14½x18¼ in., 1971
No. KI1473

WATERCOLOR NO. 23
Watercolor, 19x24 in., 1971
No. KI1474

Alfred DiLauro

Born 1930 in Philadelphia. DiLauro studied in Philadelphia at the Pennsylvania Academy of the Fine Arts. He now works in New York during the winter and spends his summers in Provincetown, Massachusetts. He is also a film maker.

THE ANGEL
Paper collage, 13½x16½ in., 1968
No. AT401

This large head, seen in profile, is based on the angel of the Annunciation in Jacopo da Pontormo's sixteenth-century fresco decoration of the Capponi Chapel in San Felicitá in Florence.

Roberto Donis

Born 1934 in San Luis Potosi, Mexico. Since graduating in 1952 from the Esmeralda School of Painting and Sculpture in Mexico City, Donis has worked in the United States and Europe. He is now the director of an art school in Oaxaca, Mexico. Formerly known as a figurative artist, he has turned in recent years to pure form and color.

PAINTING NO. 33
Ink and acrylic, 27¼x21½ in., 1965
No. MC1672

Gustave Doré

Born 1832 in Strasbourg, France; died 1883 in Paris. Known chiefly as an illustrator, Doré was also a figure and landscape painter who traveled widely in search of exotic subjects. Arriving in Paris at the age of fifteen with little formal training, he soon became associated with the journalist, caricaturist and publisher, Charles Philipon, and with the beginning of Philipon's new venture, *Le Journal pour rire*. A year later he exhibited two pen sketches at the Salon. His drawings for Balzac's *Contes Drôlatiques*, Shakespeare's *The Tempest*, Milton's *Paradise Lost* and *The Bible* are classic examples of book illustration.

MOUNTAIN LANDSCAPE
Oil on canvas, 29⅞x45¾ in., ca. 1876
No. 567

Always a romantic painter, Doré's dramatically lighted landscape probably reconstructed an Alpine scene. The painting is signed in the lower right.

Drago (Dragos Kalajic)

Born 1943 in Belgrade, Yugoslavia. Drago attended art school in his native Dalmatia but later moved to Rome where he now lives. The artist says he is trying to create an "image-myth" which will act as a symbolic mirror of the contradictions in present social and moral codes. He develops compartmentalized canvases where fantastic organic shapes are seen separately, sometimes covered in scratchy webs of graffiti.

COMPOSITION—GUNMAN WITHOUT HONOR
Mixed media on canvas, 39x64¼ in., 1964
No. RO2025

Gustave Doré, *Mountain Landscape*

Charles Loring Elliott

Born 1812 in Scipio, New York; died 1868 in Albany, New York. After first studying architectural drawing in Syracuse, Elliott worked with the painter John Quidor in New York. Despite Quidor's mocking idiosyncratic approach, Elliott preferred straight realistic portraiture. After leaving Quidor's studio, Elliott spent several years in upstate New York painting portraits. He returned to New York City around 1839. The two most important influences on his work were the paintings of Henry Inman, whom he met in 1844, and early photography. He tried to reproduce both the naturalism and the strong tonal effects of photography. After Inman's death in 1846, Elliott became the most sought after portrait painter in New York. His sitters included William Cullen Bryant, Henry Wadsworth Longfellow, Cyrus Hall McCormick and James Fenimore Cooper. Elliott became a member of the National Academy in 1847.

PORTRAIT OF JOHN BIGELOW
Oil on canvas, 44x34 in., 1853
No. 570

During his long life, Bigelow (1817–1911) was at various times author, editor, politician and diplomat. From 1848 to 1861 he, with William Cullen Bryant, was owner and editor of the *New York Evening Post*, a liberal newspaper which favored free trade and denounced slavery. After the paper was sold Bigelow became Consul General at Paris and in 1865, Minister to France. Ten years later he began one term as New York's Secretary of State. He was also the author of several books dealing with history and politics. Elliott's portrait of him was painted in 1853 when Bigelow was co-editor and co-owner of the *New York Evening Post;* a copy of the newspaper is seen on the table to the left of the sitter. The standard vocabulary of upper-class American portraiture, such as the classical column and red velvet drapery, is prominent, but it is the intelligent sincerity of Bigelow that predominates. The painting is signed at the lower right, "Elliott 1853."

England/Anonymous

SHELLS ON A MARBLE LEDGE
Watercolor, 10x12½ in., 19th c.
No. 253

A still life of shells reflects the Victorian craze for decorating mantels and whatnots with small objects and natural curiosities.

England/Anonymous

SNIPE
Watercolor, 6¾x9¾ in., ca. 1850
No. LN1491

SNIPE
Watercolor, 6¾x9¾ in., ca. 1850
No. LN1492

Two watercolors of birds by an anonymous artist are careful ornithological renderings that were popular in the nineteenth century. They probably were originally published as scientific studies.

Wojciech Fangor

Born 1922 in Warsaw, Poland. Fangor, who studied at the Academy of Fine Arts in Warsaw, held his first exhibition in that city in 1949. His earliest paintings followed the socialist realist tradition; he was also a poster and exhibition designer. During the mid-fifties Fangor turned to totally nonrepresentational painting. In 1962 he came to the United States where later he found work teaching at Fairleigh Dickinson University in New Jersey. Fangor's paintings are based on optical sensations created by the careful blending of abstract color areas. Gently undulating, curved forms or concentric circles from which light seems to radiate are his favorite motifs.

M 13
Oil on canvas, 56x56 in., 1968
No. 180

M 55
Oil on canvas, 36x36 in., 1969
No. 742

Luis Feito

Born 1929 in Madrid. Feito, who was a seminary student before studying art, received his degree from the San Fernando Academy of Art in Madrid in 1954. In the same year a grant, awarded jointly by the Spanish and French governments, provided him with the means to study painting in Paris. At first working in a geometric style, Feito soon abandoned it for a freer technique. Unrestricted forms in glowing color are spread on the canvas where certain areas are enriched by thickly applied pigment. In early works his paint is sometimes embellished by textural additives like sand and gravel. Feito makes his home in Paris.

UNTITLED
Gouache, 19½x25½ in., 1972
No. MA2042

Charles Loring Elliott, *Portrait of John Bigelow*

Jean Michel Folon

Born 1934 in Brussels, Belgium. Folon first studied architecture, then turned to painting. His early experiences were not wasted, however, since one of his chief themes concerns modern man's reaction to an urban, industrialized environment. The incongruities of contemporary life and the isolation of people in crowded centers interest him. His linear whimsical style sometimes suggests that of Paul Klee. Folon, who has made books and films, is also a photographer. His work has appeared on the covers of *The New Yorker* and *Time*. He lives in Burcy, France.

THE TAPE MEASURE
Watercolor, 20⅞x28¾ in., 1970
No. ML1528

A small figure, with tape measure for head, wanders in a barren landscape, suggesting the monotony of today's depersonalized life.

Jim Forsberg

Born 1919 in Sauk Center, Minnesota. Forsberg studied at the Minneapolis School of Art, the St. Paul School of Art, the Art Students League and the Hans Hofmann School of Art. His work reflects the influence of Hans Hofmann in its patches and splashes of spontaneous color. He lives and works in Provincetown, Massachusetts where he is the visual arts chairman of the Fine Arts Work Center.

UNTITLED
Oil on canvas, 39½x31½ in., 1969
No. 831

The perspective of a roadway disappearing between brilliantly colored trees has been tipped and flattened so that the spectator is made aware of the picture surface with its heavy impasto.

France/Anonymous

PAIR OF GAME BIRDS
Oil on canvas, 51x41 in., 18th c.
No. 281

The authorship of this painting is still unresolved. A former attribution to Jean-Baptiste Oudry (1686–1755), the French painter of animals and still life, has been rejected since the style is less deliberately dramatic than his. Although it is probably the work of an eighteenth-century French artist, it has also been thought to be seventeenth-century Dutch in origin. It is hoped that more information will emerge after the restoration of this canvas which is now in progress.

France/Anonymous, *Pair of Game Birds*

France/Anonymous

STILL LIFE
Oil on canvas, 17x13½ in., ca. 1860
No. 1931

The objects in this small still life lend themselves to the artist's interest in reflecting surfaces. An approximate date for the work can be assigned through identification of the ornate silver *sur-toute-la-table* with similar pieces first exhibited at the Great International Exposition of 1851 in London. The flagon to the left is fashioned in a shape that originated around 1840 while the vase lying on its side is decorated in a style which became prevalent around 1860.

Washington F. Friend

Born 1820 in Washington, D.C.; date and place of death unknown. Little is known about Friend's early life and schooling except that his parents were English and that he taught both music and drawing in Boston. After suffering heavy financial losses in a Boston theater fire, he organized a "floating museum" on the Wabash River late in the 1840's, but this venture failed and he turned again to painting. In 1849 Friend began a three-year tour of Canada and the United States with the idea of creating an enormous panoramic painting of the land's scenic wonders. The work was first unveiled in Quebec and then exhibited in other cities in Canada, the United States and England. Queen Victoria requested a showing of it at Buckingham Palace. Friend often accompanied his panoramic display by singing American and Canadian folk songs.

NIAGARA FALLS, SUMMER
Watercolor, 23x48 in., ca. 1850
No. LN768

This watercolor was undoubtedly made by Friend as a preparation for his panorama. Niagara Falls was a favorite subject for many nineteenth-century American landscapists, expecially the Hudson River School painters. To underline the grandeur of the scene, Friend included a few dwarfed human figures. The painting is signed in the lower left corner.

NIAGARA FALLS, AUTUMN
Watercolor, 23x48 in., ca. 1850
No. 1297

Niagara Falls, Autumn with its colorful foliage was probably also a study for Friend's panorama. The falls are here seen from a different view. A third watercolor of the falls in winter is known to be in another collection and undoubtedly a fourth of spring exists somewhere. If these were, indeed, studies for the panorama, they were extremely detailed and finished ones, though not surprising since a highly topographical style was popular at the time.

Walter Gay

Born 1856 in Hingham, Massachusetts; died 1937 in Paris. Gay went to Paris in 1876 to study painting and remained in Europe for the rest of his life. He worked under the conservative teacher, Léon Bonnat, and later became a member of the Society of Painters and Sculptors. Specializing in interiors, particularly those of eighteenth-century French buildings, Gay ignored the revolutionary artistic events which developed in Paris during the early twentieth century. The rooms in his compositions, though always devoid of figures, suggest a human presence.

INTERIOR OF THE MUSEE CARNAVALET
Oil on canvas, 22½x20 in., ca. 1895–1900
No. 438

This faithful impression of a gallery in the Carnavalet, a Paris museum devoted to French eighteenth-century culture, is characteristic of Gay. He painted many rooms in the same museum. Sunlight slants through the window, illuminating walls and objects. Though Gay was not an Impressionist, this scene is filled with atmospheric effects reminiscent of the discoveries of Monet and his followers.

Rodney Gladwell

Born 1928 in Didcot, Berks, England. Gladwell, who studied for a time at the Académie Colarossi in Paris, lives in London. His work shows the early influence of the School of Paris with a gradual progression toward abstraction.

RED AND BLUE
Gouache, 30x22 in., 1968
No. 1834

Washington Friend, *Niagara Falls, Summer*

Walter Gay, *Interior of the Musée Carnavalet*

Richard LaBarre Goodwin

Born 1840 in Albany, New York; died 1910 in Orange, New Jersey. Richard LaBarre Goodwin was the son of a minor but prolific painter, Edwin Wyburn Goodwin. After being wounded at the Battle of Bull Run, the son spent the next twenty-eight years as an itinerant painter in New York State, settling briefly in Syracuse during the 1880's. At the start of his nomadic life he chiefly painted portraits, but in the 1880's turned to still life, probably influenced by the popularity of William Harnett. After 1890 Goodwin lived in Washington, D.C., then in Chicago and later he traveled in the West. His favorite subject was the cabin door decorated with equipment for and booty from the hunt.

PAIR OF HANGING WOODCOCKS
Watercolor, 19x14½ in., ca. 1880–90
No. 170

Shadows cast by nail and woodcocks seem to project this scene directly into the viewer's vision. The watercolor, signed in the lower right, is typical of the artist's *trompe l'oeil* technique. An almost identical small oil painting of this composition belongs to the Graham Gallery, New York.

Goodwin, *Hunting Cabin Door*

HUNTING CABIN DOOR
Oil on canvas, 77x39¾ in., ca. 1890–95
No. 322

The weathered cabin door was Goodwin's specialty. Relying on a *trompe l'oeil* technique reminiscent of seventeenth-century European still-life painting, he even went so far in this case as to make his signature appear to be carved rather than painted. An ironic touch to the composition is the small envelope at the top right of the door addressed to "E.W. Goodwin/Albany" and postmarked "March 21, 1840." E.W. Goodwin was the artist's father, and the date of the postmark is five days before Richard LaBarre Goodwin's birth in Albany.
For colorplate see page 22.

Keeley Halswelle

Born 1832 in Richmond, Surrey, England; died 1891 in Paris. Born to a Scottish family living near London, Halswelle became an Associate of the Royal Scottish Academy in 1866. The artist spent time in Rome, Venice, Edinburgh and London. Early in his career he specialized in Italian peasant scenes, only later turning to the British and Scotch landscapes for which he is better known. He exhibited at the Royal Academy in London from 1862 to 1891. Halswelle was also an illustrator for publishers in London and Edinburgh. His work appeared in the *Illustrated London News* and in Robert Chamber's *Illustrated Shakespeare*.

A HEATH FIRE
Oil on canvas, 6¼x15½ in., ca. 1880–90
No. LN1486

A small loosely brushed sketch where fleeting aspects of fire and billowing smoke are dominant. The painting previously belonged to a descendant of the artist.

Patrick Heron

Born 1920 in Leeds, England. From 1937 to 1939 Heron studied at the Slade School in London. He is known not only as a painter but also as an art critic and polemicist. Since the publication of his book *The Changing Forms of Art* in 1955 he has devoted more time to painting. In recent years he has headed toward hard-edge abstractions based on interacting color areas. For him color is vitalized by the shapes it takes, the space it occupies and its relationship to neighboring colors. Titles of the Bank's two gouaches are indicative of the artist's approach. Heron has taught at the Central School of Arts and Crafts in London and now lives in St. Ives, Cornwall.

ULTRAMARINE INVADING CRIMSON WITH OPEN SCARLET DISC
Gouache, 23x30 in., 1968
No. 389

LEMON, RED AND ULTRAMARINE MOVING IN ORANGE
Gouache, 23x30 in., 1970
No. LN1487

Patrick Heron, *Lemon, Red and Ultramarine Moving in Orange*

Clinton Hill

Born 1922 in Payette, Idaho. Hill graduated from the University of Oregon and later attended the Brooklyn Museum Art School where he received a degree in 1950. He spent the following two years in Paris and Florence and in 1956 went to India on a Fulbright grant. Exposure to the metaphysical aspects of Hinduism may have inspired the mystical quality of his abstract color compositions. The two canvases in the Bank's collection are composed of tangential squares of atmospheric color. Hill, who occasionally assisted Mark Rothko, may have been influenced by this artist's use of luminous color.

UNTITLED
Acrylic on canvas, 23x80 in., 1968
No. 1289

Five equal rectangles alternate patterns of color gradations.

UNTITLED
Acrylic on fibreglas, 24x28 in., 1969
No. 676

Four squares compose a larger square. The colors are again graded in value with a resulting play of spatial planes.

Claude Raguet Hirst

Born 1855 in Cincinnati, Ohio; died 1942 in New York. Little is known about Hirst. Specializing in small still-life paintings, usually of books and pipes, she preferred watercolor, though occasionally painted in oils. The artist exhibited at the National Academy where she attained a certain degree of popularity. After William Harnett returned from Europe in 1886 the two painters worked in neighboring studios. There is no doubt that he strongly influenced her. Interest in Hirst's paintings diminished as the years went by, and she died in poverty during her late eighties.

STILL LIFE WITH BOOKS AND VASE
Watercolor, 7x10 in., late 19th c.
No. 521

Hirst delighted in painting the crisp pages and worn leather bindings of old books. She developed a skillful watercolor technique as evidenced by her faithful handling of textures. Here she includes a book open to an illustrated German love poem. The painting is signed in the lower right corner, "Claude Raguet Hirst/N.Y."
For colorplate see page 23.

Margo Hoff

Born 1916 in Tulsa, Oklahoma. A 1944 graduate of the School of the Art Institute of Chicago, the artist now lives in New York. She has traveled widely and taught at colleges and universities in the United States and in Lebanon and Uganda. Her work includes paintings, wall hangings, prints, costume designs, book illustrations and murals. Recently she has been engaged in collage, using cut and painted canvas combined with other media. Her collages are abstract, though in her paintings and prints, landscape and human figures are prominent.

BRIDGE TO ORANGE
Acrylic on canvas, 38x50 in., 1970
No. 391

NIGHT TOWN
Painted canvas collage, 51x79 in., 1971
No. NW1730

One of the first large canvas collages made by this artist, it foretells a whole series of similar architectural hangings.

Hon Chi-Fun

Born 1922 in Hong Kong. Entirely self-taught, Hon Chi-Fun gave up the business world to become a painter when he was thirty-five. His first works were watercolor landscapes; now he is known for his graphics and large paintings, both of which are, as a rule, abstract.

OURS TO GIVE
Acrylic on canvas, 52x52 in., 1969
No. NA1584

Using Chinese characters in an overall design, Hon Chi-Fun shows the influence of optically focused art in the interaction of his colors which seem to move in space.

Margo Hoff, *Bridge to Orange*

C.R. Hurlbut,
Still Life with Violin

C. R. Hurlbut

No biographical material on this artist has been found.

STILL LIFE WITH VIOLIN
Oil on canvas, 36x28 in., ca. 1892
No. 1877

The only known painting by Hurlbut, this still life follows the *trompe l'oeil* tradition popular among nineteenth-century American artists. William Harnett's canvas of 1886, "The Old Violin," from which a chromolithograph was made and widely circulated, undoubtedly inspired the composition. The painting is signed and dated in the lower right corner.

John O'Brien Inman

Born 1828 in New York; died 1896 in Fordham, New York. Inman's first teacher was his father, Henry, a well-known portrait painter. At the age of twenty-five the son became an exhibiting member of the American National Academy and while still young made his name as a portrait painter, mostly in the South and Southwest. In 1866 he went to Paris where he remained for twelve years, and then to Rome. At this time he turned to genre painting, specializing in seventeenth- and eighteenth-century subjects, some of which show the influence of Meissonier whom he admired. Inman also did still-life paintings of ornate objects combined with fruit and flowers. He returned to the United States in 1878 and settled in New York.

STILL LIFE
Oil on canvas, 11¾x19¾ in., 1851
No. 131

An early still life by Inman illustrates a mid-nineteenth-century taste for sentimental, historicizing accessories. A velvet curtain drawn halfway in the background is a device borrowed from baroque painting.

Eugène Isabey

Born 1803 in Paris; died 1886 in Montevrain, France. Son and student of the painter Jean Baptiste Isabey, Eugène originally planned to be a sailor, but early success at Salon exhibitions soon persuaded him to become an artist. His favorite subjects were marine scenes and landscapes. Very much a part of nineteenth-century French Romanticism, Isabey's coastal scenes suggest the stormy excitement of a seafaring life.

THE COVE
Oil on canvas, 28x38 in., 1827
No. 157

In this early painting by Isabey it is possible to assume some influence from the English landscapist, Richard Parkes Bonington, who worked in Paris until 1827, producing canvases with similar subject matter. Glowing with light, the scene predicts a later nineteenth-century interest in atmospheric painting. In the Salon of 1827 Isabey exhibited several views of Normandy; *The Cove*, which is signed and dated 1827, may have been inspired by the same scenery.
For colorplate see page 14.

Marvin Israel, *Untitled*

Marvin Israel

Born 1924 in Syracuse, New York. Israel studied at Syracuse University and received an MFA from Yale in 1955. He has worked as a commercial art director for the fashion magazines *Seventeen* and *Harper's Bazaar*. Since 1960 he has been living in New York and teaching at the Parsons School of Design, and has also taught at the Rhode Island School of Design and the School of Visual Arts. Israel's paintings, often menacing, deal with dreamlike anxieties.

THREE ADJOINING ROOMS
Oil on canvas, 60x47¾ in., 1969
No. 651

Israel's cold interiors and empty chairs have a symbolic unpleasantness, enhanced by the acidity of his color. In this painting the scattered clothing and shadow images on the wall of the next room indirectly reveal the nature of the subject.

UNTITLED
Acrylic and pastel on canvas, 41x29½ in., 1968
No. 288

Another interior that creates a sense of dislocation.

Norman Ives,
Red and Black Ink on Paper

Italy/Anonymous

A special type of religious folk art, votive painting offers thanks for the intercession of Heaven in preventing misfortune, no matter how minor. Found primarily in Catholic countries along the Mediterranean and in Latin America, *ex voto* paintings are produced by untrained village artisans. Usually they are technically crude but can often be perceptive human documents.

VOTIVE PANEL
Oil on wood, 20x11¾ in., 1892
No. AT740

This scene, in which a housemaid leaps from a balcony to save a small boy about to fall or jump from another balcony below, has been tilted on the picture surface in a manner that accentuates the impending danger. The Virgin appears at the top of the panel as an assurance of salvation. At the bottom of the picture an inscription reads, "Miracolosamente scampati tutte e due il 7-6-1892 Teresa Sciuto e Nicolino Balsamo—Acireale" (Both saved by a miracle on July 6, 1892—Teresa Sciuto and Nicolino Balsamo—Acireale [Sicily]).

VOTIVE PANEL
Oil on wood, 19½x10 in., 1878
No. AT741

The Virgin and Infant Jesus hover in the sky, prepared to prevent an accident from occurring to a construction worker. The inscription reads, "Miracolo concesso a Mucitta Carmelo il 16-Luglio-1878" (A miracle given to Mucitta Carmelo on July 16, 1878).

Norman Ives

Born 1923 in Colón, Panama. Ives, a graduate of Wesleyan University in 1950, earned both a BFA and MFA from the Yale School of Art and Architecture in 1951 and 1952 respectively. The following year he began teaching at Yale and has since been on the faculties of the Rhode Island School of Design, the Royal College of Art in London, and the University of Hawaii. He is presently living in Woodbridge, Connecticut. Working in collage, relief structures and graphics, he deals with forms derived from type faces. His compositions suggest the geometric jostle of newsprint, probably because he has worked as a typographical designer.

RED AND BLACK INK ON PAPER
Paper collage on masonite, 36x24 in.,
ca. 1965–70
No. 556

Robert Jacobsen

Born 1912 in Copenhagen, Denmark. With no formal art training but encouraged by a group of artist friends, Jacobsen made his first wood sculpture in 1930. After seeing an exhibition of German Expressionism in 1931, he was particularly interested in the work of Klee and Nolde. Five years later the Danish painter, Asger Jorn, advised Jacobsen to exhibit his sculpture. He moved to Paris in 1947, where his work became more abstract and was executed almost exclusively in metal. He was one of the first artists to use scrap iron. The hammered and welded surfaces of his sculpture are usually rough and occasionally polychromed.

PROJECT FOR SCULPTURE
Gouache, 25½x19½ in., ca. 1965–66
No. AT533

This gouache has an expressionistic freedom and freshness recalling the work of certain COBRA artists (see p. 39) who may have influenced Jacobsen.

Clarence Johns

Born during the nineteenth century in Pittsburgh; died 1925 in Pittsburgh. Johns studied art at the Pennsylvania Academy of the Fine Arts in Philadelphia and completed his training in Paris. He specialized in paintings of animals. For many years he served on the jury of the Carnegie International Exhibition in his native city.

STILL LIFE WITH TWO HANGING BIRDS
Oil on canvas, 27x22 in., 1866
No. 167

A familiar composition in nineteenth-century American still life, this painting of dead birds is signed and dated.

Asger Jorn

Born 1914 in Vejrum, Denmark; died 1973 in Copenhagen. Jorn studied in Paris with Fernand Léger in 1936. A year later he was working on a large-scale decoration for Corbusier's Pavilion des Temps Nouveaux at the Paris International Exposition. Returning to Denmark after World War II, he continued to paint despite the German occupation and was also responsible for secretly printing the German-banned publication, *Land og Folk*. A man of wide interests, Jorn was an archeologist, sociologist, and expert on Nordic folklore as well as a painter. In Paris after the war, he became one of the leaders of COBRA (see p. 39).

WHO IS HAMLET?
Collage, 23¾x16¼ in., 1964
No. PR1623

A subtle use of collage here shows a restraint unusual for Jorn. The title is enigmatic but obviously refers to the artist's Danish forebear. The work recalls both Cubism and Léger.
For colorplate see page 26.

Max Kahn

Born 1904 in Slonin, Russia. When he was three years old, Kahn's family moved to the town of Peoria, Illinois where he grew up. He graduated from Bradley College in Peoria and began his training as an artist in 1928 when he went to Paris for a year. There he studied sculpture with Bourdelle and Despiau and learned drawing from Friesz. On his return from Paris, Kahn enrolled at the School of the Art Institute of Chicago from which he graduated in 1934. He became a member of the faculty in 1944, having also taught at the John Herron Art Institute in Indianapolis and the School of Fine Arts at San Miguel de Allende in Mexico. Kahn's specialty is the color lithograph, a process which he himself carries out each step of the way. His compositions are large and tend toward Expressionism. He lives in Chicago.

MONUMENT TO THE SEA
Oil on canvas, 32x36 in., ca. 1967
No. 2035

Kapo (Mallica Reynolds)

Born 1911 in Byndoss, St. Catherine, Jamaica. Kapo, a self-taught artist, is also the founder and leader of a revivalist cult in Kingston where he lives. The primitive spiritualism of his work springs from religious involvement but also has deep roots in his African heritage. He is both painter and sculptor.

THE CONQUEROR
Oil on board, 32½x23 in., ca. 1960
No. KI1476

A self-portrait of the artist in his role as a religious leader.

Khoo Sui-Hoe

Born 1939 in Kedah, Malaysia. Khoo studied at the Nanyang Academy of Fine Arts, Singapore in 1959. Since then he has been working in Singapore. His paintings are strongly romantic and at times suggest surrealist influences.

TWO IN THE WIND
Oil and collage, 34½x34½ in., 1972
No. SI2011

William Kienbusch

Born 1914 in New York. Kienbusch received his BFA from Princeton in 1936 and later studied in New York at the Art Students League, in Paris at the Colarossi Academy and later with Abraham Rattner. Returning to New York in 1941 he worked under Stuart Davis at the New School for Social Research. Kienbusch's favorite theme is the landscape of New England, especially Maine. He never recreates a specific scene but combines various aspects of the American Northeast in loosely brushed lyrical compositions. He lives in New York.

PINES AFTER SNOWSTORM
Casein, 26½x39 in., 1956
No. NA1585

This picture is signed and dated in the lower right corner.

Edmund Kieselbach

Born 1935 in Brezno, Czechoslovakia. In 1957 Kieselbach moved to West Germany where he began his studies in art. He now lives in Bochum, Germany.

IRON PULSE
Watercolor, 23¼x30¼ in., 1965
No. BS1368

An imaginary animal, seen in semi-abstract form, is composed of nuts, gears and bolts all supported by a strange air machine. The work is signed and dated.

Jiri Kolar

Born 1914 in Protivin, Czechoslovakia. Kolar has been a cabinetmaker, poet and artist. Traditional classifications do not apply to his work. His collages are rarely two-dimensional arrangements; they are more often three-dimensional and intended to be seen from all sides. Although Kolar no longer writes poetry, he relies frequently on printed words as integral parts of his work. He has experimented with various techniques such as "rollages," papier-mâché and photoscreens.

THE ARCHANGEL AND TOBIAS
Rollage, 35½x23⅝ in., 1966
No. BS1369

Kolar invented a word, "rollage," for the technique used here. He cuts many reproductions of the same painting into strips and rearranges these into totally new and often perverse ensembles. In this case he has reassembled Antonio and Piero Pollaiuolo's *Tobias and the Angel* (Turin, Galeria Sabauda) to create a kaleidoscopic image.

BUTTERFLIES
Collage, 11½x9 in., 1967
No. NA1587

A decorative and painstakingly designed composition of multicolored bits of paper.

DREAMING CATHEDRAL
Photoscreen, 38½x23½ in., 1967
No. MC1674

RICIL'S DOUX
Photoscreen, 40x30 in., 1967
No. 1194

Kolar juxtaposes a face and a mascara kit in a puzzling surrealist effect.

WINDOW TO THE WORLD
Relief collage, 16x21 in., 1968
No. AT600

A collage of maps with a three-dimensional window superimposed.

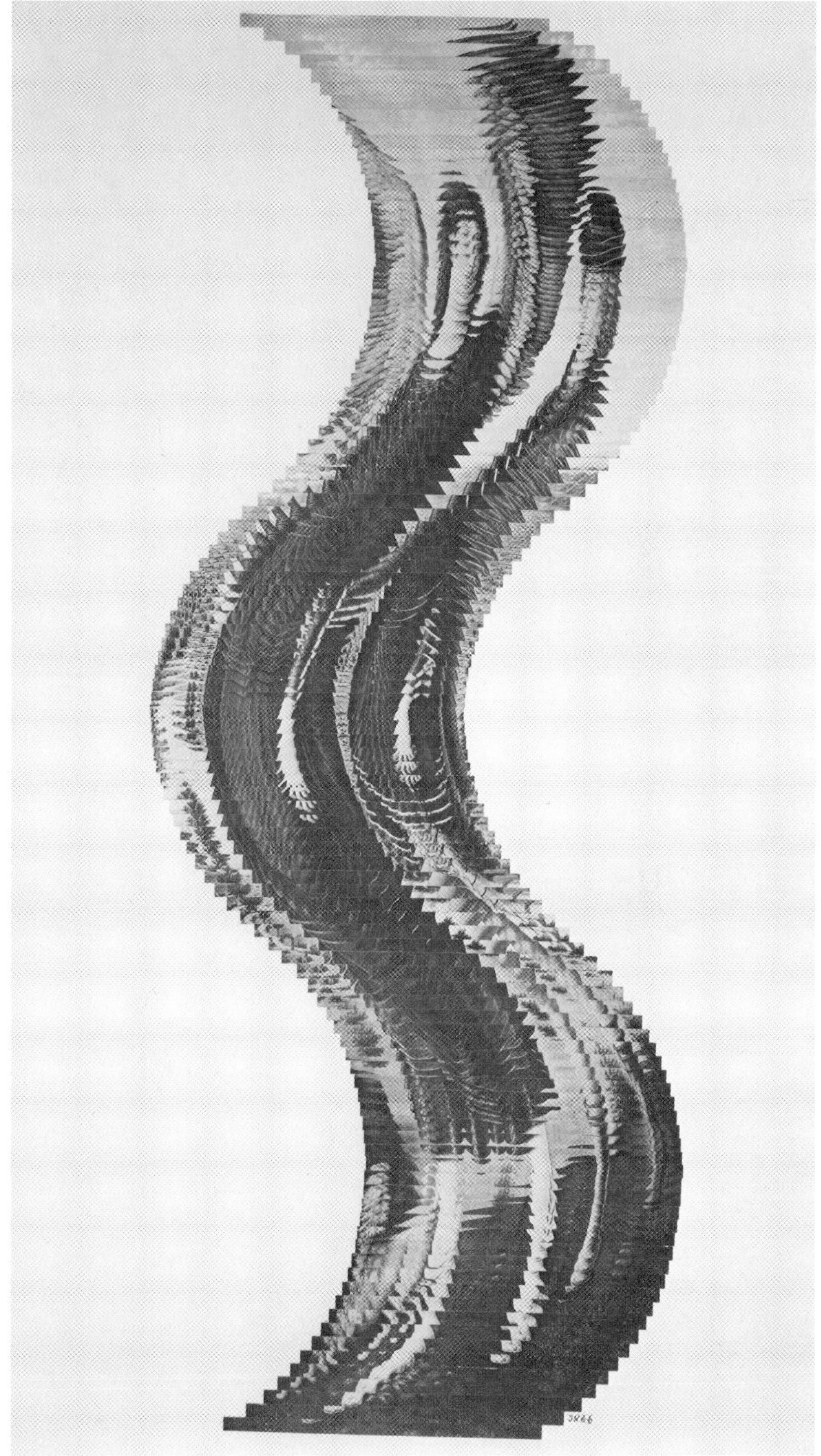

Jiri Kolar, *The Archangel and Tobias*

Nicos Kouroussis

Born 1937 in Mitsero, Cyprus. Kouroussis studied art in London from 1960 to 1964 at St. Martins and Hornsey Colleges of Art. He is considered one of the leading artists in Cyprus and brings a hard-edged abstract clarity to his themes, which are often erotic.

UNTITLED
Oil on canvas, 31¾x29½ in.
No. BE1347

Donald Kunkel

Born 1933 in New Jersey. Kunkel attended art classes at Boston University. He left before graduating to travel abroad and to study in Paris at the Sorbonne. Since 1960 he has been a permanent resident of Ibiza, one of the Balearic Islands off the coast of Spain. Kunkel's paintings, frequently done in monochromatic tones, are usually inspired by the anatomy of the human spine. His ambiguous variations on this theme take on either the look of landscape or pure abstraction.

UNTITLED
Gouache, 22¼x19¼ in., 1968
No. 1074

UNTITLED
Gouache, 20¼x18¼ in., 1968
No. 1075

Both works in the Bank's collection are related to the human spine.

Daniel Labra

Born 1956 in Madrid. The son of artist José Maria Labra, Daniel has been drawing since he was very young and has developed a special interest in color rhythms. He intends to enter the Madrid College of Art where he will also study music.

CHAS
Watercolor, 12½x18½ in., 1973
No. MA2028

CHAS
Watercolor, 12½x18½ in., 1973
No. MA2029

These two watercolors are abstract color studies.

Ellen Lanyon

Born 1926 in Chicago. A student of Max Kahn and Joseph Hirsch, Lanyon received her BFA from Roosevelt College in 1948 after also attending the School of the Art Institute of Chicago and the University of Chicago. In 1950 she earned a MFA from the State University of Iowa, and in 1951 spent a year in London at the Courtauld Institute under a Fulbright grant. She has taught painting and drawing at the School of the Art Institute of Chicago, Rockford College, the University of Illinois and the Saugatuck School of Art. Although her painting includes conventional subjects, much of it is concerned with fantasy and with the threat of slightly irrational delusions.

THE AFRICAN VIOLET
Watercolor, 15¼x22½ in., 1971
No. 1824

Berto Lardera

Born 1911 in La Spezia, Italy. Lardera, a self-taught sculptor, produced his first works in 1941–42 while living in Florence. Five years later he moved permanently to Paris. The artist's early pieces were figurative, but soon he turned to nonobjective sculpture executed in iron, copper, aluminum, Cor-ten and stainless steel. He sometimes combines several different metals in a single sculpture. Cutting his shapes irregularly from metal sheets, Lardera welds them into intersecting forms. He seldom works from models or sketches, but arranges his metal pieces spontaneously into final compositions.

UNTITLED
Paper collage, 40½x29 in., 1959
No. 286

With forms recalling his sculpture Lardera here created a two-dimensional abstract collage of colored paper and corrugated cardboard. The work is signed and dated in the lower right.

Thomas Lawrence

Born 1769 in Bristol, England; died 1830 in London. The son of an unsuccessful innkeeper, Lawrence spent his childhood in small English towns where he attended school for only two years, starting at the age of six. A precocious draftsman, he went to London in 1786 and as early as 1789 was already at work on portraits of the royal family. Shortly thereafter he was elected an Associate of the Royal Academy though he was two years younger than the mandatory age. In 1792 he was appointed Principal Painter in Ordinary to the King, a post made vacant by the death of Sir Joshusa Reynolds. Lawrence, who limited himself to portrait painting, followed the tradition of the English portrait school, though his later work became more innovative. One of his more important projects, commissioned by the Prince Regent (later George IV) for the Waterloo Chamber of Windsor Castle, was a series of some thirty full-length portraits of those European leaders who had played a significant role in the downfall of Napoleon. Not only did the artist paint the royalty and aristocracy of Britain but he also traveled to Europe for the Waterloo Chamber —to Aix-la-Chapelle in 1816 to do portraits of the Emperors of Russia and Austria, the King of Prussia and Prince Metternich; to Rome in 1819 for portraits of Pope Pius VII and Cardinal Gonsalvi; to Paris in 1825 for portraits of Charles X and the Dauphin. In 1820 he was elected President of the Royal Academy. Although he was one of the most successful painters in history, achieving every honor and demanding the highest prices from his sitters, he was constantly hounded by creditors. At his death the contents of his studio were sold to pay his debts. One of Lawrence's indulgences was a superb collection of Old Master drawings which unfortunately was dispersed when his property was sold.

FREDERICK, DUKE OF YORK
Oil on canvas, 36x27½ in., ca. 1815
No. 1204

Frederick Augustus (1763–1827), Duke of York and Albany, second son of George III and brother of George IV, made his career in the army where in 1794 he was Commander-in-Chief in Flanders. An able military administrator, he achieved the rank of Field Marshall. The association between Lawrence and the Duke of York began soon after the artist's arrival in London. The first royal likeness Lawrence exhibited at the Royal Academy was that of the Duke done in 1789. He painted the Duke at least ten times. The Bank's portrait, similar to a larger version made in 1816 for the Waterloo Chamber, may have been a preliminary painting for this full-length, more formally attired likeness. In the Bank's version, the Duke wearing a military coat with the Star of the Garter is revealed both as self-indulgent and overweight. The painting, executed somewhat broadly, foretells a later nineteenth-century freedom.
For colorplate see page 15.

Edward Lear

Born 1812 in the suburbs of London; died 1888 in San Remo, Italy. The son of a Danish stockbroker who lived in London, Lear with no formal training as an artist, supported himself from the age of fifteen by drawing. While staying at Knowsley Hall, the home of the Earl of Derby, he made drawings of animals in the menagerie there and also entertained the Earl's grandchildren with whimsical poems which later became Lear's first *Book of Nonsense*. Subsequently in Italy he decided to become a landscape artist. Though he traveled widely he made periodic visits to England, and on one occasion was invited to give drawing lessons to Queen Victoria. Lear's travels, which are reflected in his art, took him to Greece, Turkey, Albania, Malta, Egypt, the eastern Mediterranean countries and as far as India and Ceylon, but his home remained Italy. There, Englishmen often commissioned him to depict travel scenes.

ROMAN CAMPAGNA, ALEXANDRIAN AQUEDUCT
Oil on canvas, 26x54 in., 1864
No. 566

When traveling, Lear made on-the-spot drawings which he later turned into romantic topographical paintings. Usually he wrote notations on the drawings to help him remember details. His monogram appears in the lower left corner of this picture, and an inscription on the back reads, "Campagna of Rome Alexandrian Aqueduct/painted by me in 1864 for Sir Walter Jones, Bart./from my drawing made in 1860/Edward Lear." The artist painted the same subject, also in 1860, for another Englishman, Henry R. Stansfeld.
For colorplate see page 20.

Federico Madrazo y Kuntz,
Portrait of Mariano Fortuny

John Lee Joo For

Born 1929 in Penang, Malaysia. Lee Joo For is the first Malaysian artist to graduate from the Royal College of Art, London. He also studied at the Brighton College of Art and the Camberwell School of Art in England. He is now chairman of the art department at Malaysian Teachers' College in Johore Bahru. He has won the best playwright award of the Malaysian Drama Festival for three consecutive years and is a poet and novelist as well. His artistic style takes its form from primitive images combined with contemporary abstraction.

BEGINNING OF LIFE
Oil on canvas, 31½x54 in., 1971
No. SI1924

Luis Lopez-Loza

Born 1939 in Guadalajara, Mexico. Lopez-Loza attended the Esmeralda School of Painting and Sculpture in Mexico City as well as the school of engraving and applied arts at the National University of Mexico. In 1963 he studied at the Graphic Arts Center of Pratt Institute in New York. Lopez-Loza produces large colorful paintings composed of rhythmically repeated abstract motifs taken from geometry, zoology and botany. He has been commissioned to do large murals for public buildings both in Mexico and abroad. In 1972 he received a John Simon Guggenheim fellowship to work in New York where he now lives.

ARCHITECTURAL DISTORTIONS
Oil on canvas, 39x31¼ in., 1969
No. MC1675

Federico Madrazo y Kuntz

Born 1815 in Rome; died 1894 in Madrid. The son of José Madrazo, a well-known neoclassical painter, Federico came to Spain at the age of four when his family moved from Italy. At fourteen he entered the Academy of Painting in Madrid while also working with his father in the family studio. In 1832 the seventeen-year-old artist went to Paris to study with Ingres, and there gained a taste for romanticism which characterized his work in subsequent years. A stay in Rome during 1841 brought him in contact with the Nazarene School of German painters, and under the influence of Overbeck for a time. But his style was best suited to the vibrant portraits which he produced in Madrid as official court painter, an office he held in addition to being director of the Academy of Painting and the Prado Museum.

PORTRAIT OF MARIANO FORTUNY
Oil on panel, 10½x8¼ in., date unknown
No. 1876

This small painting, in the accomplished manner which made Madrazo so sought after as a portraitist, is a likeness of his son-in-law, the popular nineteenth-century Spanish artist, Mariano Fortuny y Carbó. Fortuny, a master of historical paintings with exotic themes, was lionized by his peers as well as the public. Madrazo exhibited a portrait of Fortuny at the Paris Exposition of 1878; the Bank's picture, inscribed as a copy made by Madrazo for his grandson, may be a replica of the Paris painting.

Conrad Marca-Relli

Born 1913 in Boston. Marca-Relli began to paint in New York when he was seventeen, having spent his early years in Europe. In 1935 he joined the WPA federal art project for three years, followed by a stay in Mexico and military service in World War II. By 1964 he was established as a painter and has since divided his time between studios in New York, Rome and more recently in Sarasota, Florida. Marca-Relli, a fringe member of the abstract expressionist school of the fifties, has become increasingly interested in formal structures. His collages and sculptures of the sixties and seventies are devoted to interlocked, abstract shapes, ostensibly held in place by adjustable tabs and grommets.

SUMMER SUITE D
Paper and burlap collage 10/50, 20x26 in., 1970
No. RO1767

Mardyanto

Born 1927 in Surabaya, Java. Mardyanto, who is known by one name only, attended school in central Java, but has had no formal training in art. He now lives in Jakarta where he specializes in batik paintings. The inspiration for his abstract designs comes from both traditional batik patterns and organic sources.

BATIK PAINTING
Dyed cloth, 36x34½ in., 1972
No. JA2010

A brilliant red background sets off a circle veined with spiny meanders, representing earth and sun superimposed.

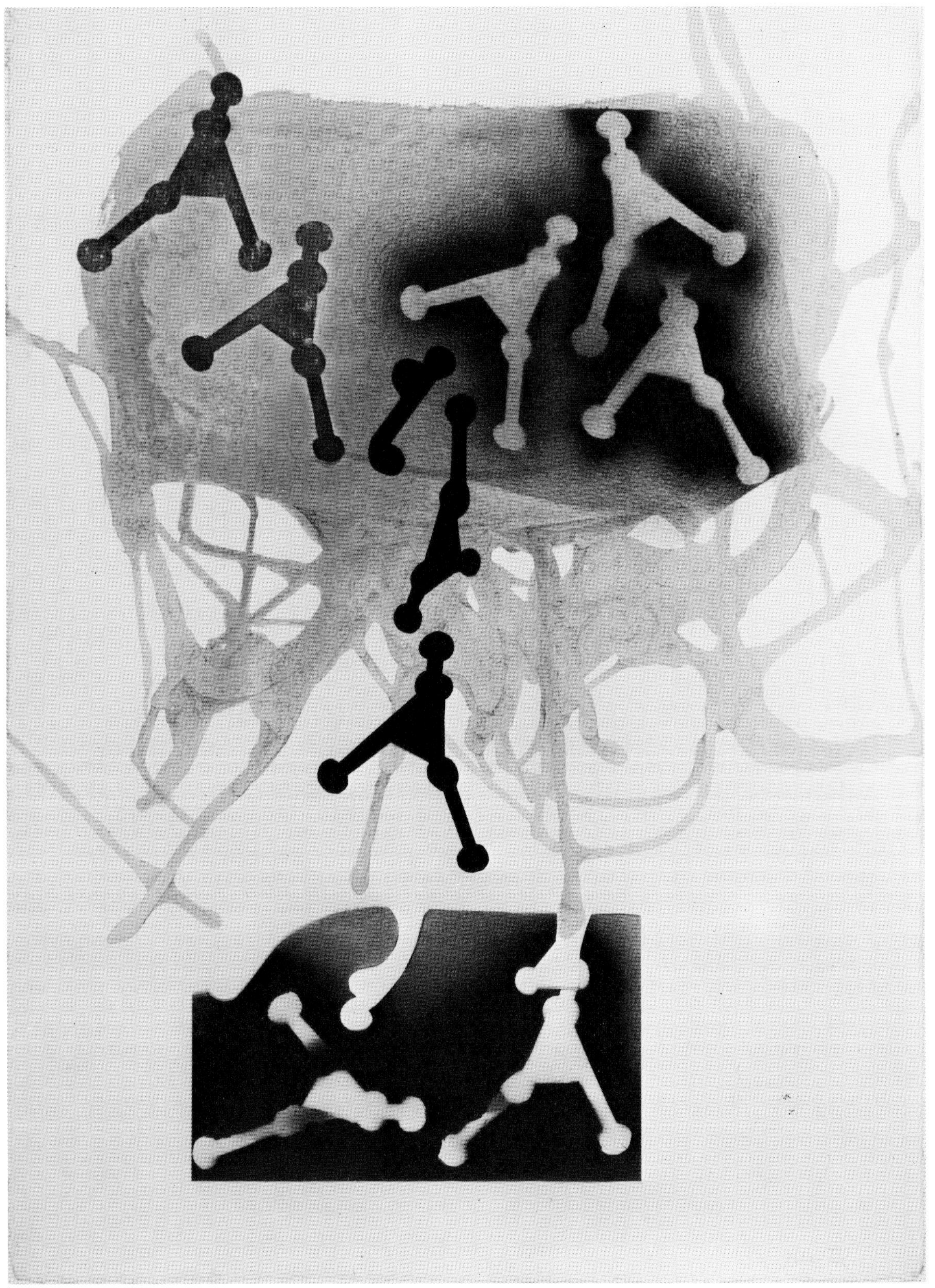

Martyl
Electric Circuit
(*Synapse Series*)

Martyl

Born 1918 in St. Louis, Missouri. Martyl began painting when she was twelve years old. She graduated from Washington University in St. Louis and spent two summers studying with Boardman Robinson at the Colorado Springs Fine Arts Center. The artist, who uses only her first name professionally, is the wife of nuclear physicist, Alexander Langsdorf, Jr. The impact of the atomic age, both as a scientific triumph and emotional shock, is expressed in a series of her paintings dating from the mid-forties, the same period in which she was art editor of *The Bulletin of Atomic Scientists*. Known for her work as a muralist, examples of which are in government buildings in Washington, D.C. and on the sanctuary wall of the Unitarian Church in Evanston, Illinois, she also paints landscapes of the Midwest and of the countries she visits on frequent travels abroad. She lives in Roselle, Illinois.

ELECTRIC CIRCUIT (SYNAPSE SERIES)
Acrylic polymer and collage, 35x27 in., 1971
No. 1207

Martyl's electronically derived shapes refer to her interest in nuclear fission. The negative and positive forms set up a polarized tension.

GREEK STILL LIFE
Paint, charcoal and collage, 25x35 in., 1968
No. AT424

In the late sixties Martyl visited numerous archeological digs in the Near East and Greece. For several years she drew on these travels as inspiration for various works of art, of which this still life is an example.

Fernando Maza

Born 1936 in Buenos Aires. Maza is a self-taught artist who uses orthographic projection as the basis for his carefully rendered paintings and constructions. His forms are cubes, pyramids, arches and derivations of numerals which take on the character of public monuments in a city of the future. The artist lives in Buenos Aires.

THE HOUSE OF SERAPHIM
Acrylic on canvas, 41x66 in., 1970
No. CA2192

Richard Merkin

Born 1938 in Brooklyn, New York. Merkin earned his BFA at Syracuse University in 1960. After a year of graduate study at the University of Michigan he completed his MFA at the Rhode Island School of Design with the aid of a fellowship from the Tiffany Foundation. He joined the faculty of the same school the following year and has continued to teach there, although he makes his home in New York. Slashing away at contemporary life, Merkin is a bitterly satiric painter who also works with graphics and collage.

ASCHENBACH
Tempera on pasted paper and board,
12x35¾ in., 1972
No. 1919

Inscribed "The Lido," this painting depicts an enigmatic man in panama hat and sunglasses, intended, of course, as the image of Aschenbach from Thomas Mann's *Death in Venice*.

Georges Michel

Born 1763 in Paris; died 1843 in Paris. Michel's knowledge of landscape was chiefly gained at the Louvre where he copied the paintings of such seventeenth-century Dutch artists as Ruysdael and Van Goyen. He was also employed by the Louvre and by private Parisian collectors to restore Dutch seventeenth-century landscape paintings. Michel's early style recalls the light-filled scenes of Ruysdael. His later, less derivative work is more romantic, though his stormy skies and lonely windmills were undoubtedly influenced by Rembrandt. His luminous landscape paintings were a prelude to the Barbizon School.

FLOODED RIVER IN STORMY WEATHER
Oil on paper mounted on canvas,
18x26½ in., after 1810
No. LN523

This painting with its dramatic sky and free brush work is typical of Michel's later style. The artist roamed the countryside making fully designed preliminary compositions, a departure from contemporary French academic practice that saw painters sketching directly from nature but combining their impressions in the studio.

Robert Middaugh

Born 1935 in Chicago. Middaugh studied at the University of Illinois, the University of Chicago and received a BFA from the School of the Art Institute of Chicago in 1964. He has been an architectural draftsman and a commercial artist. At present he is working in the Bank's Art Program. Middaugh creates imaginary mythologies built on fantastic figures, landscapes and architecture. He lives in Chicago.

THE CONCIERGE AWAITS
Acrylic on board, 9x7¾ in., 1971
No. 1828

This work is from a series of architectural landscapes. Fear of the unknown is emphasized in the darkened interiors of the buildings and by their subtle deviation from normal structural associations.

Prafulla Mohanti

Born 1938 in the state of Orissa, India. The youngest son of a peasant family in the village of Nanpur, Mohanti was awarded a scholarship to study architecture in Bombay. From there he travelled to England where he worked as a city-planner for the Greater London Council. Now a painter, Mohanti is also interested in the dance. Although he continues to make his home in London, he also spends time in India working with a group of artisans from Nanpur where he hopes to build a permanent craft center.

SPRING
Gouache, 30¾x22¾ in., 1969
No. RO1819

Here brilliant color and a decorative motif are reminiscent of Indian folk art.

Enrique Moreno

Born 1944 in Madrid. Moreno graduated in 1968 from the San Fernando Academy of Fine Arts in Madrid. He was professor of drawing at the Spanish Polytechnic Institute in Tangiers until 1972 and has since devoted himself to painting. Moreno is interested in a view of reality that depicts man's environment as a means of interpreting the human condition.

CLOSET NO. 2
Acrylic on board, 45½x33½ in., 1973
No. MA2005

A still life of garments sagging on hangers in a closet where rumpled clothes overflow half-open drawers. Two real panels from a wardrobe closet have been incorporated in the painting.

Keizo Morishita

Born 1944 in Tokyo. Morishita began studying art in Tokyo but in 1963 won a scholarship which enabled him to travel in Europe. He went to Milan where he enrolled at the Academy of the Brera. His work has been influenced by Marcel Duchamp, certain of whose motifs he has borrowed, but Morishita is also interested in hard-edge abstraction. He lives in Milan.

WITH MARCEL DUCHAMP
Acrylic on canvas, 45¼x34¾ in., 1970
No. ML1532

Morishita has based this painting on Duchamp's famous chocolate grinder motif which is best known from the large glass construction, *The Bride Stripped Bare by Her Bachelors, Even.*

Robert W. Nickle

Born 1919 in Saginaw, Michigan. Nickle studied at the University of Michigan and Illinois Institute of Technology. Interested only in collage, Nickle relies on found objects, on worn, torn, soiled or otherwise obsolete discards. Although influenced by principles governing the *Merz* constructions of Schwitters, Nickle's work remains highly personal in its tenderly structured compositions where muted color and velvety textures result from unlikely combinations of rejected materials. The artist is a professor of drawing and design at the University of Illinois Circle Campus in Chicago.

UNTITLED 1967
Collage, 13x17½ in., 1967
No. 1825

Like all of Nickle's work, the front of this collage is attached directly to the covering glass while a second piece of glass, visible only on the reverse of the picture, makes a window showing the artist's photograph and his signature.

Masuho Ohno

Born 1936 in Yokohama, Japan. Ohno is a graduate of the fine arts course at Bunka Gakuin. A member of the New Geometric Art Group since 1966, his paintings, often based on the square, are composed in such a way as to produce an optical sensation of movement. The artist lives in Tokyo.

WORK 72-3-4
Acrylic on canvas, 28x23½ in., 1972
No. TK1770

Robert Andrew Parker, *Bristol Blenheim*

Rinaldo Paluzzi

Born 1927 in Greensburg, Pennsylvania. Paluzzi was a student at John Herron Art Institute in Indianapolis where he earned a BFA in 1953 and an MFA in 1957. Before graduation he spent two years studying in Rome in 1950 and 1951, returning to Italy in 1958 on the proceeds of a Tiffany grant. In 1963 Paluzzi moved to Madrid where he now has his studio. His main concern is with light, space and movement, presented through strictly formalized abstraction.

TWO OPENINGS
Acrylic on canvas, 25½x31½ in., 1972
No. MA2050

Using a brilliant rich red over solid black, Paluzzi achieves the effect of reverberating color layers.

Robert Andrew Parker

Born 1927 in Norfolk, Virginia. A graduate of the School of the Art Institute of Chicago in 1952, Parker studied there with Max Kahn and won two scholarships. Another scholarship took him to the Skowhegan School of Painting and Sculpture during 1952 and the following winter he worked in New York at Atelier 17 with Stanley William Hayter. Since then he has had a grant from the National Institute of Arts and Letters in 1962, and a Guggenheim Fellowship in 1969. He specializes in watercolor, often using it in combination with drawing. His themes are taken from history and literature, from such writers as Auden, Cummings and Isherwood, and are liberally embroidered by imaginative touches that are often satiric. Parker lives in Carmel, New York.

BRISTOL BLENHEIM
Watercolor, 30x38 in., 1968
No. 667

The artist's interest in World War II and subjects pertaining to British history is clearly the basis for this ironic, yet romantic vision of a fighter plane diving over a rainbow.

Phaidon Patricalakis

Born 1935 in Drama, Greece. In 1960, after two years of study at the Vacalo School of Art, Patricalakis entered the Académie Julian in Paris and subsequently studied sculpture and pottery as well at the Académie du Feu. Since 1961 he has designed scenery and costumes for the theatre in France, England and Greece. He paints in brilliant Mediterranean colors, weaving elements from his Greek heritage into the School of Paris style he has adopted. The artist lives in Athens.

A COUPLE IN LOVE, WITH A MERMAID
Acrylic on canvas, 27¼x39½ in., 1971
No. AT1342

Robert Peterson

Born 1943 in Elmhurst, Illinois. Afflicted from early childhood with a progressive hearing loss, Peterson turned to drawing as a means of expressing himself. He lives in Albuquerque, New Mexico where he grew up and often paints the surrounding landscape as well as still lifes conceived with precise fidelity.

EGGS ON A PLATE
Oil on canvas, 18½x19¾ in., 1970
No. BS1370

During 1970–72 the egg was repeatedly featured in Peterson's highly realistic paintings.

Fernand Pierre

Born 1922 in Port-au-Prince, Haiti. Pierre was already painting at the age of twenty after beginning his career as a cabinetmaker. He has never studied painting but was inspired to become an artist by his neighbor, Hector Hyppolite, the pioneer Haitian painter. Pierre fills his canvases with fruits, flowers, animals and birds; his favorite theme is a bountiful imaginary tree, laden with large fruits and vegetables. Among the murals in the Episcopal Cathedral of Port-au-Prince is Pierre's interpretation of the Visitation.

FRUIT TREE
Oil on pressboard, 24x36 in., ca. 1970
No. KI1477

UNTITLED
Oil on pressboard, 24x30 in., 1970
No. KI1478

UNTITLED
Oil on pressboard, 24x30 in., 1970
No. PN2008

TREE
Oil on pressboard, 24x20 in., 1973
No. 1936

All four paintings are variations on Pierre's favorite theme, the tree of plenty.

ZEBRAS
Oil on pressboard, 18x36 in., 1973
No. 1935

An imaginary scene of numerous zebras, a subject also popular with Pierre.

A.D. Pirous

Born 1932 in Meulaboh, Aceh, Sumatra. On completion of his studies at the Institute of Technology in Bandung, Java in 1970, Pirous went to the United States under a Rockefeller Grant to take courses in graphics and design at the Rochester Institute of Technology in New York. Since 1971 he has been teaching art at his alma mater in Bandung where he lives. His brightly piled-on pigments show the influence of Abstract Expressionism.

UNTITLED
Acrylic, 39½x31½ in., 1971
No. JA2009

This is the first in a series of paintings based on calligraphy which the artist initiated in the early seventies.

Jacques Poli, *Blue Screw on Red Background*

Michelangelo Pistoletto

Born 1933 in Biella, Italy. Pistoletto learned to paint from his father, an art restorer. His early works from the late fifties were conventional life-size portraits. In 1960 he developed his first mirror painting and in 1963 began making collages on stainless steel. He attaches a photographic image printed on tissue paper to a highly polished steel surface, usually concentrating on human figures, occasionally on animals. As a rule he alters the photographic image by drawing or painting on the reverse side of the tissue paper. The viewer becomes an integral part of the composition as he sees himself reflected in the background.

SELF-PORTRAIT WITH PLANT
Collage on stainless steel, 78x47 in., 1965
No. 296

Typical of Pistoletto is this informal candid camera self-portrait showing the back of the artist as he leans over to tie his shoelace. The collage with its life-size figure has a compelling realism. *For colorplate see page 25.*

Jacques Poli

Born 1938 in Paris. An artist who devotes himself to the supremacy of mechanization in contemporary life, Poli paints outsized, hard-edge representations of tools and machine parts. He lives in Paris.

BLUE SCREW ON RED BACKGROUND
Oil on oilcloth, 39⅜x39⅜ in., 1970
No. BS1371

Gaetano Pompa

Born 1933 in Forenza, Italy. Pompa received his training in Rome where he now lives. His paintings and graphic works combine robot-like human figures—their faces often swathed in wrapping—with typography and scattered symbolic designs.

THE DANCER
Mixed media on canvas, 59½x29½ in., 1964
No. RO2026

This stylized painting, even to the areas of gold pigment, shows the influence of archaic and medieval Italian compositions.

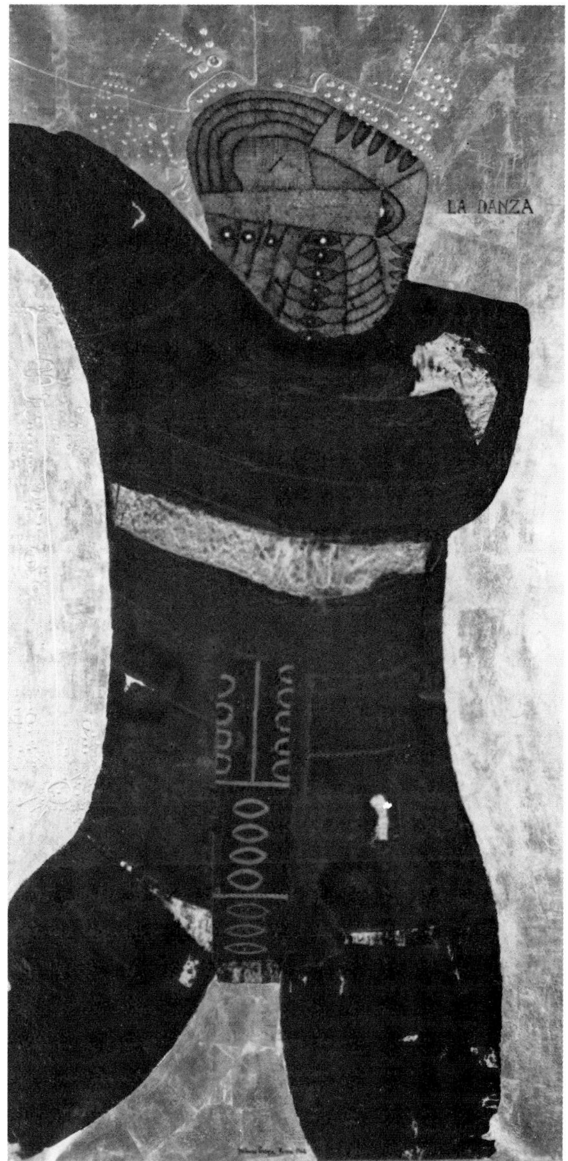

Gaetano Pompa, *The Dancer*

George Pyne

Born 1800 in England; died 1884 in England. Chiefly a painter of architectural interiors and topographical scenes, Pyne worked at Windsor, Kent, Cambridge and Oxford. He exhibited with the Old Watercolor Society in London and published some works on perspective and design.

CHRIST CHURCH HALL, OXFORD
Watercolor, 14x12 in., 19th c.
No. LN2043

A highly detailed interior view of a dining hall with tablecloths, silverware and china in place.

Giuseppe Recco

Born 1634 in Naples, Italy; died 1695 in Alicante, Spain. Recco was sent as a youth to Lombardy where it is thought he studied with two famous still-life painters, Evaristo Baschenis and Bartolomeo Bettera. On his return to Naples he worked with his father Giacomo Recco, a little-known still-life painter. Recco's favorite subjects were tables loaded with opulent harvests from sea and field. In certain larger works he depicted kitchens filled with food and the implements necessary for its preparation. No human figures appear in his paintings. The artist occasionally did the still-life sections in compositions by Luca Giordano. Recco, called to Spain by Charles II who had knighted him earlier, died shortly after arriving there.

STILL LIFE WITH WATERMELONS
Oil on canvas, 29¼x39 in., ca. 1670–75
No. 341

Rich displays of fruit and vegetables were popular subjects in seventeenth-century Naples and Spain. The artist's signature, obscured by shadow, appears in the lower right corner. *For colorplate see page 9.*

Thomas Miles Richardson

Born 1813 in Newcastle-on-Tyne, England; died 1890 in London. Richardson learned from his father, a watercolorist of the same name. The younger Richardson established himself as a painter in Newcastle, but moved permanently to London in the late forties. A member of the Old Watercolor Society and the Royal Scottish Academy, he exhibited at the Royal Academy from 1837 to 1848. Chiefly a landscapist, he painted scenes from the Scottish Highlands and from the Continent, especially from Italy. Richardson was also a competent lithographer.

PARTRIDGES AND PHEASANT
Watercolor, 6½x16¾ in., 19th c.
No. LN1488

Dead game is shown against a background of grasses and underbrush, all of which lends itself to a variety of textures. The monogram of the artist is seen in the lower right.

George Rodney

Born 1936 at Innswood, St. Catherine, Jamaica. From 1957 to 1961 Rodney attended the Jamaica School of Art, followed by two years at the Art Students League in New York where he won the 1962 Robert Ward Johnson Memorial Award. Although he began as a figurative painter influenced by Augustus John, Rodney's work became semi-abstract in the late sixties. He is employed by the Jamaica Broadcasting Corporation as an artist and lives in Kingston.

WOMAN IN A LANDSCAPE
Acrylic on canvas, 36x29¾ in., 1970
No. KI1479

LANDSCAPE
Acrylic on canvas, 36½x12 in., 1970
No. KI1480

Thomas Miles Richardson, *Partridges and Pheasant*

Severin Roesen

Dates of birth and death unknown. Roesen, originally a painter of porcelain and enamelwork in Germany, came to the United States around 1848. From 1850 to 1857, records show that he lived in New York where he also exhibited. For the next fourteen years he made his home in Williamsport, Pennsylvania; from there he seems to have disappeared in 1871. There is no proof to the story, sometimes appended to his biography, that Roesen died in a Philadelphia poorhouse. Most of the artist's works are devoted to sumptuous displays of fruits, sometimes so excessively abundant that two marble ledges—one above the other—are needed to hold the bounty. Occasionally, brimming glasses were added to the composition.

STILL LIFE WITH PEACHES
Oil on panel, 14x18 in., after 1850
No. 1838

A comparatively subdued composition for Roesen, this still life has a realism typical of nineteenth-century American painting. The arrangement rests on Roesen's usual marble ledge, but his signature here is printed rather than formed by vine tendrils, the latter a device Roesen favored. *For colorplate see page 16.*

Thomas Leeson Rowbotham, Jr.

Born 1823 in Dublin, Ireland; died 1875 in London. Rowbotham was a pupil of his father whom he succeeded as professor of design at New Cross Naval Academy. An active member of the Institute of Painters in Watercolors, he made romantic landscapes often resulting from travels abroad and in England.

STILL LIFE
Watercolor, 6¾x10½ in., 1874
No. LN2004

This sketch, made at the Portsmouth dockyard, shows a group of objects found at quayside.

G. R. Sarjent

Dates of birth and death unknown. Sarjent exhibited at the Royal Academy in London from 1811 to 1849. He lived in London and was a watercolorist who painted landscapes, architecture and interiors of well-known places.

WESTMINSTER SCHOOL
Watercolor, 14¾x19⅞ in., 1839
No. LN1489

Here Sarjent depicts a classroom in the Westminster School. Names of former students appear on the wall. The work was exhibited at the Royal Academy the year it was painted. At the Royal Academy in 1836 and 1848 Sarjent showed other interior scenes of the same school. The watercolor is signed and dated in the lower left.

Seah Kim Joo

Born 1939 in Singapore. The son of Chinese émigrés from Fukien Province, Seah attended Nanyang Academy of Fine Arts in Singapore. After graduating in 1961 he joined a group of ten young artists who were traveling in Southeast Asia where they worked and exhibited together. In 1965 he began studying the art of batik, an ancient Indonesian technique of wax-resist dyeing. Seah transposes this process to painting and also produces large architectural murals in the medium. His works, almost always layered with translucent color, are punctuated by flickering patterns. The artist is also a sculptor and lives in Singapore.

COMPOSITION
Batik painting, 41x41 in., 1970
No. SI2006

Arthur Secunda

Born 1927 in Jersey City, New Jersey. After attending New York University, Secunda studied at the Art Student's League in New York, the Académie Julian in Paris where he worked under André Lhote and Ossip Zadkine, the Meschini Institute in Rome and the Esmeralda School of Painting and Sculpture in Mexico City. Although known as a printmaker, Secunda is also a sculptor and painter. He now lives in California. Strong color and bold abstract shapes are basic to his work.

OPEN WIDE THE HEAVENS
Paper collage, 38¼x23¾ in., 1972
No. 1844

JELLY BELLY
Paper collage, 23½x18 in., 1972
No. RO2020

G.R. Sarjent, *Westminster School*

Antonio Segui, *Elephant*

Antonio Segui

Born 1934 in Córdoba, Argentina. Segui studied law and painting in his native Argentina and later went to Europe in 1952. He lived in Mexico from 1957 to 1961 and subsequently moved to Paris. Since 1963 he has divided his time between France and Argentina. During the 1960's Segui's paintings, drawings and wood constructions dealt with brutalized human forms and were often imbued with his own leftist political views. More recently, as in the Bank's untitled drawing, he has turned to semi-surrealist scenes of rudderless boats and disoriented passengers. In the early seventies Segui produced strange close-up portraits of elephants in nebulous landscapes and also ironic tintype-style family portraits.

MAN WITH TIE IN LANDSCAPE
Oil on canvas, 57½x45 in., 1967
No. 330

Here the landscape is idyllic and the man grotesque, a combination Segui particularly likes.

ELEPHANT
Mixed media including charcoal and pastel, 51x51 in., 1973
No. 1929

Although Segui has never studied elephants in their own habitat, his imagination—stimulated by trips to the zoo and by the study of photographic essays on Africa—has prompted him to create a series of intimate, superrealistic "portraits" of this animal.

Yoshio Sekine

Born 1922 in Wakayama City, Japan. Sekine received his art training in Japan where in 1948 he was awarded the Mainichi Newspaper prize. Since 1960 he has been obsessed with the abacus as a theme. His paintings, usually dark in color, seem abstract but the abacus, which he transforms into bold new patterns, is always his point of departure. The artist lives in Tokyo.

ABACUS NO. 106
Oil on canvas, 51x38 in., 1966
No. FR1006

ABACUS NO. 210
Oil on canvas, 32x25¾ in., 1970
No. MC1676

WORK 94
Oil on canvas, 28½x23¾ in., 1966
No. TK1768

Yoshio Sekine, *Work 94*

Leon Polk Smith

Born 1906 in the Indian Territory, now Oklahoma. Smith, part Cherokee Indian, put himself through Oklahoma State College, graduating in 1933. Four years later in New York he became an admirer of Mondrian's paintings and began to work in a similar style, but was also influenced by American Indian design. In the fifties he reduced his palette to two colors per painting and introduced interlocking curved forms inspired, Smith says, by the seams of baseballs and basketballs. This interest in shape and contour anticipated the hard-edge color school of the sixties. The artist has been the recipient of a Guggenheim grant and a Tamarind Lithography Workshop grant and in 1968 was artist-in-residence at Brandeis University. He now lives on Long Island, New York.

UNTITLED
Collage, 40¾x26½ in., 1960
No. FR534

This collage, composed of two large free-form areas of color, is typical of Smith's later work. Here, the intersection between the color areas defines and divides the space. In addition, the two colors interact on each other to form new color relationships.

CORRESPONDENCE: WHITE-ORANGE
Oil on canvas, 36x68 in., 1964
No. 535

The undulating division between the two colors in this painting gives movement to otherwise static planes. Taking a cue from Smith's title, the viewer sees an interaction or a "correspondence" between the two colors.

Frans Snyders

Born 1579 in Antwerp, Belgium; died 1657 in Antwerp. A painter of animals and still life, Snyders was the pupil of Peter Breughel the Younger and possibly of Henrik van Balen. In 1602 he became a master in the Guild of St. Luke at Antwerp and in 1608 made a trip to Italy where he spent one year. He carried out important commissions for the Spanish court and in his native city, but is probably best known for his collaborations with Rubens. Snyders was frequently responsible for the animal and still-life portions in large compositions in which Rubens provided the human figures and landscapes. Snyders' style was always sumptuous and filled with lively brushwork.

STILL LIFE WITH HARE, DOVE AND ARTICHOKES
Oil on wood panel, 49¼x32¾ in., ca. 1625
No. 333

This tabletop still life, once assigned to the French painter Alexandre-François Desportes (1661–1743), according to John Walsh of the Metropolitan Museum of Art seems more likely to be Flemish and as first suggested by Georges de Lastic of the Musée de la Chasse, Paris and later confirmed by Frans Baudouin, director of the Rubenshuis in Antwerp, seems closer to the work of Frans Snyders. Desportes studied with Snyders' pupil, Nicasius Bernaerts, and might conceivably have completed an exercise in the manner of Snyders for his teacher. But the close similarity to Snyders' style and the extraordinary number of exactly reproduced motifs presupposes an almost complete knowledge of the Flemish artist's lifework. The informal hodgepodge of kitchen items, food and animals which make up the composition are precisely the ingredients of a Snyders' still life and correspondences to each object can be found in one or another known painting by him. Particularly noteworthy are the black and white bird on the left which appears in a signed and dated work of 1613 (last known in a private collection in Munich) and the hen and rooster seen in the lower right corner of the Bank's painting which can be found in the large bird still life belonging to the Wallraf-Richartz Museum, Cologne, signed and dated 1614. Examples can also be cited for the various fruits, the basket, the copper tub, the dove, the delftware and brace of small birds. It is clear that Snyders used many of the same studio props over and over again without bothering to add much by way of compositional invention to the basic arrangement of game and other edibles in his paintings. The Bank's panel has evidently been cropped on all four sides. *For colorplate see page 10.*

Sotiris Sorogas

Born 1936 in Athens, Greece. In 1961 Sorogas studied painting and the theory and history of art in Athens. Later he attended courses in Byzantine icon painting. Since 1964 he has been a teaching assistant at the National Technical University of Athens. His work is essentially playful in feeling.

UNTITLED
Acrylic on canvas, 21x17½ in., 1970
No. AT1327

UNTITLED
Acrylic on canvas, 21x17½ in., 1970
No. AT1328

Giangiacomo Spadari

Born 1938 in the Republic of San Marino. Spadari, who now lives in Milan, insists that the artist must express new ideas; for him repetition is not art. He uses flickering, splashing patterns to transform scenes composed like newspaper photographs.

BULL FIGHT
Acrylic and fluorescent paint on canvas, 39x46¾ in., 1969
No. ML1535

The excitement of a bullfight is caught in the rapid shifting design of Spadari's painting.

Giangiacomo Spadari, *Bull Fight*

Giuseppe Spagnulo

Born 1936 in Grottaglie, Italy. Spagnulo began his studies at the Faenza Institute of Art and then continued at the Academy of the Brera in Milan, the city where he still lives. He is primarily a sculptor who creates powerful abstract wood or metal structures that recall various types of mechanized equipment.

UNTITLED
Paper collage, 26½x38¼ in., 1970
No. ML1536

This collage, in its stark monumentality, is closely related to Spagnulo's sculpture.

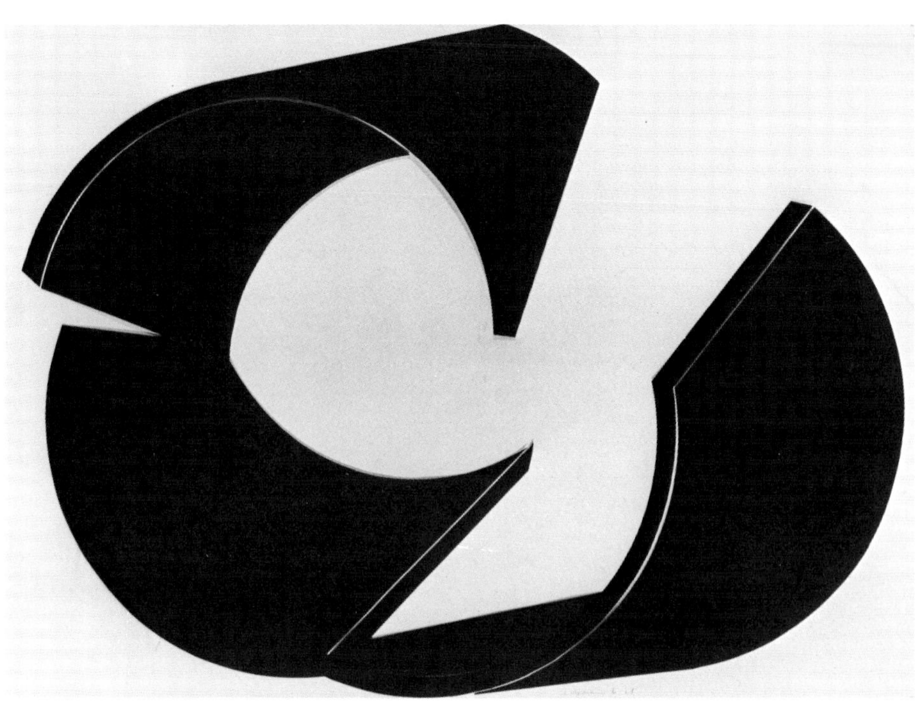

Giuseppe Spagnulo, *Untitled*

Nancy Spero

Born 1926 in Cleveland, Ohio. Spero earned a BFA from the School of the Art Institute of Chicago in 1949 and afterward went to Paris where she studied with André Lhote and at the Ecole des Beaux Arts for one year. Since the beginning of the woman's liberation movement, she has been politically active in art and has recently contributed to two print portfolios on political themes. She tends toward Expressionism highlighted by caustic social comment. Spero works exclusively in gouache, ink and typewriter collage on paper. Her home is in New York.

WAR SERIES
Gouache and collage, 24x19 in., 1968
No. 597

Stars containing human heads appear at the crossing and terminal points of a silver swastika. Spero says the picture symbolizes Fascism and its victims.

Julian Stanczak

Born 1928 in Borownica, Poland. At the outbreak of World War II Stanczak left Poland to spend the next decade traveling in Russia, Iran, Iraq, West Pakistan, East Africa and England. During 1949–50 he studied at the Borough Polytechnic in London. He came to the United States in 1950 where he attended the Cleveland Institute of Art, earning his BFA in 1954. Two years later he received his MFA from Yale where he studied under Josef Albers and Conrad Marca-Relli. Stanczak, who lives in Seven Hills, Ohio, has taught at the Cleveland Institute of Art since 1964. Like his friend, Anuszkiewicz, he is a leading op artist whose work has been influenced by the theories of Albers. He uses color to dazzle the eye by means of lines superimposed at graduated intervals over geometric shapes.

SEQUENCE
Acrylic on canvas, 36x36 in., 1969
No. GU320

Hedda Sterne

Born 1916 in Bucharest, Rumania. After studying art in Bucharest, Paris and Vienna, Sterne came to the United States in 1941, settling in New York where she still lives. Her early work was surrealist; later she experimented with abstract metal constructions, finally turning in the sixties to serene abstracted landscapes. As an outstanding draftsman, she has been preoccupied with drawing during her entire career. In the late sixties and early seventies she concentrated on drawing, with special emphasis on the human face and on ambiguous growing forms. In 1967 she received a grant from the Tamarind Lithography Workshop in Los Angeles.

MADAME HAIMAN
Acrylic on canvas, 54x72 in., 1969
No. 310

Not originally intended as a portrait this large black and white work, as it progressed, assumed the likeness of a woman the artist had known in Rumania. The entire canvas is filled with a pattern of black lines. A pale face emerges from interwoven tonal layers.

Hedda Sterne, *Madame Haiman*

Alfred Stevens

Born 1823 in Brussels, Belgium; died 1906 in Paris. After completing his studies under the Belgian painter, François Joseph Navez. Stevens went to Paris where he remained the rest of his life. There he discovered his personal métier, making a triumph of painting *les femmes parisiènnes* in the intimate rounds of daily life. His choice of theme suited the moment when women were playing an important role in society under the leadership of the Empress Eugénie. The same subject matter was reflected in the contemporary writings of his good friend, Alexandre Dumas. In 1880 Stevens' doctor ordered him to the seashore for relief from turpentine fumes, and thus began a lifelong interest in painting coastal seascapes. Although clearly affected by Impressionism, he made his real conquests in the official Salons where Impressionism was taboo. His older brother, Joseph, was also a popular Salon painter, and a younger brother, Arthur, became a highly respected art dealer and critic who wrote influential articles for *Le Figaro* in support of Manet.

SAILING VESSELS ON A CHOPPY SEA
Oil on canvas, 28½x23½ in., ca. 1885
No. 1854

Departing from the intimate charm of his genre scenes, Stevens here handles a romantic seascape with loose brush strokes and a rapid scumbling technique. Though not strictly an impressionist work, this luminous picture shows a strong affinity for the contemporary interest in natural light. *For colorplate see page 18.*

Tom Strobel

Born 1931 in Nashville, Tennessee. While fulfilling his military service, Strobel was placed in charge of an army art center in Munich, Germany, an experience which led him to apply to the School of the Art Institute of Chicago after his discharge. Following graduation in 1960 he received a Fulbright grant for the study of Gestalt psychology and painting at the Düsseldorf Academy of Art in Germany. Strobel remained in Europe for three years, returning in 1963 to the United States where he has since been teaching painting at the School of the Art Institute of Chicago, at Illinois Institute of Technology and at Northwestern University. Strobel's themes are usually taken from nature. He achieves a variety of effects with sponge, palette knife and spraygun techniques. He lives near Chicago.

ILLINOIS LANDSCAPE
Oil on paper, 24x35 in., 1966
No. 679

Combining the effects of spraygun painting with hairline brush strokes, Strobel created a texturally varied field of dead grass beneath a winter sky.

Gilbert Stuart

Born 1755 in North Kingstown Township, Rhode Island; died 1828 in Boston. After studying with the painter Samuel King in Newport, Stuart was apprenticed to Cosmo Alexander, a Scottish portrait painter. With Alexander he traveled through part of the South and in 1772 to Scotland, but shortly returned to Newport after Alexander's death. In 1775 Stuart settled in England where two years later he became a student of Benjamin West. Despite West's hopes of turning Stuart into a history painter, the younger artist remained a portraitist. English nobility as well as lesser persons flocked to his studio; their portraits were often exhibited at the Royal Academy. Despite Stuart's success, he left London and his many creditors in 1787 for Dublin. Here again important people sat for him, but once more he was forced to leave because of debts. Although not sympathetic to the cause of the American Revolution, in 1793 he returned to America where important leaders of the new republic sat for him. His portraits of George Washington are known to all Americans. After his return to the United States, Stuart lived briefly in New York, Philadelphia and Washington, finally settling in Boston in 1805. His English portraits were influenced by eighteenth-century British painting, but his American ones have the forthright vigor of the New World. During his brief years in Ireland he painted with a dash and freedom somewhat in contrast to his more conservative English style.

COLONEL HUGH NUGENT
Oil on canvas, 30½x25¼ in., ca. 1787–1792
No. 1205

This portrait, with its stippled background and free use of unblended pigment, is typical of Stuart's ebullient Irish period. The sitter belonged to a distinguished Irish family connected with the army. The painting was purchased directly from the Colonel's descendants and subsequently sold to the Bank. *For colorplate see page 13.*

James B. Sullivan

Born 1830 in Troy, New York; died after 1871 in Chicago. Sullivan came to Chicago in 1855 and two years later founded the firm of J.B. Sullivan and Brothers, specializing in "painting, decorating and frescoes." Little more is known about his life or work.

THE CONFLAGRATION OF 1871
Oil on canvas, 52x65 in., ca. 1871
No. 826

The second home of The First National Bank of Chicago, which stood at the corner of State and Washington Streets, was left with a major portion of its walls intact after the Chicago fire of 1871. A photograph of the building taken the next day shows it from almost exactly the same view as is seen in this painting. It is therefore possible that Sullivan who was a friend of Lyman Gage, then cashier and later president of the Bank, painted this scene from the photograph, embellishing it with dramatic foreground ruins and smoldering sky. *For colorplate see page 17.*

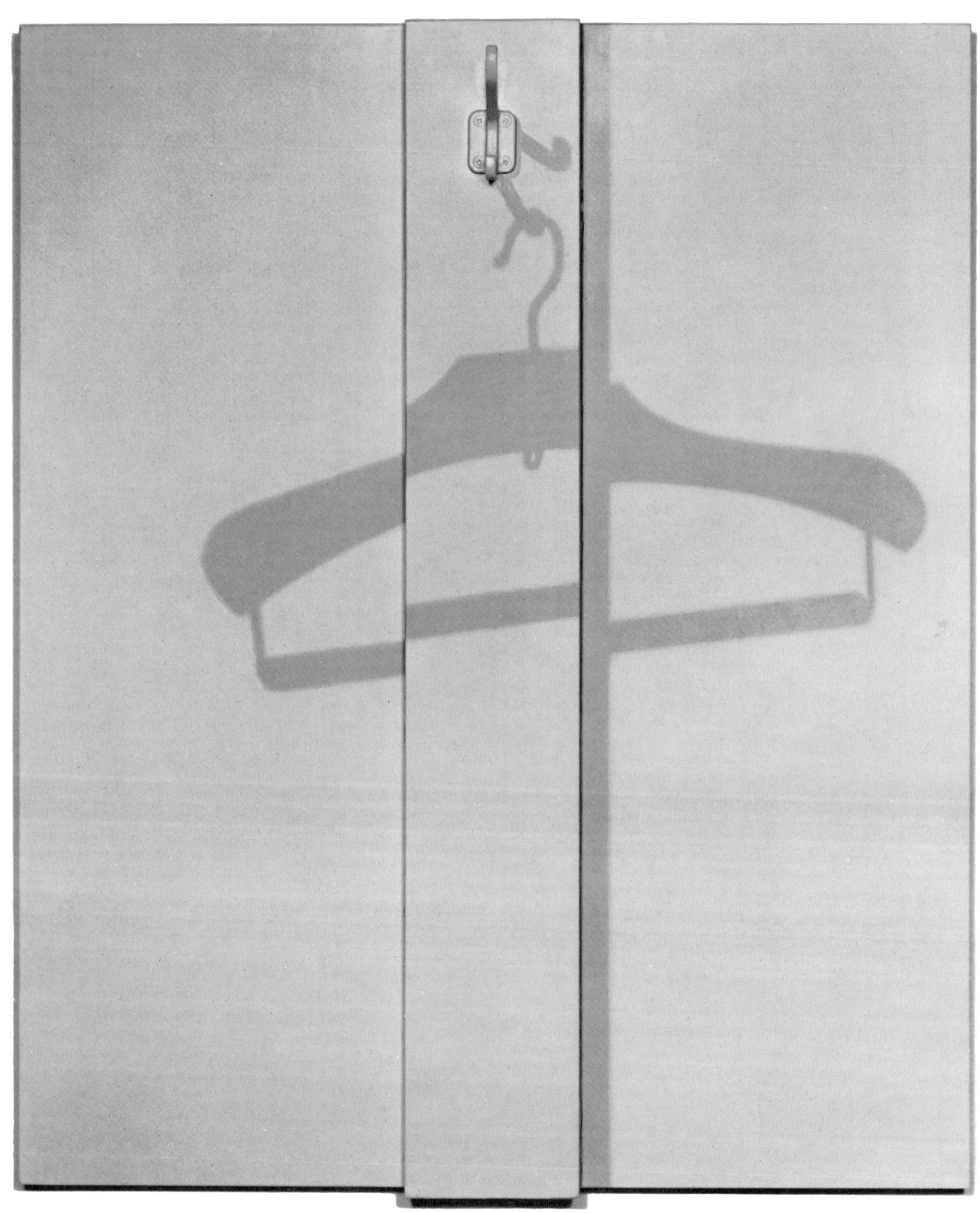

Jiro Takamatsu, *Shadow of a Hanger*

J. Swaminathan

Born 1928 in Simla, India. Swaminathan first chose medicine as a career and then turned to journalism, to short stories for children and to art criticism. Deciding to become a painter, he entered the art department of Delhi Polytechnic and later obtained a scholarship to study at the Academy of Fine Arts, Warsaw, Poland. In 1968 Swaminathan was awarded a Jawaharlal Nehru Fellowship to write a thesis on tradition in contemporary Indian art. The following year he became a member of the international jury at the São Paulo Bienal in Brazil. His paintings place mystical motifs against geometric backgrounds. The artist lives in Bombay.

THE SQUARE IN THE RECTANGLE
Oil on canvas, 30x50 in., 1965
No. 1818

This painting belongs to a series which Swaminathan calls color-geometry. He often adds evocative symbols like the eye and hand depicted here.

Shu Takahashi

Born 1930 in Hiroshima, Japan. Takahashi, who lives in Rome, graduated from the Musashino School of Fine Arts in 1950. He is noted for the bold, hard-edge style from which he creates brightly colored forms somewhat anatomical in derivation.

UNTITLED (OCHRE COMPOSITION)
Tempera, 27¼x20½ in., 1970
No. 1221

UNTITLED (ORANGE COMPOSITION)
Tempera, 27¼x20½ in., 1970
No. 1220

Jiro Takamatsu

Born 1936 in Tokyo. Takamatsu, who still lives in Tokyo, graduated from the department of painting at Tokyo University in 1958. Like some of his contemporaries, he seems to have bypassed Japanese tradition, replacing it with an assimilation of Western motifs. He has experimented with problems of distance in a series called "Points and Threads," with the elongation and reduction of shadow forms and with "solidified perspective," the last an attempt to achieve the illusion of two-dimensional perspective in three-dimensional form. Takamatsu has also done stage and film sets and created the "Mirror Plaza" of *Expo 70* at Osaka.

SHADOW OF A HANGER
Oil on panel with metal hook, 25¾x21½ in., 1970
No. 1095

The painted shadow of a nonexistent hanger is suspended from a real three-dimensional hook.

Eduardo Tamariz

Born 1945 in Mexico City. From 1963 to 1967 Tamariz was a student at the Esmeralda School of Painting and Sculpture in Mexico City where he took first prize in sculpture. He is a versatile artist, his work ranging from heavy and even massive sculpture to delicately shaded abstract paintings. Tamariz works in Mexico City.

STAMP
Encaustic, 24x32 in., 1969
No. MC1678

IMPACT
Encaustic 24x32 in., 1969
No. MC1677

These strongly outlined abstract forms recall Tamariz's sculpture.

Francisco Toledo

Born 1940 in Juchitán, Oaxaca, Mexico. Toledo, a Zapotec Indian, studied painting in Mexico City and worked for a time with Rufino Tamayo. In the sixties he was in Paris to learn graphic techniques from Stanley William Hayter. Since then he has been active both in Europe and Mexico. Living among the traditions of his native state of Oaxaca, he draws on themes from Mexican folk and pre-Hispanic art to produce woodcuts, lithographs and tapestries filled with phantasmagoric scenes of beasts and people. Toledo's color is strong.

THE PITCHER
Oil on paper (monotype), 23½x27¼ in., 1969
No. MC1679

This monotype was executed by transferring to paper a design painted in oil on a metal plate or piece of glass.

Tay Chee Toh

Born 1941 in Rengit, Johore, Malayasia. Tay studied at the Nanyang Academy of Fine Arts, Singapore from 1958 to 1960. Although formerly a figurative painter, in 1972 he turned to more abstract designs always based, however, on natural forms and usually deriving from aquatic life. He specializes in dye-printed batiks and lives in Singapore.

BATIK PAINTING
Dyed fabric, 60x72 in., 1972
No. SI2019

Lucas Gregorio Valdés y Morales

Born 1661 in Seville, Spain. Died 1724 in Cadiz, Spain. Apparently Lucas Valdés began his artistic apprenticeship at an early age under the guidance of his father, the baroque painter Juan de Valdés Leal, who founded the Public Drawing Academy at Seville in 1660 and was president of the Academy of Painting there from 1663 to 1666. An etching in Torre Farfan's book on the life of St. Ferdinand is signed by Lucas Gregorio with the date 1672 and the inscription, "age eleven years." However, since the elder Valdés instructed his children in art, it is quite possible the work, seemingly too skillful for a child who even in maturity failed to equal his father's talent, is largely by the hand of the parent. Lucas became his father's assistant and worked with him in the decoration of churches and other commissions. After his father's death in 1690 and in order to help his widowed mother, Valdés took the position of professor in mathematics at the Naval Academy in Cadiz. Six paintings done without the collaboration of his father are in the Church of the Old Priests in Seville.

PAINTING CROWNED QUEEN
OF THE ARTS
attributed to Lucas Gregorio Valdés y Morales
Oil on canvas, 49x39 in., ca. 1693–95
No. 251

The theme here is the triumph of Painting among the Arts. An elaborate setting, borrowing architectural elements from late Gothic, Italian Renaissance and Moorish sources, assumes the general outline of a church interior where, however, a double-arched entry replaces the expected choir screen. In addition there is no altar. "Painting," a female figure in jeweled robes, seated on a dais, is being crowned by a king wearing armor. The sovereign is possibly Charles II of Spain, a notion strengthened by the Hapsburg double-headed eagles seen in the pendentives of the dome, as well as by a standard, bearing the Holy Roman Empire insignia SPQR. "Painting" is identified by an easel which stands behind her dais. Among the crowd in attendance are allegorical personifications of various Arts—Geometry, Philosophy and Astrology—as well as three women, with harpsichord and other instruments, representing Music. In the lower right-hand corner Mercury, messenger of the gods, banishes "Bad Painting" with his demonic muses who knock down easel, mahl stick and paint pots as they disappear below. On the columns above, wreath-crowned statues holding palettes and brushes or compasses represent famous artists. One is labeled "Apelles," the Greek painter of antiquity, another "Urbino" for Raphael, and a third, "Rubens." The latter two inscriptions have been rewritten in a different style than the first but probably without changing the original names. St. Luke, patron saint of painters, and his evangelical symbol, the bull, are seen as sculpture in a small shrine at gallery level. The significance of his presence is underlined by the St. Luke's Guild coat of arms seen in the dome and by a second bull and an easel found in the right-hand spandrel of the upper arch on the left side of the painting. Above the same arch is a cartouche on which the following appears:

En Trono Eminentissimo elevada
  (Raised on a most imposing throne,
la eloquente Pintura y sus primores,
  (Eloquent Painting and her qualities,
delineando ensalzada
  (Depicted in heightened manner,
Rethoricos colores,
  (terms of color, and rhetorical themes,
por dibujos y sombras sublevada
  (Glorified through lines and shadows,
repartiendo sus luces q̄ la abonan
por su Reina los Artes la coronaro
  (Displaying her prowess which designates her as the deity whom the Arts crown their Queen.)

Lucas Gregorio Valdés y Morales, *Painting Crowned Queen of The Arts*, detail

At the bottom of the canvas, two putti hold a tablet which must have carried the signature of the artist and the date of the painting. It is possible that traces of a "B" remain, which may signify the name of Valdés in its alternate Spanish spelling. It is not unlikely that such a painting could have been made by Lucas Valdés for the chapel of the Guild of St. Luke in the church of San Andres at Seville, although this work is not known to have been in the Guild's collection when it was dispersed in the nineteenth century.

Anton Van Dalen

Born 1938 in Amsterdam, the Netherlands. Anton Van Dalen was a student at the Amsterdam School of Graphic Arts from 1952 to 1955. In 1962 he emigrated to Toronto, Canada and eventually to New York where he is now living. Van Dalen's obsession with leaves started in 1967 when ecologists were beginning to influence public opinion. Entire canvases are covered with foliating patterns which in some cases combine to form familiar objects. The first painting of this type was an enormous eye composed of leaves, but soon Van Dalen focused his attention exclusively on consumer items—Polaroid cameras, computer cards and magazine covers—all fabricated from sap-green leaves. If the first impression suggests Surrealism, the dominant factor is the artist's moral stand against a world wasting itself in superfluous consumerism.

LEAVES—WATCH
Oil on canvas, 74x34 in., 1967
No. 673

An enormous wrist watch composed of leaves hangs against a background of more leaves. The effect is unsettling.

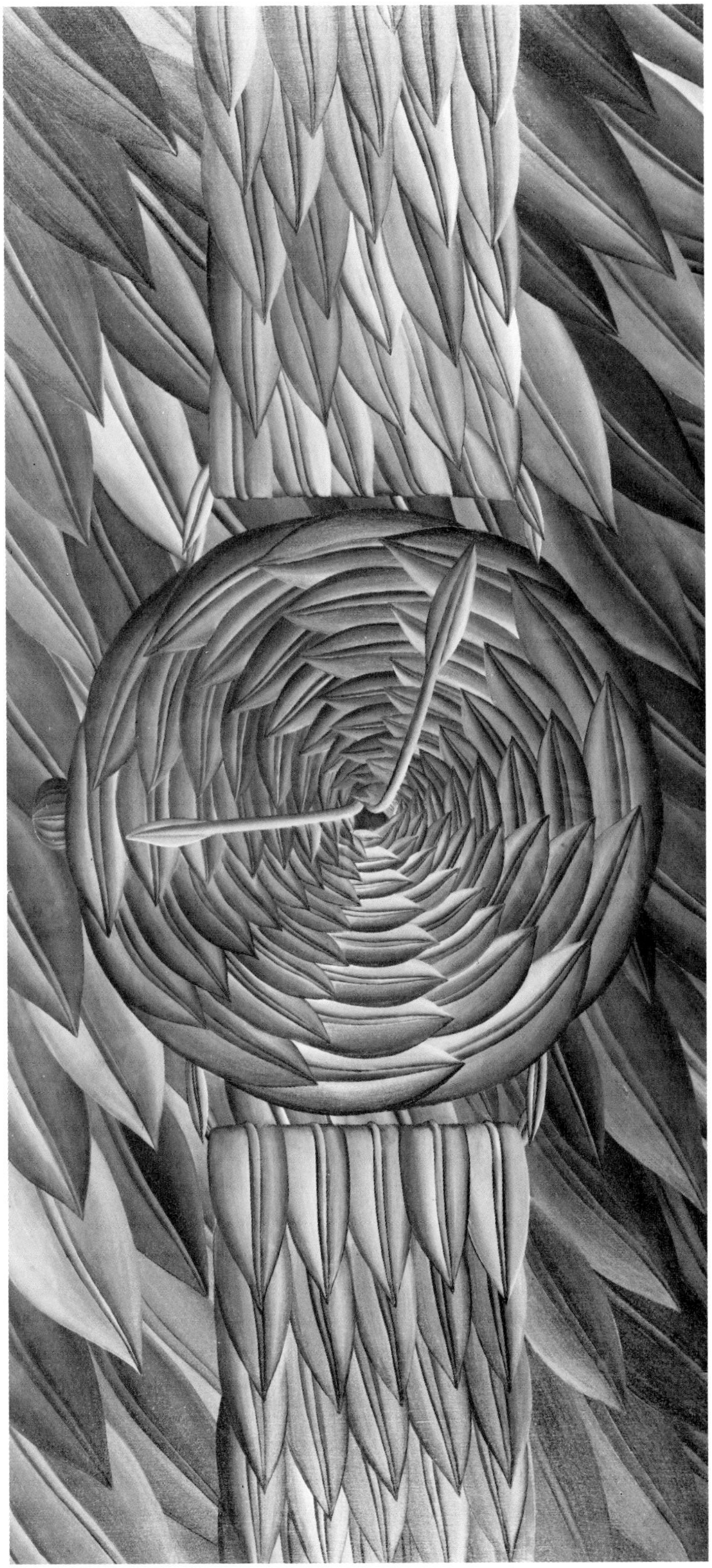

Anton van Dalen, *Leaves-Watch*

Bartholomew van der Helst, *Portrait of Lieutenant Admiral Egbert Meeuwszoon Kortenaar*

Bartholomew van der Helst

Born 1613 in Haarlem, the Netherlands; died 1670 in Amsterdam. Van der Helst, one of the most popular Dutch portrait painters, was probably a pupil of Nicolas Eliasz and in his early work also influenced by Hals and Rembrandt. But in his mature style, van der Helst brought a marked change to the introspective manner of Dutch portrait painting by adding an elegance borrowed from Van Dyck. Arriving in Amsterdam in 1636, van der Helst received his first group portrait commission the next year. By 1643 he had succeeded Rembrandt as the leading portrait painter in the city.

PORTRAIT OF LIEUTENANT ADMIRAL EGBERT MEEUWSZOON KORTENAAR
Oil on canvas, 21½x17½ in., ca. 1650
No. 1840

This portrait in *grisaille* is the original for an engraving by Arnold Houbraken. Van der Helst painted two other portraits of Admiral Kortenaar, who died at the Battle of Lowestoft in 1655 during the Anglo-Dutch War. One is now in the Rijksmuseum in Amsterdam and the other is at the Maritime Museum, Greenwich, England. William van der Velde is thought to have painted seascapes as backgrounds in some of van der Helst's work. Here, however, collaboration cannot be affirmed.

Louis Michel Van Loo

Born 1707 in Toulon, France; died 1771 in Paris. Van Loo was the nephew of the painter Carl Van Loo and the son of Jean-Baptiste Van Loo, under whom he studied. Louis Michel became an important rococo artist who won the *Prix de Rome* in 1727 and worked in Italy until 1733. In 1736 he was summoned to Madrid by Philip V of Spain to become court painter, and in 1752 was made director of the San Fernando Academy of Painting in Madrid. After his return to Paris in 1753 he exhibited in the Paris Salon, showing his work there annually until 1769. He became director of the Ecole des Elèves Protégés in 1765. Van Loo embodied the spirit of French eighteenth-century painting in all its decorative elegance. His best known portraits are full-length figure paintings of Louis XV and the 1767 painting of Diderot in the Louvre.

PORTRAIT OF M. DE LA CROIX VAN CRUCIUS
Oil on canvas, 26x21½ in., 1767
No. 1930

Van Loo sometimes painted double portraits of married couples, either on the same canvas or in pairs. This oval portrait of M. de la Croix van Crucius belongs to the second category; the pendant picture of his wife, who was from the well-known Huguenot family, the Girardots, is in a New York collection. The picture is signed and dated and is in the original frame which bears the stamped signature of "J-B Charpentier," a registered cabinetmaker in eighteenth-century Paris.
For colorplate see page 11.

Robert Van Rosen

Born 1900 in Kiev, Russia; died 1964 in New York. After studying art in Rumania, Van Rosen emigrated to the United States where he continued his studies at the Master Institute of United Artists in New York. His career as a designer also included the invention of the Van Rosen Videometric Comparator, a machine used by several industrial corporations to test legibility and visual impact. He designed stage scenery for both the Provincetown Playhouse and the Yiddish Art Theatre. From 1926 to 1928 Van Rosen was director of the Roerich Museum in New York; from 1940 to 1942 he was art director of *THINK*, the IBM publication. In 1950 he became a commercial designer and consultant in packaging.

STAGE DESIGN FOR THE YIDDISH THEATRE
Casein, 19x24 in., 1929
No. AT666

A backdrop of machinery, smoke and flames apparently sets the scene for a drama with social content.

José Varona

Born 1930 in Mendoza, Argentina. Varona first planned to become an architect, but in 1952 he turned to the study of design at the Ernesto de la Corcora School of Fine Arts in Buenos Aires. In 1955, after spending a year in Europe, he returned to Argentina as a costume and scenic designer, working for the Theatre Colón, the ballet and the National Comedy. Soon he became a designer for television, advertising and films as well, but in 1962 a job for the San Francisco Opera took him to the United States. He became a textile designer in New York where he still lives. Since 1966 Varona has devoted himself to opera, creating productions for companies in New York, Berlin, Hamburg, Paris and Sydney.

COSTUME SKETCH—"LE COQ D'OR"
Watercolor, 16½x13 in., 1967
No. 665

This fanciful costume sketch for *Le Coq d'Or* shows the figure of a soldier, possibly King Dodan, dressed for battle. The treatment of the drawing is suited to the fantasy of Rimski-Korsakov's opera, based on an ancient Russian fairy tale.

Diecilis Vital

Born 1920 in Jacmel, Haiti. The son of a painter, Vital works with strong color in the primitive style popular in Haiti. All his paintings are set in his home town of Jacmel.

UNTITLED
Oil on pressboard, 24x32 in., 1971
No. PN1609

A view of Jacmel, showing houses, distant fields and a river. The perspective, as always with Vital, is perpendicular.

Andrew John Henry Way, *Grapes*

Renato Volpini

Born 1934 in Urbino, Italy. In 1957 Volpini graduated from the Urbino Institute of Art and the following year moved to Milan, where he now lives. A printmaker as well as a painter, he also works in collage. Volpini's style is melodic, using large, translucent areas of color accentuated by contour lines of varying widths.

UNTITLED
Collage with tempera, 26¼x36¼ in., 1971
No. ML1541

Andrew John Henry Way

Born 1826 in Washington, D.C.; died 1888 in Baltimore. A landscape, still-life and portrait painter, Way studied privately with artists in Cincinnati and Baltimore. In 1850 he went to Paris where he remained for four years interrupted by excursions to Italy. Upon his return to the United States he settled in Baltimore and became the city's foremost still-life painter.

GRAPES
Oil on canvas, 18⅛x12⅛ in., 1881
No. 1295

GRAPES
Oil on canvas, 18⅛x12⅛ in., 1881
No. 1296

Way was fascinated by grapes and painted them repeatedly. In this pair of canvases he contrasts green and purple varieties of grapes, the glossy clusters set off against a background of wooden panel painted with an exactitude reminiscent of Harnett and Peto. The paintings are signed and dated in the lower left.

The Ghost

Robert Jay Wolff

Born 1905 in Chicago. Wolff was a student at Yale from 1923 to 1926 when he left to study art in Paris. After returning to the United States his interest in contemporary art education led him to collaborate with Laszlo Moholy-Nagy and Gyorgy Kepes in founding the Institute of Design where he remained until 1942. Wolff headed the art department at Brooklyn College for many years. His personal style has remained committed to the two-dimensional surface of the picture plane with a growing emphasis on disciplined simplification. Interrelationships of color are the basis for his compositions; for him color actually becomes a dimension. Wolff has written widely on art. A book by him, entitled *Art and Learning*, was published in 1971.

THE GHOST
Casein, 9⅞x9⅞ in., 1958
No. 1307

The Ghost, Wolff says, belonged to an "imagery of short duration in my work. It was one of a series of casein studies that acted as preparations for larger paintings." The final oil painting, for which this is a study, is in the artist's collection.

CAPE COD TIME PIECE
Oil on canvas, 20x46 in., 1966
No. 877

With nothing more than the geometry of rectangular color areas, the artist has produced a painting filled with the hour-by-hour changing light of Cape Cod where Wolff sometimes works in the summer.

Zenderoudi

Born 1937 in Teheran, Iran. Since 1961 Zenderoudi has lived in Paris. His recent work consists of complicated abstract compositions based on Persian calligraphy.

UNTITLED
Gouache, 38x41 in., 1970
No. FR1697

UNTITLED
Gouache, 38x41 in., 1970
No. FR1698

Both gouaches are concerned with calligraphy.

Karl Zerbe

Born 1903 in Berlin, Germany; died 1972 in Tallahassee, Florida. Zerbe's family moved to Paris the year after his birth but returned to Germany in 1914, this time to Frankfurt. He first studied chemistry and then worked in an architect's office in Munich. Later he attended the Munich Academy of Art. Zerbe spent three years in Italy, returning to Munich in 1926. He came to the United States, finally settling in Boston in 1934. Chiefly an Expressionist, he enlivened his work with richly textured surfaces. He was one of the first artists to experiment with acrylic paint. Zerbe headed the painting departments at the Boston Museum School and later at Florida State University.

BIG OWL NO. 1
Gouache, 35½x23½ in., 1969
No. 829

In the late sixties, and until the time of his death, Zerbe's interest in ornithology led him to create many dramatic "portraits" of birds.

Zuka (Zenaida Gurievna Booyakovitch)

Born 1924 in Los Angeles. Zuka, as she is known professionally, graduated from the University of Southern California. She began her studies in painting with Dan Lutz in California, and then moved to New York where she worked at the Art Students League and studied with Yasuo Kuniyoshi. She now lives in Paris. Zuka treats her subjects, mostly historical figures, in a series of flat silhouettes emphasized by strong color. Her methods recall forms from Japanese woodcuts and, even more, from early American paintings.

LINCOLN
Oil on canvas, 77¼x39 in., 1969
No. 1626

At once compassionate and satiric, this portrait of Lincoln shows him swathed in his famous shawl.

Horst Antes

Born 1936 in Heppenheim, Germany. Antes studied at the Academy of Fine Arts in Karlsruhe from 1957 to 1959 and presently teaches at the same school. His theme is always the human figure, but usually represented without a torso. Sometimes a head or hand alone suffices; sometimes a head directly attached to legs. Depending on the artist's mood, these elisions can be whimsical or frightening, but as a rule his apparitions are unnerving. He is considered one of Germany's most important living artists.

SMALL HAND
Polished chrome and steel 6/6,
25¼x16½x11 in., 1968
No. FR1694

The barred cage which surrounds this monumental hand evokes a sense of imprisonment. Though Antes is better known as painter and printmaker, he also makes occasional sculptures.

HEAD
Silkscreen on metal 9/35, 17¼x17¼x1¼ in.,
1969
No. BS1366

A head seen in profile with frontal, staring eye is one of Antes' recurring themes. This multiple is a wall plaque.

Horst Antes, *Small Hand*

Richard Anuszkiewicz

Born 1930 in Erie, Pennsylvania. Anuszkiewicz received a BFA from the Cleveland Institute of Art and an MFA from Yale where he was a student of Josef Albers who influenced him greatly. The younger artist, like his teacher, has long been interested in optical color experiments. With a strong emphasis on linear devices he creates visual illusions that give his paintings a sense of palpitating motion. He lives in New Jersey near New York City.

VOLUMES
Silkscreen on plastic, 26 ft.x61 ft. 6 in., 1970
No. 1123

With nineteen sets of a variable multiple which he designed earlier, Anuszkiewicz created a vast wall decoration specifically for the mezzanine floor of the Bank. Using only the multiples, he made a unique work of art which under his direction can be varied from time to time. The present arrangement of box-shaped "volumes" creates a vibrating energy. *For colorplate see page 24.*

Jean (Hans) Arp

Born 1887 in Strasbourg, Germany; died 1966 in Basle, Switzerland. One of the most important figures in twentieth-century art, Arp began his career as a poet and later studied at the School of Applied Arts in Strasbourg, at the Weimar Art School and at the Académie Julian in Paris. Settling in Switzerland during 1909, two years later in Lucerne he organized the Moderne Bund, an exhibition of pioneer artists including Gauguin, Hodler, Matisse and Picasso. In 1914 Arp met Max Jacob, Modigliani and Apollinaire in Paris, also Max Ernst in Cologne. His associations with them were instrumental in establishing the Zurich Dada movement in 1915. Several young writers and artists, fleeing to neutral Switzerland during the first World War, formed a group which questioned, attacked and negated the traditions of Western art, literature and life. In addition to Arp the group included the German writers Hugo Ball and Richard Huelsenbeck, the German artist Hans Richter, the Rumanian poet Tristan Tzara and the Rumanian painter Marcel Janco. Rejecting all past reason and rules, the Dadaists relied on a kind of fatalistic nihilism. At the outbreak of World War II Arp moved to Grasse in southern France and then to Switzerland, later making three trips to the United States. Throughout his life, he experimented with all manner of materials and was known for his reliefs, cutouts, drawings, sculpture and poetry. His curvilinear simplified forms, usually anthropomorphic, are often witty and always sensuous.

RELIEF CONCRET D
Duraluminum 1/5, 18x26x4 in., 1961
No. 356

As early as 1916 Arp began experimenting with abstract reliefs, a new form he based on arrangements made "according to the laws of chance," by dropping cutout shapes at random on a flat surface. Though his first reliefs were of wood, he later turned to metal, creating a series in duraluminum during 1960–61. Each shape in *Relief Concret D* relates to its neighbor as well as to the surrounding empty spaces. The surface of the metal has been carefully chased in order to absorb and reflect light.

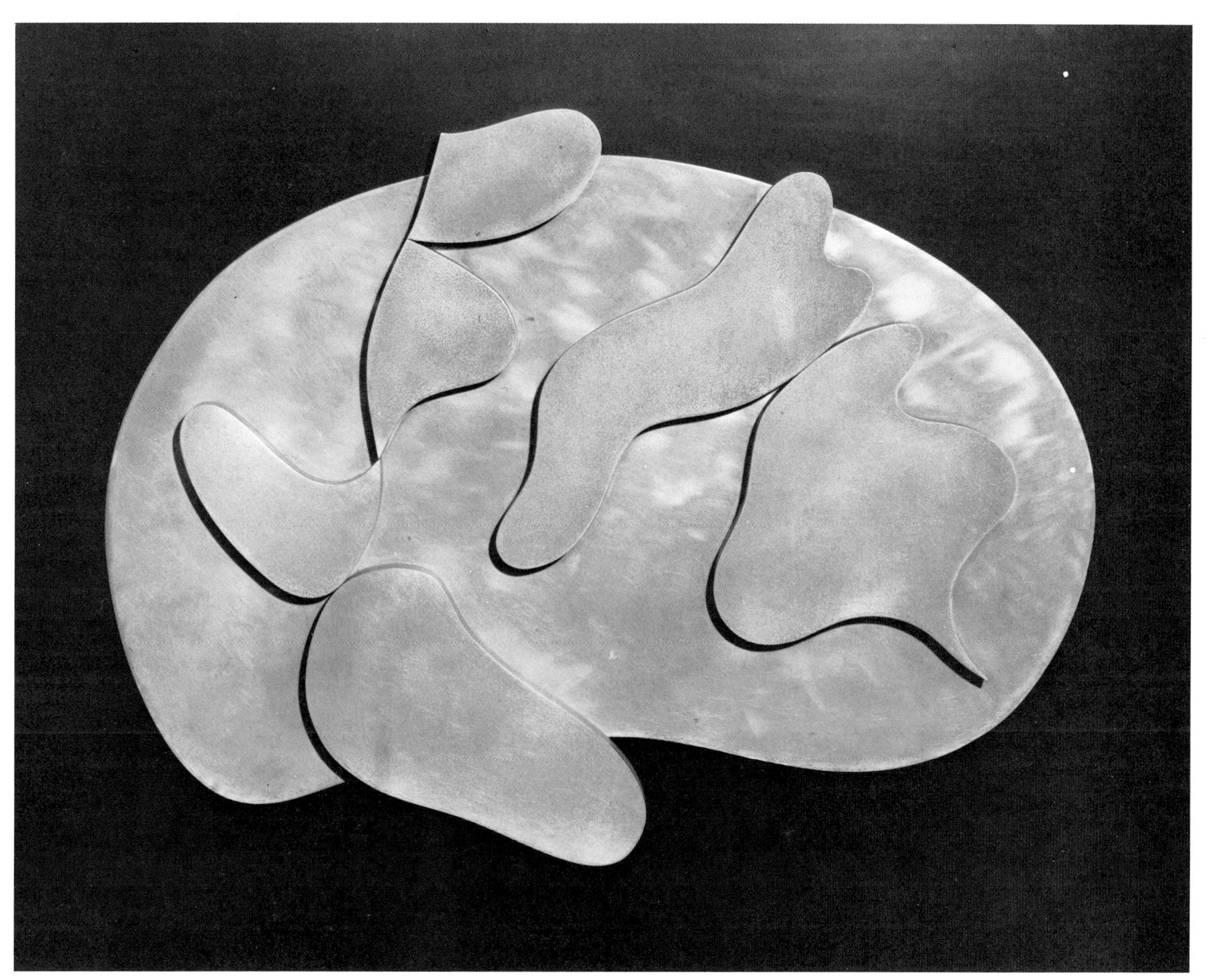

Jean (Hans) Arp, *Relief Concret D*

Joannis Avramidis

Born 1922 in Batumi, Russia. The son of Greek parents living in Russia, Avramidis studied painting at the art school in Batumi and also in Greece where he stayed from 1939 to 1943. He continued to study painting in Vienna and remained a painter until 1953 when he turned to sculpture. His sculpture, often semi-abstract, derives from the human body. Each work is preceded by a series of drawings, the starting point always an aspect of human anatomy. His early sculpture shows the influence of Arp. Avramidis, who usually works in bronze or aluminum, lives in Vienna.

TORSO
Bronze 4/6, 33x7¼x7¼ in., 1960
No. GN1435

A satin-smooth seductive torso that suggests the influence of Arp. The sculpture is signed.

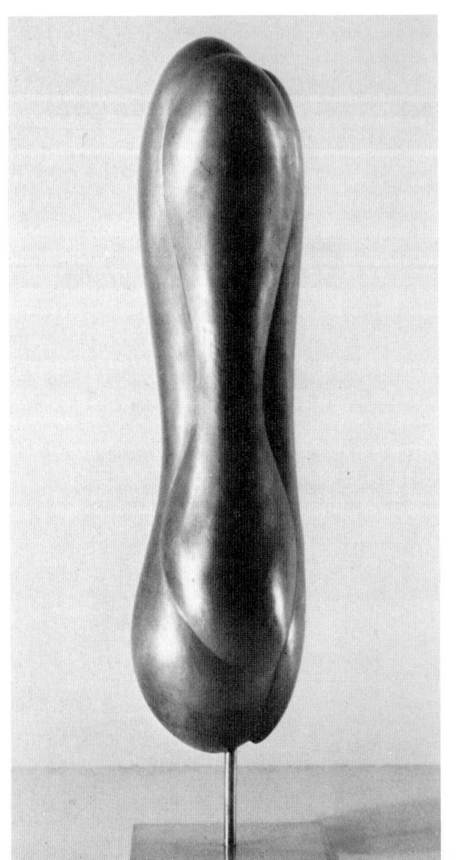

George Gray Barnard

Born 1863 in Bellefonte, Pennsylvania; died 1938 in New York. Barnard began drawing and modeling animal figures during his boyhood. At seventeen he studied at the School of the Art Institute of Chicago and later in Paris at the Ecole des Beaux-Arts. By the time he left France in 1894, he had received acclaim at the Salon du Champ de Mars and had been elected an Associate of the Société Nationale des Beaux-Arts. In America in 1902 Barnard was commissioned to do several important groups of sculpture for the exterior of the new Pennsylvania State Capitol. In order to carry out this project, which was finally installed in an abbreviated form, he returned to France where he remained until 1913. While there he amassed a large collection of medieval sculpture, part of which he sold and part of which he took back to New York, installing it in a private museum he called The Cloisters. The collection was purchased from Barnard in 1925 by John D. Rockefeller and given to the Metropolitan Museum as the basis for the present Cloisters, now in Fort Tryon Park. Barnard's sculpture, influenced by the works of Rodin, whom he met in Paris, and by those of Michelangelo, was monumental in scale and often romantic in feeling, but always realistic.

ABRAHAM LINCOLN
Marble, 20x12x13 in., 1919
No. 323

In 1910 Barnard was commissioned by the Taft family to create a full-length bronze statue of Abraham Lincoln to be placed in a Cincinnati park. Using as models both a life mask of Lincoln (made by Leonard Wells Volk in 1860 in Chicago) and a six-foot, four-inch Kentucky rail-splitter, Barnard unveiled the sculpture in 1917. It was both highly praised and severely criticized, members of Lincoln's family calling it "grotesque." Barnard made several other likenesses of Lincoln, among them marble busts most of which were similar except for minor details. The Bank's marble carving was owned by the artist's family until it came to Chicago, and it is one of the few versions finished entirely by the artist himself. There are similar versions at the Metropolitan Museum in New York, the Musée du Luxembourg in Paris, the Lincoln School in New York and in two private collections.

George Gray Barnard, *Abraham Lincoln* —

David Barr

Born 1939 in Detroit. Now a professor of art at Macomb County Community College in Michigan, Barr received his BFA in 1962 and MA in sculpture in 1965, both from Wayne State University. Stylistically he belongs to the international structurist movement, descending from Constructivism and Neo-Plasticism. As a rule he confines his wooden reliefs to vertical elements controlled by variations of dimension and color.

NO. 6
Acrylic on wood and masonite, 24x30x3 in., 1966
No. 1837

The inherently static character of Barr's wooden strips is belied by careful manipulation. Within a strictly vertical formula the strips are so interrelated as to suggest tension and motion. The work is a wall relief.

Varujan Boghosian
(for biography see p. 41)

ONE OF FOUR
Mixed media, 33½x18x7¾ in., 1968
No. 306

Some of Boghosian's favorite objects—a doll and weathered wood—make up this assemblage. The title of the work, Boghosian says, relates to one of the four characters in the Orpheus myth; the antique sexless doll, with its movable arms and its body partly hidden, is intended to suggest Orpheus.

Emile Antoine Bourdelle

Born 1861 in Montauban, France; died 1929 in le Vésinet, France. Bourdelle's introduction to sculpture came in the workshop of his father who was a cabinetmaker in Montauban. From these modest beginnings he went on to study art in Toulouse and finally in 1884 at the Ecole des Beaux-Arts in Paris. In 1893 he entered the studio of Rodin where he worked not as a pupil but as an assistant. During this period he maintained the integrity of his own style, which was often influenced by archaic Greek and Gothic sculpture. The range of his work was wide and he is known for portrait busts and intimate smaller figures as well as large-scale monuments. Bronze was his preference, though one of his most important large statues, the *Virgin of Alsace*, is in stone.

BEETHOVEN WITH CRAVAT
Bronze 4/10, 12½x10½x9¾ in., 1890
No. PR177

Beethoven's image obsessed Bourdelle. From 1888 until his death the sculptor made over thirty versions of the composer, ranging from an isolated hand to brooding faces. Though Bourdelle never knew Beethoven, he tried repeatedly to recreate the musician's personality. All Bourdelle's bronzes are limited to editions of ten. This is no. 4 and was cast at the Susse Foundry.

GREAT WARRIOR OF MONTAUBAN
Bronze 5/10, 70½x62½x20 in., 1898
No. 324

This sculpture, considered Bourdelle's masterpiece, represents one of the principal figures in a monument to those Montauban citizens who defended their city during the Franco-Prussian War of 1870–71. The artist began the monument in 1893 and completed it in 1902, making numerous studies for the various figures, each of which portrays a different aspect of war. The female figure of France represents the ideals for which men fight; the *Warrior* dramatizes virility and force, while a dying figure symbolizes the agony of war. The heroic scale, rough surface and exaggerated muscularity of the *Warrior* all suggest indomitable power. The surface of the sculpture catches the light with an impressionistic Rodinesque technique. The original plaster model is in the Musée Bourdelle in Paris. The number of bronzes is limited to ten of which the Bank owns cast no. 5. Other casts of the *Great Warrior* are in the Joseph Hirshhorn Museum in Washington, D.C., the Jerusalem Museum and the Chrysler Collection. The figure was cast at the Susse Foundry.

Above, *The Monument at Montauban*, and at right, Emile Antoine Bourdelle, *The Great Warrior of Montauban*

Emile Antoine Bourdelle

← WOMAN WITH RAISED ARMS
Bronze 6/10, 22¾x7⅜x5¾ in., 1909
No. 176

Between 1905 and 1912 Bourdelle executed a series of standing female figures. Despite their relatively modest size, he gave them monumentality by exaggerating their amplitude. Here the simplicity of the woman's garment also contributes to a sense of scale. The original plaster model for the *Woman with Raised Arms* is in the Musée Bourdelle in Paris. The edition, cast by the Susse Foundry, is limited to ten, of which this is no. 6.

Harvey Breverman

Born 1934 in Pittsburgh. Breverman received degrees from Carnegie Institute, where he studied with Balcomb Greene, and from Ohio University. He has also taught at both of these schools and is presently a professor of art at the State University of New York, Buffalo. As a printmaker, Breverman has won many awards and grants, including one from the government of the Netherlands which gave him the opportunity to work as artist-in-residence at the State Academy of Fine Arts, Amsterdam in 1965. His work is figurative and naturalistic.

FIGURE WITH MEDALS
Bronze 2/15, 14¾x10¾x1 in., 1969
No. 536

In 1969 a number of leading printmakers in the United States were invited to the Kalamazoo Art Center Sculpture Workshop to learn a variety of methods for casting metal sculpture. In the process, their own basic familiarity with metal—the creation of a negative plate from which a print is made—was transposed into the new experience of working with the positive plasticity of metal sculpture. This wall relief by Breverman is one of four sculptures in the Bank which were made at Kalamazoo by graphic artists.

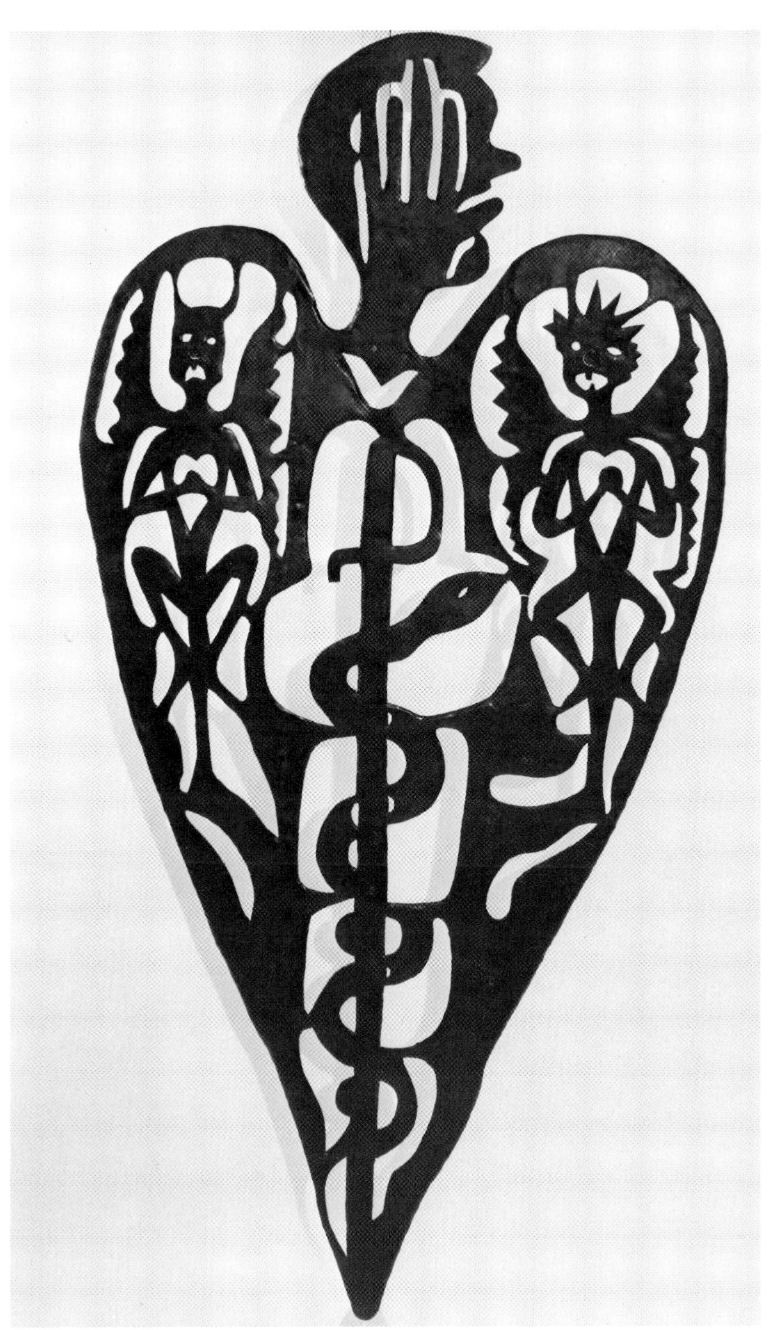

Murat Brierre, *Infidel Heart*

Murat Brierre

Born 1938 in Port-au-Prince, Haiti. Using a material readily available in Haiti, Brierre cuts his sculpture from steel oil drums. His figures are fantastic images based on his Afro-Haitian heritage and especially on Voodoo practices. He works in flat iron silhouettes which become cutout wall reliefs. The artist now lives in Brooklyn, New York where he has a studio.

INFIDEL HEART
Iron, 57x34 in., 1972
No. 1309

This relief is composed of a large heart terminating in the profile of a man's head which in turn surrounds the silhouette of a hand. Two winged devils cavort within the heart on either side of a slithering snake. The sculpture has a violence typical of Brierre.

COCKFIGHT
Iron, 14x33¼ in., 1972
No. KI1468

In another cutout relief two cocks, spurs flying, are intertwined so that each head is crowded into the cavity of the other's body. The cockfight is popular in Haiti.

UNTITLED
Iron, 32x11 in., 1971
No. PN1604

A small relief in which arms and legs spring from six grimacing masks. The composition is tied together in one continuous form.

Pol Bury, *Sphere in Four Parts*

Pol Bury

Born 1922 in Haine-Sainte Pierre, Belgium. After studying art in Mons, Belgium, Bury started his career as a surrealist painter, but at thirty-one abandoned painting for sculpture. The mysteries of movement are his basic concern, movement activated by electric motors. The separate but related elements of his sculpture seem almost imperceptibly propelled by some inner psychological force. Bury uses a variety of materials such as aluminum, stainless steel, copper, brass, wood and nylon. Since 1961 he has lived in or near Paris. In 1964 his work was featured in the Belgian Pavilion at the Venice Biennale.

SPHERE IN FOUR PARTS
Brass 6/8, 12x20 in. diameter, 1969
No. 696

Powered by an electric motor, four metal sections of a sphere creep at random over the surface of a round metal base. The slowly moving pieces collide or pass each other in an unpredictable ballet. Eight examples of this work were cast; the Bank's is the sixth.

Alexander Calder

Born 1898 in Philadelphia. The son and grandson of sculptors, the younger Calder was initiated early into the world of art. His first formal training, however, was as a mechanical engineer at the Stevens Institute of Technology where he received a degree in 1919. In the early twenties he studied drawing and painting at the Art Students League in New York. Considered one of America's greatest sculptors, Calder is credited with having invented the mobile, a sculpture that moves. He also is known for his stabiles, a title given to Calder's large immobile structures by Arp. Calder, who made his first trip to Paris in 1926, has lived alternately in France and Roxbury, Connecticut. His sculpture is sometimes abstract, but more often it grows directly from nature. It is frequently architectural in scale and scope.

SNAKE ON THE POST
Bronze 1/6, 25½x18½x28½ in.,
executed 1944, cast 1969
No. 442

In 1944 the architect Wallace K. Harrison suggested that Calder make several projects for outdoor sculpture. As a result, the artist executed plaster models which were to have been enlarged and cast in cement. These monumental pieces, however, never materialized, but in 1968 Calder authorized the original plasters to be cast in bronze editions, a departure for him since his work is usually made from cut, welded or riveted metal sheets. Calder's early training as a mechanical engineer is evident in much of his sculpture. Here the snake, carefully balanced on its post, can both dip and rotate. All the 1944 plasters were limited to six casts in bronze; the Bank's is cast no. 1.

Alexander Calder, *Snake on the Post*⟶

Sergio de Camargo

Born 1930 in Rio de Janeiro, Brazil. At eighteen the artist went to Paris where he studied philosophy at the Sorbonne. While there he met Brancusi, Arp and Vantongerloo. In 1961 he settled permanently in Paris. Camargo is best known for his reliefs which consist of variegated wooden dowels attached to a flat surface. Each piece is cut separately, affixed at a different angle and usually painted white, thus allowing the sculpture to respond to light with great versatility.

RELIEF NO. 199
Wood, 53½x15x3 in., 1968
No. 555

RELIEF NO. 234
Wood, 39½x39½x2 in., 1969
No. 354

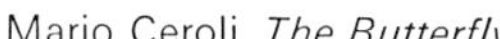

Sergio de Camargo, *Relief No. 234*

Mario Ceroli, *The Butterfly*

Cosmo Campoli

Born 1922 in South Bend, Indiana. Campoli graduated from the School of the Art Institute of Chicago in 1950, spending the next two years abroad on a fellowship which took him to Spain, France and Italy. On returning to Chicago, he and another sculptor formed the Contemporary Art Workshop where equipment and space were made available to artists. Campoli's style is expressionistic, often incorporating two of Brancusi's favorite themes, the bird and the egg. Since 1953 he has taught at the Illinois Institute of Technology in Chicago where he lives.

MOTHER KISSING CHILD
Bronze, 10½x33½ in. circumference, 1971
No. 1306

This sculpture is a study for a projected monument twelve feet in diameter which Campoli would like to execute in pink granite or rose quartz. The artist compares the two shapes to a mother and child, or to the earth and moon.

Marco Cancellieri

Born 1931 in Rome. Cancellieri attended the Industrial Technical Institute for Watchmaking and Mechanics for five years. He also supervised operations in the manufacture of metal furniture before going to Jamaica in 1962 as a dye-maker for an engineering company. He now lives and works in Rome where he is a master craftsman in fine metal work and produces metal sculpture.

UNTITLED
Metal relief, 6½x4⅛ in., 1971
No. KI1469

UNTITLED
Metal relief, 6⅜x4¾ in., 1971
No. KI1470

Both metal reliefs reflect Cancellieri's experience with the intricacies of watchmaking.

Norman Carlberg

Born 1928 in Roseau, Minnesota. After attending the Minneapolis School of Art, Carlberg graduated from the Yale School of Art and Architecture with a BFA in 1958 and an of MFA in 1961. He spent 1960 in Santiago, Chile on a teaching Fulbright grant at Catholic University. Since then Carlberg has been teaching at the Rhinehart School of Sculpture, Maryland Institute College of Art in Baltimore. Under the influence of Constructivism and Josef Albers, with whom he worked at Yale, his sculpture has remained committed to strong, simple forms. Recently a unit type of sculpture lending itself to large outdoor pieces has dominated his work.

SNOW FORM
Epoxy over plaster and wood, 56x27x17 in. 1964/66
No. 283

A polished white column branches at the top in two parts, asymmetrical but precise in form. The base, shining black in contrast, continues as a natural extension of the upper column widening enough to support the entire structure. The sculpture, despite its title, seems purely nonobjective.

Lourdes Castro

Born 1930 in the Madeira Islands. In 1956 Castro graduated from art school in Lisbon and studied in Munich for an additional year. In 1957 she moved to Paris where she still lives. Her art is based on a system of superimposing plastic foil and photo-silkscreen on one another. Castro is also interested in film-making.

SILHOUETTE OF A MAN WITH A CIGARETTE
Plastic foil and photosensitive paper 15/20, 12¼x19½x1½ in., 1967
No. GN1436

A witty multiple that is signed on the lower right side.

Alik Cavaliere

Born 1926 in Rome. When he was twelve, Cavaliere's family moved to Milan where he studied at the Academy of the Brera under the sculptors, Giacomo Manzu and Marino Marini. He became the assistant of the latter. Cavaliere also took courses at the University of Milan. Often working in series that depend on literary content, he tends to employ contrasting materials in the same work. One of his specialties is the realistic representation of plants and fruit. His sculpture is strongly *trompe l'oeil.*

THE APPLE
Bronze, 7⅝x9 1/16x4 5/16 in., 1967
No. ML1527

Made of highly polished bronze, a realistically conceived apple seems to give off its own light. Cavaliere created a series of thirty apples, each slightly different, and this is the twelfth of the series. The work is signed.

Mario Ceroli

Born 1938 in Castelfrentano, Italy. As a young man, Ceroli moved to Rome where he devoted himself to sculpture. His work is usually involved with two-dimensional silhouettes, often in groups of nearly life-size human figures cut from wooden packing crates with no attempt to conceal nail holes, lettering or any other surface aberrations. Despite the patent nonreality of these figures, Ceroli produces an element of illusionism by using shadows, both natural and simulated, in many of his sculptural environments. He has also designed stage settings for Shakespearian productions and for the cinema in Rome where he lives.

THE BUTTERFLY
Paper in lucite shadow box, 24x30x4½ in., 1969
No. 1823

A large white butterfly, made of paper, gives the transient effect of a trembling insect impaled in a specimen box.

Ferdinando Codognotto, *Owl*

Peter Chinni

Born 1928 in Mount Kisco, New York. Chinni studied at the Art Students League in New York and in Rome at the Academy of Fine Arts. He returned to New York after nine years in Italy but again in 1966 went back to Rome where he still lives. Working in bronze, stainless steel and silver, he is concerned with cosmic origins from which he takes such titles as *Earth Cycle, Awakening Mountain, Genesis* and the Bank's *Primordial Form II*. His sculpture is abstract, but as a rule is related to organic forms.

PRIMORDIAL FORM II
Bronze, 15½x23¼x11 in., 1966
No. 524

In this sculpture Chinni has given the bronze an almost black stone-like patina. Typical of his work, the curving dark form seems to have anthropomorphic overtones.

Ferdinando Codognotto

Born 1940 in San Doná di Piave, Italy. Codognotto is a self-taught artist who creates sculpture in unpainted wood. Frequently he takes his subject from nature, from birds, plants, and flowers, magnifying and transforming his images into stylized objects of fantasy. He lives in Rome where he has also created a series of puppets for the Children's Theatre and where he sometimes works as a cabinet-maker.

FLOWER
Wood, 74x9x8¾ in., 1972
No. RO2032

A huge blossom, hinged to a long stem, is mobile and can be adjusted to various angles.

OWL
Wood, 28½x18x7 in., 1972
No. RO2033

Codognotto has provided the owl with mirrors in place of eyes. The viewer sees himself reflected in, and as part of, this sculpture.

Angel Duarte

Born 1930 in Aldeanueva del Camino, Spain. Duarte attended art school in Madrid from 1945 to 1948. He became a member of the group "Equipo 57" with whom he exhibited. His art is modular and geometric. He is interested in the idea of multiple sculpture. The artist lives in Paris.

MODULAR STRUCTURE
Metal 14/15, 19½x10½x2½ in., 1969
No. GN1437

This abstract wall relief is signed on the back.

Dušan Džamonya

Born 1928 in Strumica, Yugoslavia. Džamonya completed his art studies in Zagreb in 1951. His early sculpture, which stressed the human figure, was influenced by the British artists Henry Moore and Lynn Chadwick. Since the early sixties his work has become completely abstract. His materials include nails, iron, blocks of wood and lumps of glass. In place of his past serenity, he has recently introduced disquieting, aggressive elements into his sculpture. The artist lives in Zagreb.

SCULPTURE NO. 25
Iron, 26x12x8¼ in., 1963
No. LN1485

By means of nails fused together, Džamonya has produced a threatening circle. The tension created by these multiple spikes is strong, and so also is their suggestion of hostility.

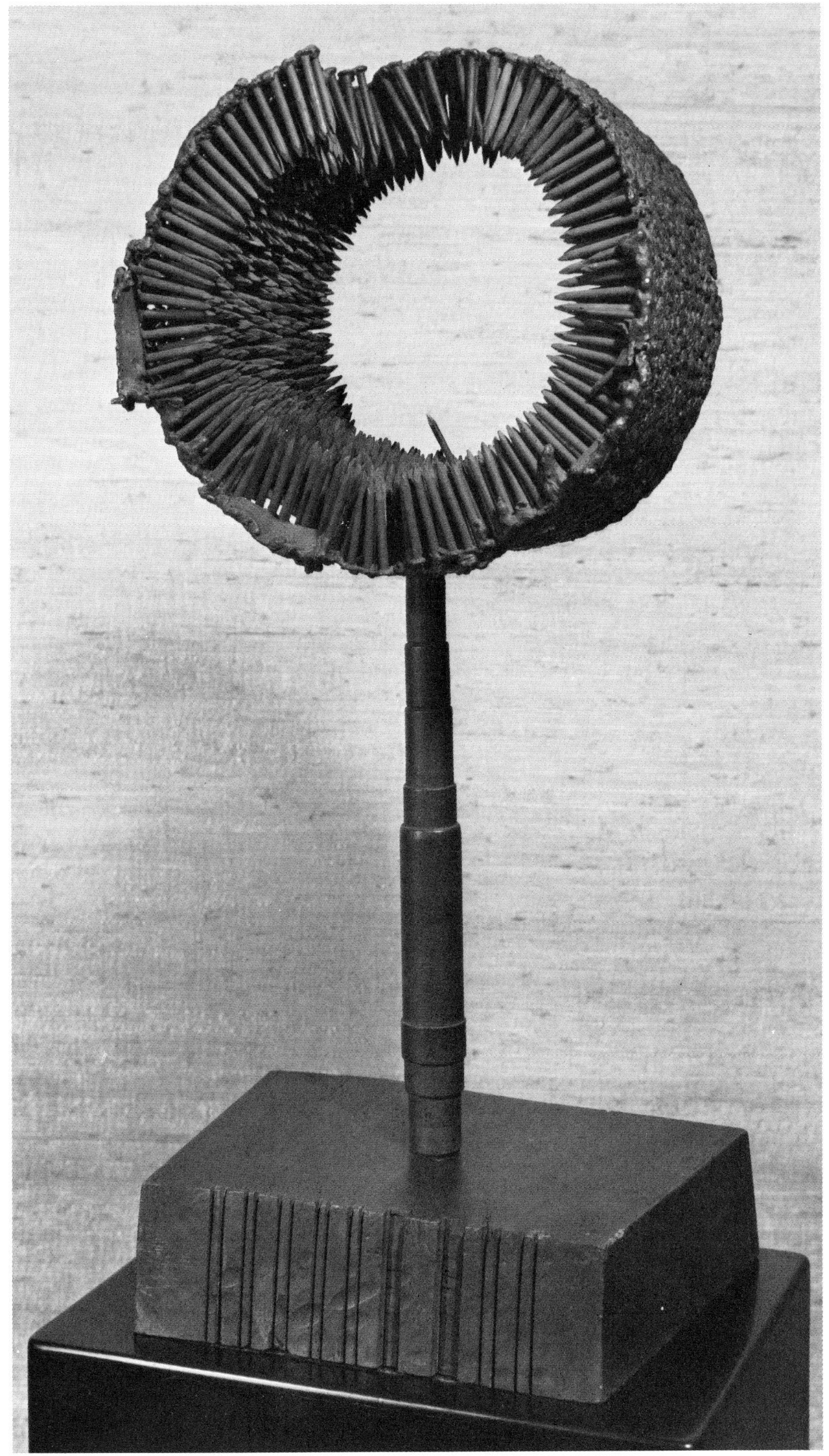

Dušan Džamonya, *Sculpture No. 25*

Julius Geissler

Born 1935 in Ulm, Germany. Geissler studied architecture at the Stuttgart Technical School but since 1956 has been working in sculpture. He began making modular structures in 1959 and turned to the use of synthetic materials—especially duroplast and aluminum—in 1964. Geissler lives in Düsseldorf where he also experiments with color and black light as elements of sculpture.

UNTITLED
Aluminum and plastic 24/50, 39x7¾x7¾ in., ca. 1970–71
No. DS1412

Polyhedral units are clustered on tall bars to form this sculpture. The work is signed and numbered.

David Hare

Born 1917 in New York. Hare, who grew up in the Southwest, first studied chemistry and then from 1938 to 1943 worked with color photography. During World War II under the influence of several French Surrealists, who had settled in the United States temporarily, he experimented with "heatages," a photographic process by which he melted the negative in order to distort the final image. Hare was editor-in-chief of the surrealist periodical *VVV* which first appeared in 1942 and continued with four issues into 1944. The editorial committee included André Breton, Max Ernst and Marcel Duchamp, all of whom may have influenced Hare in one way or another. Interested in Freudian psychology, he often looks to dreams and free association as starting points for his work. He is best known as the first serious American surrealist sculptor. In recent years he has also turned to painting and to large drawings, most of which deal with psychological symbols of mythology. The artist lives in New York.

SUICITE
Bronze, 19(with base)x27x5½ in., 1944
No. 830

A female figure, abstracted in tense coils and sadistic edges, thrusts through space on a course of self-destruction. This early and significant example of American surrealist sculpture is a unique cast, produced by the lost wax process. "Suicite," a variant of "suicide," according to the artist defines a single member of a group in which all are dedicated to taking their own lives. Date and signature both appear at the base of the sculpture.

Erwin Hauer

Born 1926 in Vienna. Hauer came to the United States to study at the Rhode Island School of Design under a Fulbright travel grant in 1956. He had already completed work at an art school in Vienna and the Academy of the Brera in Milan. His later association with Josef Albers, who was first his teacher and then his colleague at Yale, is evident in the geometric purity of his sculpture. In describing his work Hauer says, "The identical module holds the greatest fascination. Pared down to the simplest possible form, it contains the entire law of growth of the system." In 1963 after a three-year sojourn in Mexico, the artist returned to Yale as assistant professor in sculpture. He lives in New Haven.

UNTITLED
Bronze 1/3, 27¾x28½x21½ in., 1968
No. 233

The module of this sculpture is repeated in exact half measure with the curious effect of obscuring the basic form. The artist also repeats exact openings, convexities and concavities, implying a nonexistent complexity in the work. The sculpture presents a different perspective from every angle.

David Hare, *Suicite*

David V. Hayes, *Seated Beast*

David V. Hayes

Born 1931 in Hartford, Connecticut. Hayes studied at the Ogunquit School of Painting and Sculpture with Robert Laurent and at the University of Notre Dame where he began as a premedical student. He received his MFA from Indiana University, studying there again with Robert Laurent and David Smith. During 1961–62 Hayes was awarded both Fulbright and Guggenheim fellowships, thus allowing him to work in Europe. His sculpture is executed mainly in forged steel and bronze, though in recent years he has experimented with colored glass and abstract, painted steel sheet constructions. His forms, usually figurative, are highly simplified. He lives in Coventry, Connecticut.

SEATED BEAST
Forged steel, 17x18x21 in., 1963
No. 297

Richard Hunt

Born 1935 in Chicago. Hunt graduated from the School of the Art Institute of Chicago in 1957 where he won a fellowship for a year's travel in Europe. He was awarded a Guggenheim Fellowship five years later. A visiting artist at Yale and Purdue, he has also taught at the School of the Art Institute of Chicago. In 1965 he received a Tamarind Fellowship that permitted him to experiment with lithography, but he is primarily a sculptor who welds aluminum, copper and steel into organic shapes. During his student days at the Art Institute he worked part-time in a biological laboratory, an experience that influenced his sculpture. Hunt's early pieces were identified with strange insects but more recently his forms are related to anthropomorphic sources. He lives in Chicago.

NATURAL FORM
Welded steel, 14¾x32½x13¼ in., 1967
No. 332

This work is one of a series of horizontal forms produced in the late sixties and based on human and animal skeletons. It epitomizes Hunt's description of his artistic goal, "to use every element of tri-dimensionality in one sculpture."

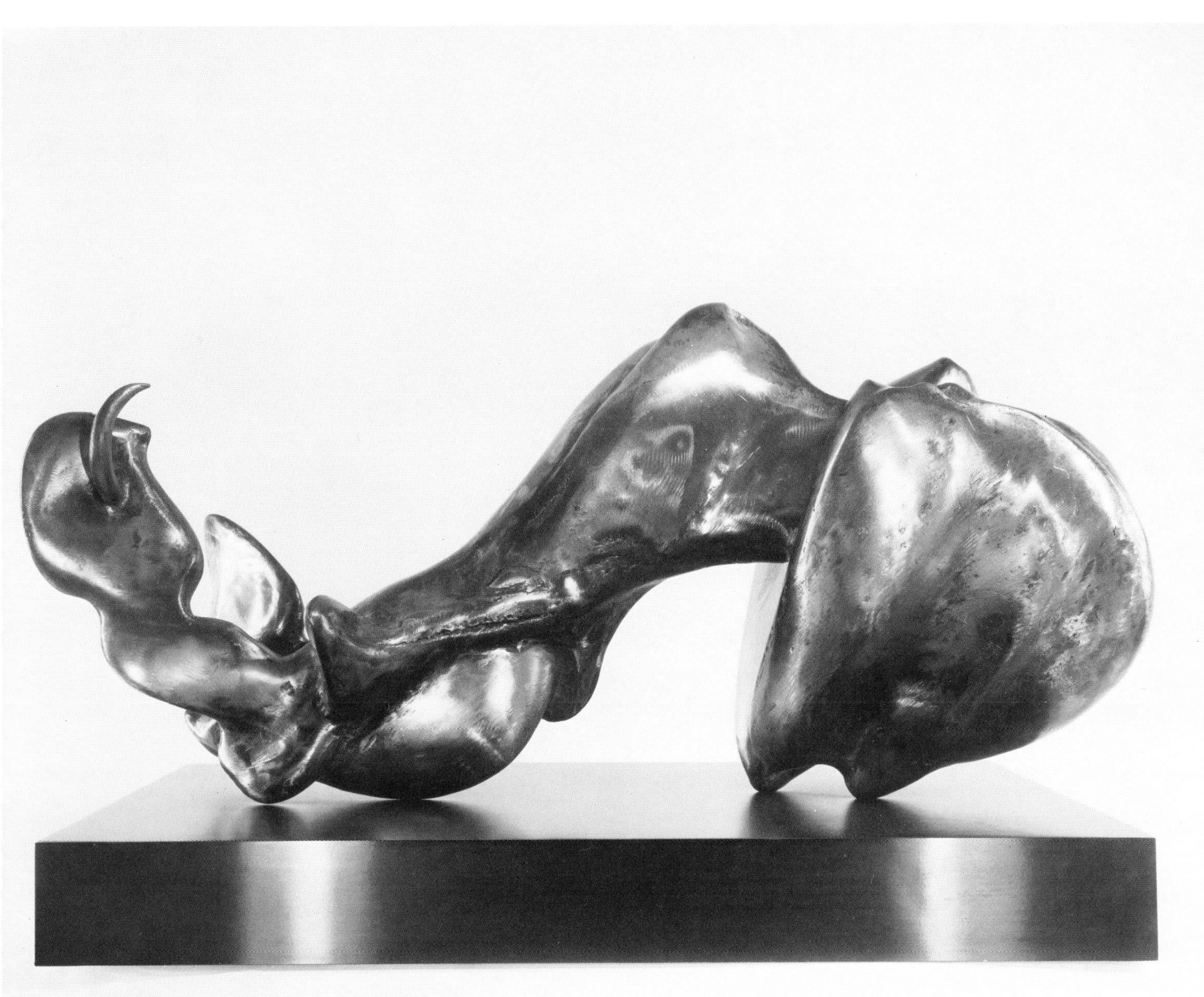

Richard Hunt, *Natural Form*

Italy/Anonymous, *Bust of a Man*

Italy/Anonymous

BUST OF A MAN
Terra-cotta, 30x23x10 in., ca. 1725
No. 1875

After the establishment of the French Academy in Rome in 1666, a classicizing element began to temper the exuberance of the Bernini tradition. This portrait bust of an unidentified, aristocratic cleric still has the sweeping presence of baroque art. One of a pair of male portraits, it is somewhat unusual because the subject's right hand has been shown instead of merely terminating the bust in a swirl of drapery, a more customary stylistic device for the period.

Italy/Anonymous

HEAD OF A BOAR
Porphyry, 10½x14¾x8 in., ca. 1550–1650.
No. 981

The art of porphyry carving was revived in sixteenth-century Italy, especially in Florence. In order to cut this unyielding stone, Vasari says, "Iron tools hardened by the juice of herbs" were needed. The Bank's carving may have come from the workshop of the Ferrucci family, well-known porphyry specialists in Florence. Since porphyry was prized for the high lustre it attains when polished, the rough surface of this work suggests it may be incomplete. An unfinished drill hole below the snout also seems to indicate that work on the sculpture was arrested before completion. Boars are still hunted in Tuscany and have been a popular subject in art since classical times. This sculpture belonged to the Serristori family of Florence and may originally have been part of a larger decorative piece connected with architecture.

Italy/Anonymous

STORY OF BALAAM
Limestone, 18½x45x2 in., date unknown
No. 1122

Here, in an Old Testament story, the prophet Balaam has been called by his king to curse the Israelites and prevent their passage through the land of Moab during the exodus from Egypt. God sends an angel to stop the prophet, and the ass on which Balaam is riding halts in the holy presence. Unaware of the angel, Balaam beats the animal who then miraculously reproaches his master in a human voice. The prophet is converted instantly by this supernatural event. The Bank's carving, based on the façade of San Leonardo, a twelfth-century Romanesque church in Foggia, Italy, differs from the original which has no blank spaces between the figures and the border ornament. Though the sculpture has been attributed to the Romanesque period, Charles Avery and John Beckwith of the Victoria and Albert Museum suggest it is a later work.

Norman Ives (for biography see p. 68)

BLACK BAS-RELIEF
Painted wood, 24x24x2⅝ in., ca. 1965–70
No. 557

WHITE BAS-RELIEF
Painted wood, 24x24x2⅝ in., ca. 1965–70
No. 558

Two relief sculptures based on typography.

Minoru Kano

Born 1930 in Tokyo. After beginning his art studies in Tokyo, Kano left in 1957 for Paris where he attended the Ecole des Beaux-Arts and the Académie de la Grande Chaumière. The first influences on his work were from classical Roman sculpture, but since 1961 he has turned more and more toward abstraction. He began working in bronze and stone, but now prefers wood, a variety of metals and synthetic resins. He wants his work to suggest untapped sources of energy, expressed by the tension of his forms. The artist lives in Paris.

TONDO
Metal, 28 in. diameter, 1973
No. BR2047

An abstract relief where contrasts in form and texture give the sculpture a sense of rotating motion.

Kapo (Mallica Reynolds)
(for biography see p. 70)

THE SPIRIT OF REVIVAL
Concrete, 11x8½x5 in., ca. 1960
No. KI1475

A small cult figure, primitive and highly expressive. When purchased from the artist, it was decorating the roof of his house.

William King, *The Interview*

William King

Born 1925 in Jacksonville, Florida. King studied engineering at the University of Florida and then turned to architecture, attending Cooper Union in New York. Inspired especially by an exhibition of David Smith's work, he changed again, this time to sculpture. He has experimented frequently with materials—bronze, wood, terra-cotta and brass—and has sometimes even combined burlap or vinyl with aluminum, a metal which he either casts or uses in sheet form. King's emphasis is usually on the human figure handled in humorous context. He lives in New York.

THE INTERVIEW
Aluminum 3/6, 52x23½x10 in., 1968
No. 315

Made from cast aluminum, *The Interview* depicts a man smoking a cigarette as he leads an unwilling child by the hand. According to the artist, the two are headed for an interview with the admissions director of a private school.

THE TEST
Aluminum (artist's proof), 20x13x6 in., 1970
No. NA1586

One of King's favorite methods is to cut flat shapes from sheets of aluminum and fit the slotted pieces together. In this way the sculpture can be taken apart and easily transported. The title refers to an encounter between a man and woman in which, according to the artist, "The guy is seeing if the girl passes 'The Test'." The Bank's example is the artist's proof in an edition of two hundred. Two other versions of *The Test* were made, one six feet high, the other seven-and-a-half feet high, each limited to an edition of six.

Jiri Kolar (for biography see p. 71)

OLD APPLE
Papier-mâché, 13x38½ in. circumference,
ca. 1965–70
No. 599

The papier-mâché surface of this object, a larger-than-life size apple, is made from thin strips of paper printed in *fraktur*, a German script dating from the sixteenth century.

Jiri Kolar, *Old Apple*

Itaru Komuro, *Momijigari*

Itaru Komuro

Born 1941 in Osaka, Japan. Komuro studied at the Uemura Takachiyo Art School in Tokyo. He has developed a three-dimensional style in which he combines weathered wood and fine calligraphy taken from the scripts of classical Noh dramas. He lives in Tokyo.

MOMIJIGARI
Wood, 13¼x19¾x4 in., 1969
No. TK1769

The title of this work refers to the Japanese aristocracy's former practice of gathering autumn foliage in the woods, a pastime which became a subject for the Noh drama. The compartments, mask and calligraphy in the sculpture are all associated with the Noh theatre.

Rudolfo Krasno

Born 1926 in Buenos Aires. Krasno began taking courses in painting and sculpture at the Academy of Fine Arts in Buenos Aires. In 1959 he received a fellowship which made it possible for him to study in Paris, where he has remained. He works in various media but is best known for his white reliefs and sculpture in the round, both of papier-mâché.

WHITE AND PAPER
Papier-mâché 3/10, 45½x22 in., 1970
No. PR1624

This all-white abstract paper relief is signed in the lower left.

WHITE BREAK IN
Papier-mâché, 25⅓x20x4¼ in., 1973
No. AM2041

One of a series of works featuring the egg, this papier-mâché sculpture is pierced by an ovoid form.

Bernard Langlais

Born 1921 in Old Town, Maine. Langlais studied at the Corcoran School of Art, The Skowhegan School of Painting and Sculpture, the Brooklyn Museum Art School, the Académie de la Grande Chaumière, and at the Oslo Academy of Art during a Fulbright year abroad. His studio and home are in Thomaston on the coast of Maine where he assembles "primitive" sculpture from pieces of cast-off weathered wood. One of Langlais' favorite subjects is the farm and its animals. His work shows the influence of American folk art.

HORSE AND FENCE
Wood, 44½x66x8 in., 1969
No. 1007

Dovetailed wooden lathes make up the horse's rough coat in this relief sculpture. Some of the wood has been burned or daubed with paint to create the textural effect Langlais wants. The piece is signed.

Bernard Langlais, *Horse and Fence*

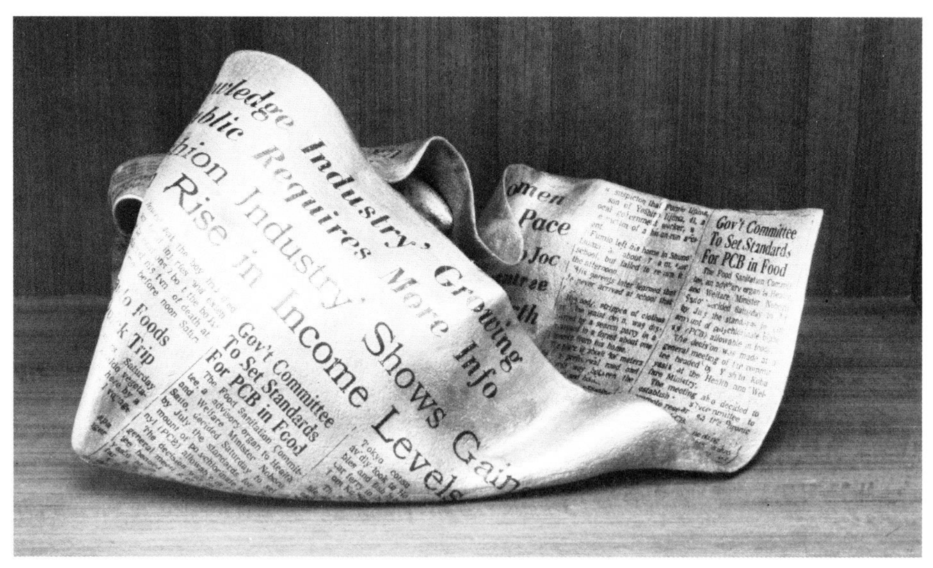

Kiyomi Mishima, *Newspaper*

Lidia Lopez

Born 1948 in Panama City. The artist has been a student of architecture at the University of Panama but is involved with works of art in many media. Influenced by Guillermo Trujillo (see p. 209), she works in an abstract style. Her home is in Panama City.

UNTITLED
Nails on board, 24x24x3 in., ca. 1971
No. PN1665

Nail heads in several sizes, pounded into a board at various depths, produce a structural pattern.

Robert Marx

Born 1925 in Northeim, Germany. Marx's family moved to the United States when he was two years old. Before becoming a printmaker he studied both architecture and painting, earning his BFA at the University of Illinois and his MFA from Heidelberg. He was a professor of drawing and design at the University of Wisconsin in 1953 and went on to teach at Flint Junior College in Michigan and at Syracuse University. Marx now lives in Newbury, Massachusetts.

HEAD OF A MAN
Bronze 2/18, 6⅜x6⅜x¾ in., 1969
No. 537

FIGURE WITH A COLLAR
Bronze 2/6, 16⅞x13⅛x1 in., 1969
No. 538

Two relief sculptures made at the Kalamazoo Sculpture Workshop (see p. 116).

Tomio Miki

Born 1937 in Tokyo. Miki began to exhibit with the "Neo-Dada Organizers" of postwar Japan when he was only twenty. The iconoclastic attitude of these young artists was exemplified by Miki's contribution to the Yomiuri Independent Show of 1958 when he splashed gasoline on his abstract paintings and set a match to them. By 1960 he joined the trend toward junkyard art, building huge sculptures from refuse. But in 1962, during a train ride, he says, "I suddenly felt myself surrounded by hundreds of ears trying to assault me." Since then he has been completely occupied with the ear—usually the left one—as subject matter. Miki's ears vary from exact reproductions to monumental abstractions; they have been produced in metal, clay and rubber, printed on plastic and used as scenery for a film. He lives in Tokyo.

EAR
Aluminum, 41¾x23¾x7⅝ in., 1972
No. TK1763

This gleaming image of a human ear is cast in aluminum. Its superhuman scale presents an abstract topography which nearly obscures the anatomical origins of the form.

Kiyomi Mishima

Born 1932 in Osaka, Japan. Mishima began her career as a painter and did not study ceramics until the late sixties. In 1971 her work was chosen as part of the large travelling international exhibition of Japanese ceramic art. Mishima makes her home in Osaka where she produces pottery and ceramic sculpture.

NEWSPAPER
Ceramic, 9¾x19½x11¾ in., 1972
No. TK1762

A graphic technique here applied to the surface of a ceramic sculpture with surprising fidelity recreates a crumpled newspaper, an English-language daily published in Japan.

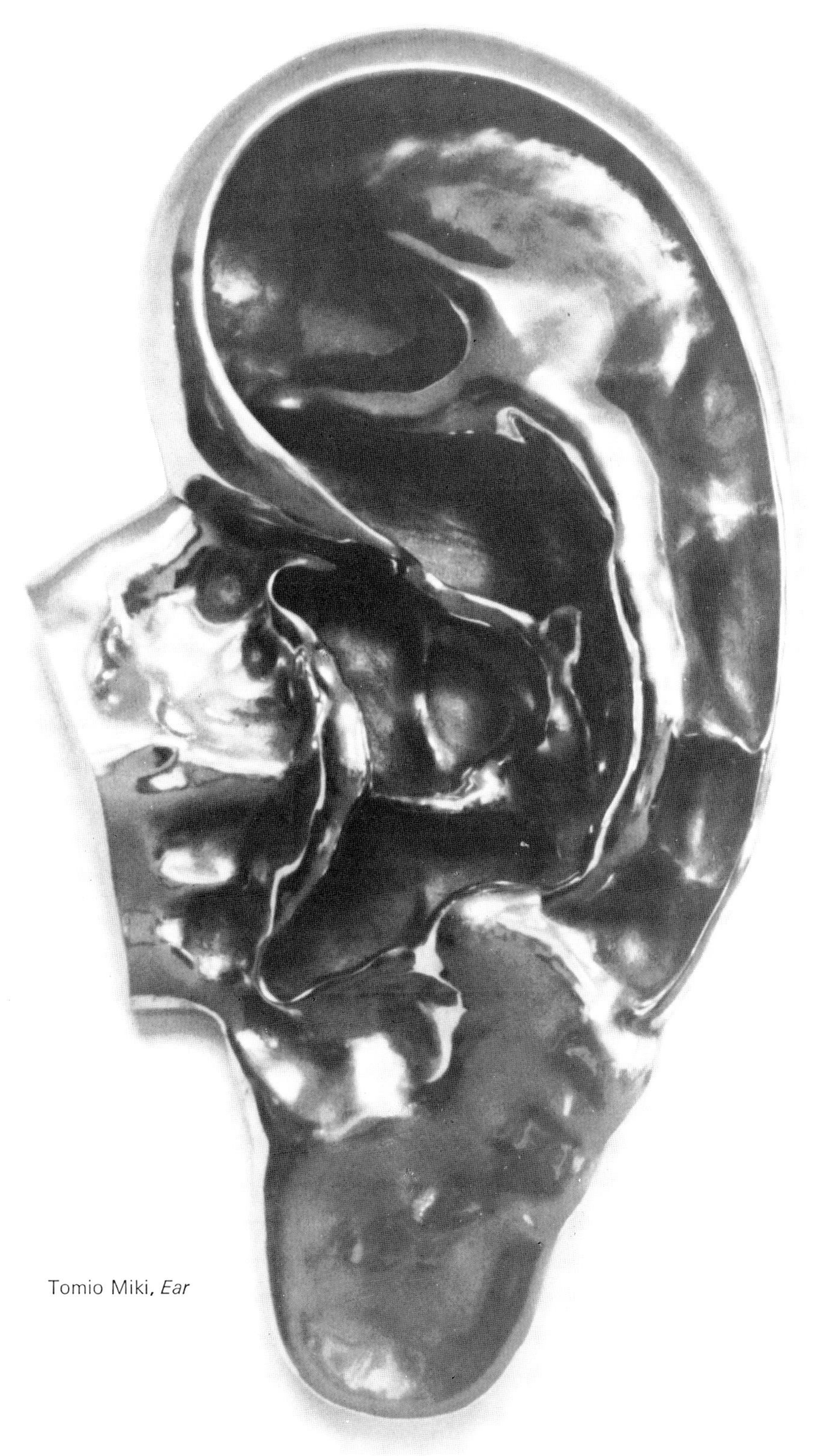

Tomio Miki, *Ear*

Louise Nevelson

Born 1900 in Kiev, Russia. After growing up in Rockland, Maine, where her family settled in 1905, Nevelson arrived in New York at the age of twenty. There she attended the Art Students League in 1929–30, and the following year went to Munich to study with Hans Hofmann. During her stay in Europe she also worked as a film actress in Berlin and Vienna. After returning to the United States in 1932, she became an assistant to the Mexican mural painter Diego Rivera. Nevelson first showed her sculpture in New York during the thirties but met with little success. However twenty years later she came into her own, and now Nevelson's work is found in major museums throughout the world. She has experimented with various materials—metals, marble, plastics, wood and terra-cotta—but seems to prefer either wood or metal. Characteristic are her carefully arranged reliefs of fragmented, discarded objects and architectural elements. These assemblages are sometimes large enough to act as walls. Her wood sculpture is always of a single color, usually black but sometimes gold or white.

BLACK EXCURSION XIV
Wood and formica, 50×45½x2½ in., 1969
No. 319

Departing from her usual method of juxtaposing diverse wooden pieces in recesses of the same material, here Nevelson begins with a formica frame and projects her composition out into space. The relief has a taut vitality dependent on the interarrangement of various wooden fragments. An aura of mystery is enhanced by black shadows cast by black forms.

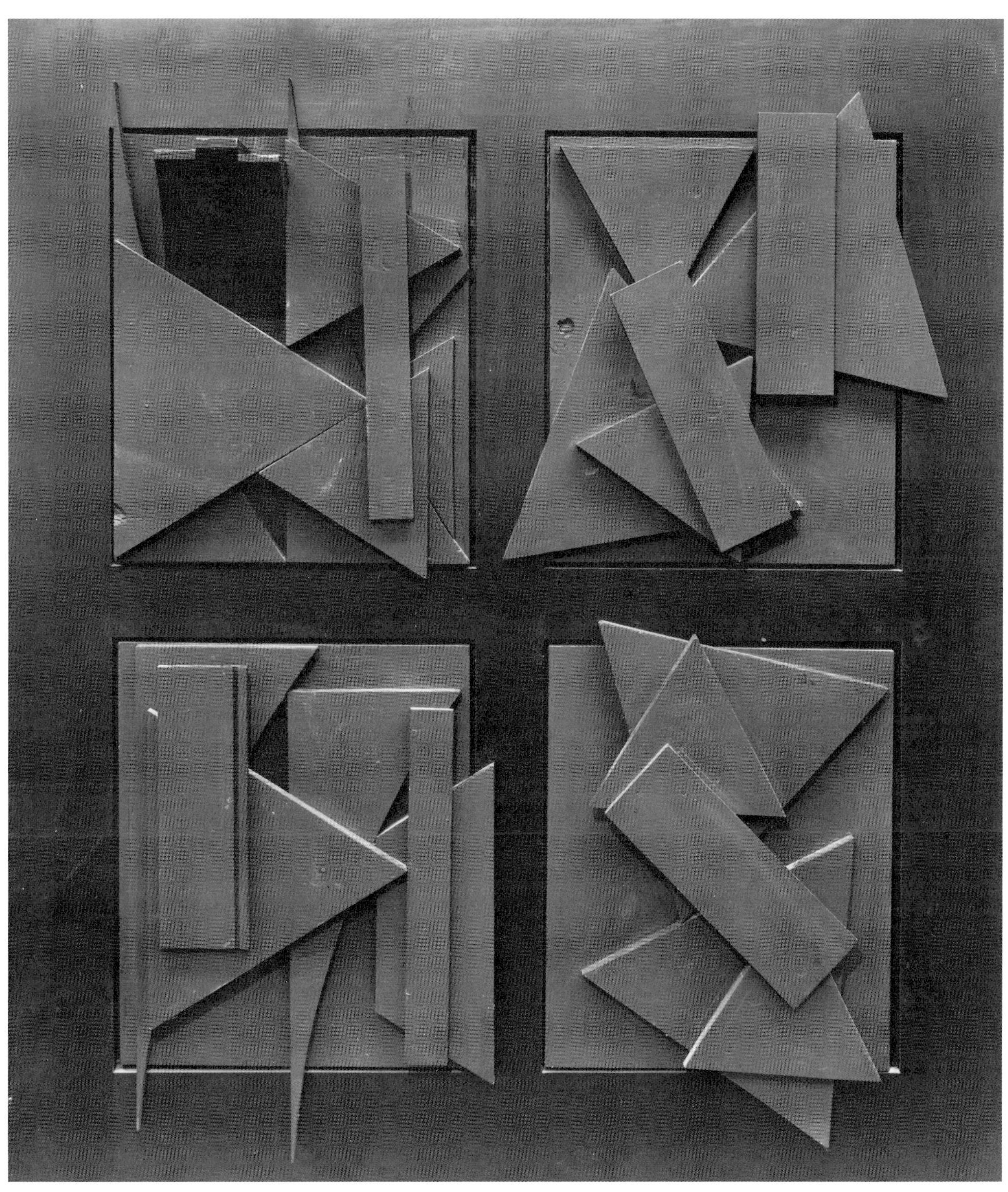

Louise Nevelson, *Black Excursion XIV*

Isamu Noguchi, *Kintaro*

Isamu Noguchi

Born 1904 in Los Angeles. Noguchi's father was a Japanese poet and professor of English and his mother was a schoolteacher of Scotch-Irish and American Indian descent. When he was two years old the family moved to Tokyo where Noguchi lived until returning to the United States to attend high school. After deciding to become an artist he apprenticed himself for a short time to the American academic sculptor, Gutzon Borglum. In 1927 with the aid of a Guggenheim Fellowship he spent two years in Paris as Brancusi's assistant. He still acknowledges Brancusi as a strong influence in his development. The other important influence on his work is the art of ancient Japan. Though Noguchi is best known for his sculpture he has also designed lamps, gardens and dance sets. Over the years he has worked in wood, metal, terra-cotta and marble, but recently he has turned to extremely hard stone, preferring granite or basalt. He divides his time between studios in New York and in Mure Cho on the Japanese island of Shikoku. Noguchi chose this village because it is renowned for its hereditary stonecutters.

KINTARO
Bronze, 21⅝x16⅛x9 in., 1931
No. 461

During a stay in Japan in 1931, Noguchi made the original terra-cotta for *Kintaro*. The simple forms reflect his interest in ancient Japanese sculpture, particularly pre-Buddhist grave figures. He borrowed the traditional pose of Kintaro, a young god of the mountains often shown dancing with an ax. One other bronze cast of Kintaro belongs to the artist's sister, Mrs. Ailes Spinden.

Thom O'Connor

Born 1937 in Detroit. O'Connor received his BA from Florida State University and his MFA from Cranbrook Academy. He is a printmaker and has been a professor of lithography at the State University of New York in Albany since 1962. In 1970 he was a visiting artist at Williams followed by two years in the same position at Vassar. He has been invited twice to the Tamarind Lithography Workshop and was awarded research fellowships at the State University of New York in 1965 and 1972. He lives in Voorheesville, New York.

THREE HEADS
Bronze 2/30, 17¾x5⅞x1 in., 1969
No. 539

A relief made at the Kalamazoo Sculpture Workshop (see p. 116).

Anthony Padovano

Born 1933 in Brooklyn, New York. After studying at Pratt Institute and Carnegie Institute of Technology, Padovano graduated from Columbia University where he now teaches. He also worked with Theodore Roszak in 1959–60 and at the American Academy in Rome in 1960–62. In 1964 he received a Guggenheim Fellowship, and in 1969 he was named New York State Council on the Arts' "Sculptor of the Year." Working almost exclusively in metal, Padovano depends on both welding and casting. His drawings as a rule are preparatory sketches for his sculpture.

TWO PIECES
Painted aluminum on chrome base,
10x18x10 in., 1970
No. 751

Two C-shaped forms with stepped contours, one with a white surface and the other black, set up interacting relationships with each other and with the mirrored surface of the sculpture's base.

Frederic Remington

Born 1861 in Canton, New York; died 1909 in Ridgefield, Connecticut. An artist who dealt almost exclusively with subjects of the Old West, Remington was very much an Easterner, living in and around New York most of his life. After a year in art school at Yale, and when only nineteen, he made his first trip to the West. Realizing that the life style of this part of America would soon be taken over by more "civilized" elements from the East, he romantically set about chronicling the last days of the Wild West. Remington made numerous trips throughout the country, constantly sketching Indians, cowboys and soldiers. His drawings appeared in *Harper's Weekly*, *Century*, and *Collier's*. After returning to New York from the West he would make his finished paintings or sculpture, using sketches done at the scene. He also wrote and illustrated books on the West.

BRONCO BUSTER
Bronze, 22x20¼x11¼ in., 1895
No. 1003

Bronco Buster was Remington's first attempt at sculpture and was typical of his interest in daring cowboy exploits. A realist in both his paintings and bronzes, he carefully delineated every possible detail. He is famous for the vitality of his figures and his ability to express violent action. Exactly how many casts of *Bronco Buster* were made is not known, but it was somewhere between two and three hundred. Forty casts came from the Henry-Bonnard Foundry. Later casts were made at the Roman Bronze Works of which the Bank's copy is one.

Jeanne Reynal

Born 1903 in White Plains, New York. Jeanne Reynal, privately educated, was apprenticed in 1930 to the Russian mosaicist, Boris Anrep. Working in his Paris studio, she learned basic mosaic techniques. Returning to the United States in 1939, she settled in San Francisco, but six years later moved permanently to New York. Reynal rejects the idea of mosaics as a means of reproducing paintings, yet she values the careful craftsmanship of earlier practitioners. Her abstract mosaics are sometimes flat, sometimes three-dimensional. Occasionally she has designed entire free-standing walls. Certain of her mosaic objects relate to the primitive art of Africa and South America. She believes strongly that mosaic compositions must respect the materials from which they are made.

UNTITLED
Mosaic, 37x10½ in. circumference, 1969
No. 672

Although nonfigurative, this three-dimensional piece has the undulating form of a reptile.

Auguste Rodin

Born 1840 in Paris; died 1917 in Meudon, France. From 1854 to 1857 Rodin, son of a Paris Police Prefecture employee, attended a school of design where his teacher was Horace Lecoq de Boisbandran. At fifteen he was awarded a medal for drawing and at that time started to study sculpture. After leaving school he worked for a number of decorating firms, learning to carve and model in a variety of materials. In 1862, saddened by the death of his sister Maria who had joined a convent, Rodin himself entered the Order of the Fathers of the Holy Sacrament as Brother Augustin, but after two years he resumed his decorating career and also made jewelry. Following his army service in the Franco-Prussian War, he formed a partnership with the sculptor Ernst Carriere-Belleuse, and later made a similar arrangement with the Belgian artist, Joseph van Rasbourgh. By 1875, when his work was first accepted in the Paris Salon, Rodin was financially able to travel, especially in Italy where he was greatly affected by the sculpture of Michelangelo and Donatello. When his first major success, *The Age of Bronze*, was exhibited at the Salon of 1877 the public suspected that it was cast from life because of its realism. Soon Rodin became one of the most influential artists of his time, creating many public monuments as well as individual figures and portraits. He ran a large studio where his assistants, including Bourdelle (see p. 114) and Despiau, did most of the actual carving from his models, but Rodin always finished the work himself. He was the most important impressionist sculptor, the surface of his highly expressive work always a foil for light. A joint exhibition of his sculpture and Monet's paintings, held in 1889 at the Galerie Georges Petit in Paris, summed up the discoveries of Impressionism by two of its strongest exponents.

THE MIGHTY HAND
Bronze, 18x11¼x7½ in., ca. 1885
No. 1940

In 1884 Rodin began work on his most dramatic monumental group, *The Burghers of Calais*, for which he made many studies including a series of hands. *The Mighty Hand* was one of these and, although never used as part of *The Burghers*, was eventually cast as a completed work. It also appears in another sculpture with a small female figure, probably one of those intended originally for the unfinished *Gates of Hell*. The sculpture is signed both by Rodin and by the founder, Alexis Rudier. It is one of five known casts of this sculpture by Alexis Rudier with whom Rodin worked personally.

Auguste Rodin, *The Mighty Hand*

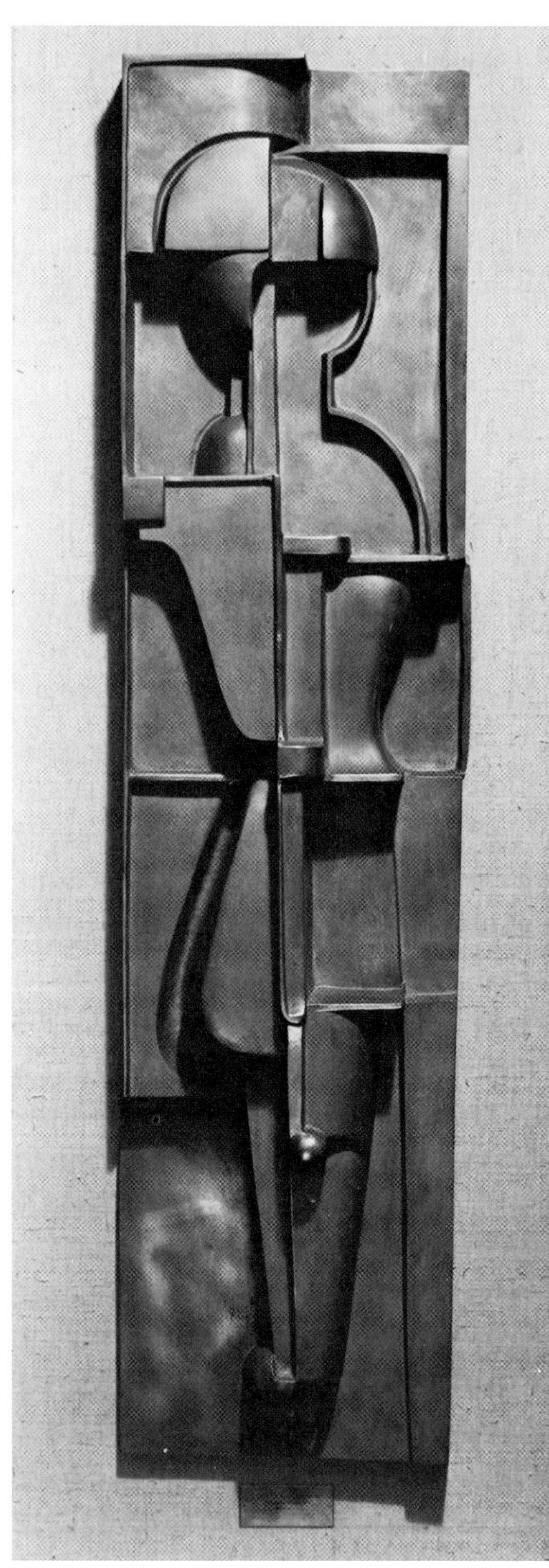

Oskar Schlemmer,
Bauplastic R

Oskar Schlemmer

Born 1888 in Stuttgart, Germany; died 1943 in Baden-Baden, Germany. Schlemmer studied painting at the Stuttgart Academy from 1909 to 1919. In 1920, at the invitation of Walter Gropius, he joined the Bauhaus at Weimar to head its sculpture workshop. In keeping with the Bauhaus tradition of interrelating the arts, Schlemmer soon expanded his department into a center for theatrical production which included theatre and stage design, mural painting and choreography. He was one of the few Bauhaus artists whose chief concern was the human figure. Influenced by Constructivism and Cubism, also by Archipenko and Léger in particular, Schlemmer reduced the figure to geometric forms always simplified and somewhat mechanized. In 1925 he moved with the Bauhaus to Dessau, leaving there four years later to become a professor at the Breslau Academy of Fine and Applied Arts. During the last ten years of his life, disturbed by constant Nazi opposition to his work, he retired to the country where he did little more than occasional jobs as a commercial artist.

BAUPLASTIC R
Aluminum 4/7, 39x10x2¾ in., 1919–20/1962
No. 188

The original model for this work was made in plaster by Schlemmer in 1919–20; an edition of seven was cast after the artist's death at the Noack Foundry, Berlin in 1962. The title plates which accompany each piece, rather than the casts, have been numbered and signed by Tut Schlemmer, the artist's widow, to whom the original model belongs. Schlemmer's interest in the constructivist movement is obvious in this early relief sculpture with its closed system of geometric forms articulated by positive and negative elements.

Seah Kim Joo (for biography see p. 86)

UNTITLED
Aluminum relief, 68½x47½ in., 1971
No. SI2007

A large metal panel of geometric design seems constantly to change as reflections on its gleaming surface form new patterns.

Christopher Shurrock

Born 1939 in Bristol, England. Shurrock began his training at the West of England College of Art from which he graduated in 1959. The following year he did graduate work at Cardiff College of Art and now makes his permanent home in Wales. His work shows a marked interest in both constructionist and kinetic art.

VIBRATION OBJECT
Wood, aluminum and acrylic on glass, 24x24x4 in., 1967
No. 258

Optical motion is set up by the play of vertical and curved lines superimposed in two planes.

David Smith

Born 1906 in Decatur, Indiana; died 1965 near Bennington, Vermont in an automobile accident. An influential sculptor of the twentieth century, Smith began his art studies with a correspondence course from the Cleveland Art School in 1923. He attended Ohio University for one year and shortly thereafter became a riveter at the Studebaker automobile plant in South Bend, Indiana, an experience which was to be of invaluable help in his later work. Earlier he had been a telephone lineman. In 1927 he studied with John Sloan and Jan Matulka. All his preliminary art training was limited to painting, but during the early 1930's he began experimenting with sculpture—first with painted wood, later with steel and iron. In 1935–36 he was in Europe—in Paris, Greece, London and the Soviet Union. In 1940 the sculptor moved permanently to Bolton Landing, New York. During World War II he took a defense job, welding at the American Locomotive Works in Schenectady. Important early influences were his own experiences as an industrial welder plus the three-dimensional constructions in wire and metal of Picasso and Julio Gonzalez. He also owed much to Cubism. Smith worked in welded iron and steel, usually in series ranging from a few to as many as thirty individual sculptures. His earliest pieces were light, lyrical and often based directly on nature. His later sculpture became more abstract, geometric and monumental, though frequently his point of departure was a recognizable object or experience. Smith believed in the validity of color in sculpture and almost always painted his machine-like constructions with shiny industrial pigment.

CIRCLE: BLACK, WHITE & TAN
Painted steel, 77x92x20 in., September 10, 1963
No. 443

In the 1960's Smith increasingly tended to paint all his sculpture. At the same time he began to include the circle more prominently in his work. In the *Zig* series from the sixties, circles appear, but not as the main geometric element. In 1962 he started a series in which the circle was dominant. Three sculptures, painted in bright colors, were created the first year, and the Bank's *Circle: Black, White & Tan* completed the series in 1963.
For colorplate see page 29.

Jesus Rafael Soto, *The Importance of the White Square*

Jesus Rafael Soto

Born 1923 in Ciudad Bolivar, Venezuela. Soto attended the School of Plastic Arts in Caracas from 1942 to 1947 and then became the director of the School of Fine Arts in Maracaibo. In 1950 the artist left his native country for Paris where he still lives. Influenced by Mondrian and Pol Bury, Soto is as deeply interested in the illusion of movement as in actual movement. He wants the viewer to become involved and often produces a sense of movement by forcing the observer himself to move.

THE IMPORTANCE OF THE WHITE SQUARE
Wood and metal, 62½x42⅛x6 in., 1965
No. 321

Although this wall relief has no moving parts, Soto's metal plates seem to vibrate as the viewer passes by. This ambiguous optical sensation, caused by finely painted thin lines, is characteristic of Soto's work and of his ability to make what is seem what it is not.

Henryk Stazewski

Born 1894 in Warsaw, Poland. Stazewski studied at the Academy of Fine Arts in Warsaw. During 1923–24 he was a member of "Blok," a group of *avant-garde* artists who published a review of the same name. He met Kasimir Malevich, the Russian abstract painter, in Poland in 1927 and later went to Paris, remaining there until 1929. During this first stay in Paris, Stazewski knew Mondrian, Van Doesburg and Vantongerloo, all artists in the forefront of nonobjective art. Returning to Paris from Poland in the early thirties, Stazewski became a member of "Cercle et Carré" and later "Abstraction-Création," both groups of abstract artists and theoreticians who held exhibitions and published reviews. During the second world war, Stazewski's creative activity ceased; many of his works in Poland were destroyed. He resumed his career in Warsaw after the war, specializing in taut geometric reliefs of wood painted white.

WHITE RELIEF NO. 23
Wood, 66¾x34⅜x2½ in., 1963
No. NA257

Using only white, Stazewski arranged abstract elements against a striated background. Shifting shadows on a configuration of six rectangles with slightly curved sides suggest suspended forms in space.

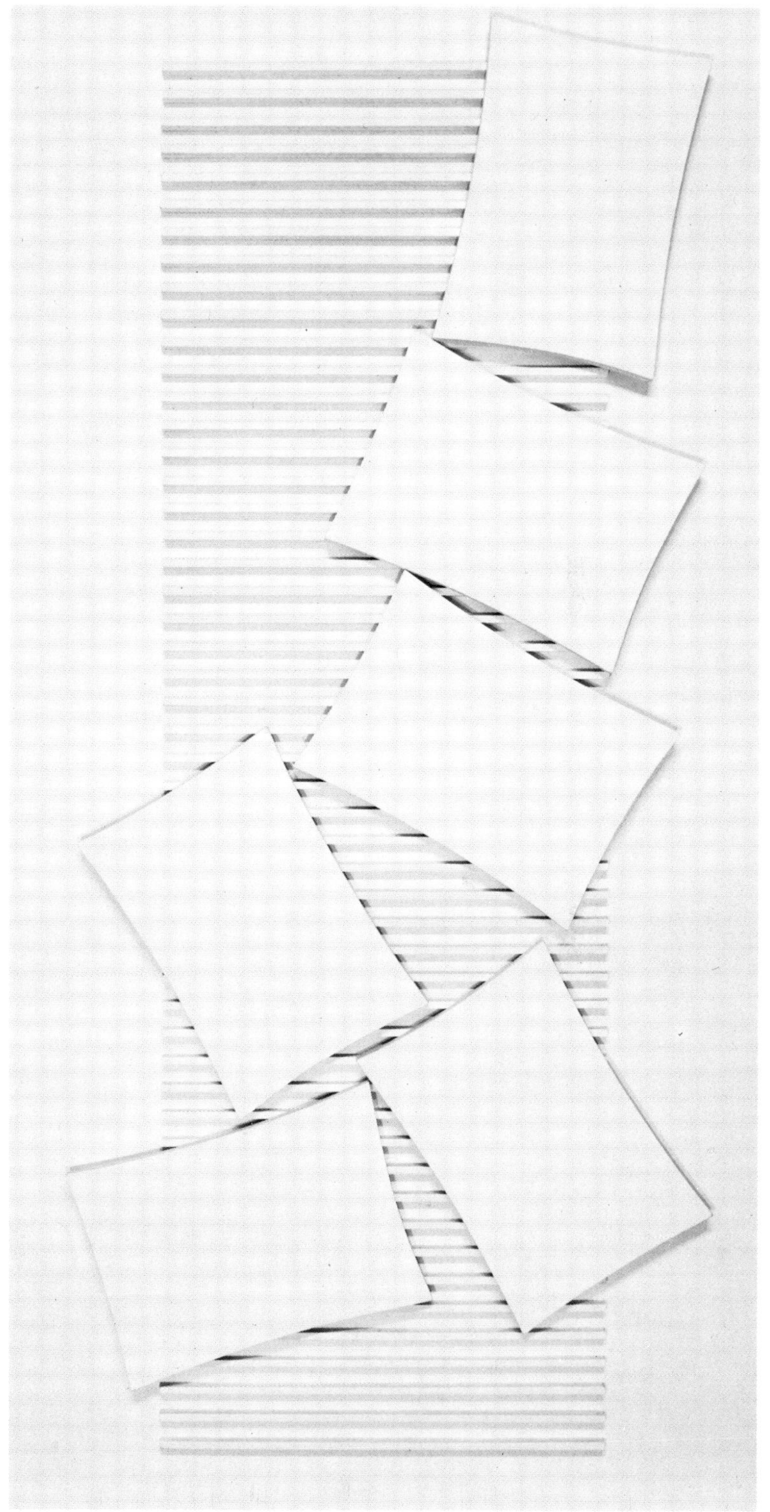

Henryk Stazewski, *White Relief No. 23*

Paul Suttman

Born 1933 in New York. After graduating from the University of New Mexico in 1956, Suttman earned an MFA from Cranbrook Academy in 1958. Two years of teaching sculpture at the University of Michigan followed and in 1960 Suttman won the first in a series of major awards which took him to Europe. He has remained there, chiefly in Rome. His work shares a quality of super-reality with the early sculpture of Giacomo Manzu, under whom he studied. Familiar objects—bottles, food, clothing—are cast in bronze or carved from marble. At times the scale of these tabletop arrangements expands to assume an aspect of monumentality.

STILL LIFE
Bronze, 19x14x3 in., 1968
No. 178

A plate, holding a neatly dissected apple and a small knife, lies on the drape of a large napkin, but the entire still life hangs on the wall in gravity-defying verticality.

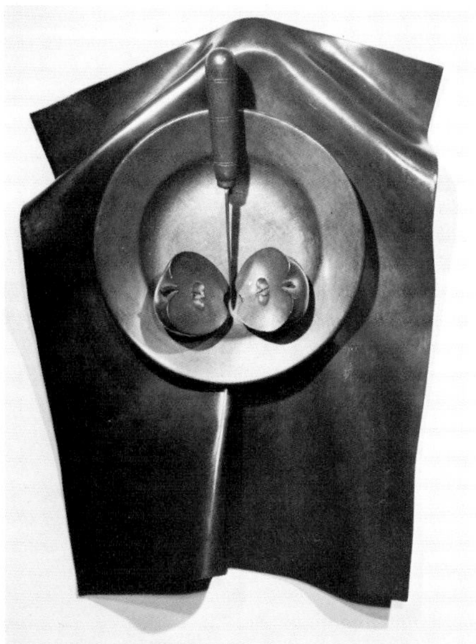

Toshiko Takaezu

Born 1922 in Hawaii. Takaezu studied at the Honolulu Academy of Arts, the University of Hawaii and Cranbrook Academy. Although her pottery began as a purely utilitarian craft, she thinks of her "vases" as separate works of art and not necessarily as vessels to be used. In fact, many of what the artist calls "vases" have no openings. Into some of these closed forms the potter seals small beads which tinkle when the object is moved, not unlike certain primitive Pre-Colombian and North Pacific works. Contours and glazes are of the utmost subtlety. All three terra-cottas in the Bank's collection are drum-shaped. The artist lives in Clinton, New Jersey.

VASE
Glazed terra-cotta, 17x10 in. diameter, 1969
No. 530

VASE
Glazed terra-cotta, 13½x8¾ in. diameter, 1969
No. 531

VASE
Glazed terra-cotta, 13½x8½ in. diameter, 1969
No. 532

Gunther Uecker

Born 1930 in Wendorf, Germany. Uecker studied painting in Wismar, in Berlin at the Weissensee Art Academy and finally at the Düsseldorf Academy of Art. With Otto Piene and Hans Mack he was influential in forming Group Zero, a German movement that stressed light and motion in abstract constructions. Founded in 1958, the group borrowed its name from space rocket countdowns. Movement is present in Uecker's work, sometimes real and activated by motors, sometimes only suggested as the spectator himself moves. During 1964–65 the artist lived in New York. He presently lives in Düsseldorf.

ZERO GARDEN
Linen-covered plywood and nails,
32x32x3 in., 1966
No. 318

In 1966 Uecker created an environment consisting of twenty-five nail-covered panels, some to be seen on the wall, others on the floor. The panels were similar since each was white and contained a circular arrangement of nails, yet each differed slightly. The ensemble was called *Zero Garden* (after Group Zero), and spectators were encouraged to wander through it. As they moved among the panels, shifting light caused the nails to produce changing shadows that in turn gave a sense of motion. The Bank's panel is one of the twenty-five.

Aijiro Wakita

Born 1942 in Tokyo. Wakita, who began to paint at the age of fourteen, graduated from the Musashino Art University, Tokyo in 1964 and then came to the United States. He studied at the Brooklyn Museum Art School from 1965 to 1966 and has remained a resident of New York where he has his studio. Wakita moved away from strictly two-dimensional work when he began incorporating pieces of string into his paintings. By 1967 he developed a sculptural technique of winding metal wire around simply shaped forms made of papier mâché, lathe-turned wood or plastic. These objects are often paired or grouped, opposed like stalactites and stalagmites.

TWO ELEMENTS
Aluminum wire on plastic core, 47x11 in. diameter, 1972
No. 1324

Two nearly ovoid forms—one mounted on a stand, the other suspended from above—achieve a fluid continuity in contour and in the paths of light reflected from their metal surfaces.

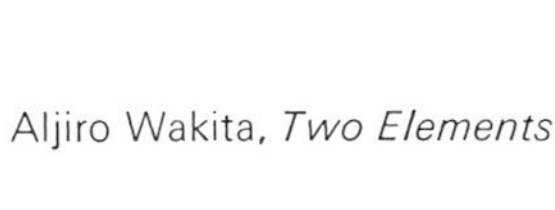

Aljiro Wakita, *Two Elements*

Willy Weber

Born 1933 in Berne, Switzerland. Weber is a self-taught artist who started as a surrealist painter and only in the early sixties turned to sculpture. He usually begins his work with a metal sheet or column which he plants with explosive charges. When the charges detonate, they cause concavities in the metal. Depending on the amount of explosive used and its precise location, the artist creates numerous effects varying from mere ripples to deep craters. Later he polishes the metal to a high shine or plates it with chrome. His gleaming sculptures with their undulating surfaces reflect and distort the surrounding world. Weber lives in Berne.

BY THE WAY
Metal, 28x23¾ in., 1969
No. ML1542

As one views this relief from different angles, it gradually suggests a woman's torso.

Mahonri M. Young

Born 1877 in Salt Lake City; died 1957 in Norwalk, Connecticut. After very little training and while still an adolescent, Young started out as an illustrator for the *Salt Lake Tribune*. A grandson of the Mormon leader Brigham Young, he left Utah in 1899 to study at the Art Students League in New York. Later he went to Europe where he traveled and also worked in Paris at the Académie Julian. He became friends with Leo Stein, though very little of the latter's enthusiasm for *avante-garde* art seemed to rub off on the young American artist. His work always remained solidly based on nature and he spent considerable time sketching animals and people from life. After successes at the Paris Salon, Young returned to New York where he remained on and off for the rest of his life. He is remembered as a draftsman, sculptor and painter.

PONY EXPRESS
Bronze 1/6, 14x22½x6 in., ca. 1937
No. 596

The idea of speed is basic to this sculpture. Undoubtedly it was influenced by Remington. The original plaster is in the collection of Brigham Young University. The bronze casts were made after the artist's death and although six were originally planned, only the two belonging to the artist's son, Mahonri Sharp Young, and to the Bank are known.

DRAWINGS

Valerio Adami

Born 1935 in Bologna, Italy. Adami completed his studies in art at the Academy of Milan in 1954. Since then he has developed a style of deceptive simplicity which shows his debt to comic strip art with its hard black contours and blank, bright blocks of color. His metaphors are nevertheless complicated and disturbing. Fragments of human anatomy mingle with misshapen furniture in banal interiors such as hotel rooms and movie theatre lobbies. Adami's art is propaganda for the systematic destruction of a bourgeois environment he finds oppressive. His home is at Arona on Lake Maggiore.

HUNTER WITH A NET
Pencil, 19½x27⅓ in., 1965
No. ML1525

Pierre Alechinsky

Born 1927 in Brussels, Belgium. After studying typography and book illustration at the National School of Architecture and Decorative Arts in Brussels, Alechinsky went to Paris in 1948 where the following year he allied himself with the newly established COBRA group (see p. 38). The direct emotion expressed in the art of this group is also found in his work. He is known for his dashing calligraphy and nervous, free brushwork. Though he settled permanently in Paris in 1951, he has traveled widely in Europe, the Orient and the United States. In 1952 he studied etching with Stanley William Hayter in Paris.

UNTITLED
Ink wash, 9x11½ in., 1963
No. 254

Alechinsky's images are often ominous. Typical is this brooding, skull-like head defined by jabbing lines. The work is signed and dated in the upper right.

Pierre Alechinsky, *Untitled*

Leonard Baskin

Born 1922 in New Brunswick, New Jersey. After studying at New York University, Yale and the New School for Social Research where he received an MA, Baskin spent time in France and Italy. Since the early fifties he has taught at Smith College. The artist received a Guggenheim Fellowship in 1953 and a medal from the American Institute of Graphic Artists in 1965. He is best known for his sculpture, though drawings, woodcuts and etchings are also an important part of his work. Baskin is an Expressionist whose images of flawed human bodies are caustic comments on the condition of man.

CHIMERA OF WAR I
Ink, 30¼x22¼ in., 1967
No. FR231

Baskin is concerned with political and moral questions and with such timeless themes as death and dissolution. This foreboding snake-like creature is a strangling personification of war. The drawing is signed in the lower right.

Jack Beal

Born 1931 in Richmond, Virginia. Educated at William and Mary College, the School of The Art Institute of Chicago and the University of Chicago, Beal now lives in New York. He is a realist who paints interiors where people and furniture are seen from close-up and unexpected perspectives.

LILY
Charcoal, 25x19 in., 1969
No. FR771

Cecil Beaton

Born 1904 in London. Educated at Harrow and Cambridge, Beaton is widely known as photographer, writer, illustrator and stage designer. He has been active on both sides of the Atlantic creating designs for film and stage productions, including *Anna Karenina, Lady Windermere's Fan, Portrait of a Lady, The Chalk Garden* and *My Fair Lady*. Beaton lives in London.

COSTUME SKETCH FOR "MARGUERITE AND ARMAND"
Watercolor, 16½x13 in., 1962
No. 664

The ballet *Marguerite and Armand*, first performed on March 13, 1963 at Covent Garden in London, featured Dame Margot Fonteyn and Rudolf Nureyev. With set and costume designs by Cecil Beaton and choreography by Frederick Ashton, the story was drawn from Alexandre Dumas' *La Dame aux Camélias*. The Bank's sketch is for the costume of Armand's father in the death scene.

George Bellows

Born 1882 in Columbus, Ohio; died 1925 in New York. In 1904 Bellows went to New York where he studied at the New York School of Art under Robert Henri. The latter was a member of "The Eight" (see p. 53), a group that influenced Bellows who was attracted to the Ash Can painters' preference for everyday experiences. He was particularly interested in laborers and boxers, and one of his most famous canvases was based on the Dempsey-Firpo prizefight of 1924. In 1919 he taught at the School of the Art Institute of Chicago. Prominent as an illustrator, Bellows made drawings for stories such as *The Wind Bloweth* by Donn Byrne and *Men Like Gods* by H.G. Wells. Bellows is especially remembered for his paintings, drawings and lithographs of human figures in motion and for his unidealized portraits and views of New York.

ILLUSTRATION FOR "THE BLACK HAND"
Ink, wash and pencil, 19½x14 in., 1921
No. 171

Bellows made illustrations for M.L.C. Pickhall's short story, *The Black Hand*, published in *Century Magazine*, October, 1921. This is one of the preparatory drawings for the illustrations and is signed on the corner of the raft with the artist's initials.

Franco Berdini

Born 1941 in Rome. After graduating in 1961 from the Institute of Art in Rome with a degree in architecture, Berdini studied painting at the Academy of Fine Arts and the Free Academy of the Nude, both in Rome. His artistic style seems to stem from his architectural studies; intricate linear patterns drawn in colored inks suggest the tensions and stress of modern constructions. Berdini lives in Rome.

THEME CA 100
Ink, 39x28 in., 1970
No. RO2034

George Bellows,
Illustration for
"The Black Hand"

Giuseppe Galli Bibiena, *Courtyard Scene*

Fred Berman

Born 1926 in Milwaukee, Wisconsin. Berman graduated from Milwaukee State Teachers College in 1948 and studied at the University of Wisconsin the next year. He taught at the Layton School of Art in Milwaukee from 1949 to 1960 and since then has been a professor of art at the University of Wisconsin, Milwaukee, with an exchange lectureship at Reading University, England during 1966–67. Although he has worked in diverse media, making wooden assemblages and printing silkscreen on plexiglas constructions, Berman's paintings, influenced he claims by Turner, are often light-struck abstractions.

PORTRAIT
Charcoal on blue paper, 24⅞x18⅞ in., 1970
No. PN1208

A portrait drawing of one of the artist's friends.

Giuseppe Galli Bibiena

Born 1696 in Parma, Italy; died 1757 in Berlin. Bibiena was a second generation member of a family famous throughout Europe for stage design and court pageants. His father Ferdinando was called to Vienna in 1712 by Emperor Charles VI to become chief decorator to the Imperial Court. Young Giuseppe accompanied his father and learned his skills as an assistant. When Ferdinando left Vienna, Giuseppe was appointed to his father's position. As chief decorator, Giuseppe was responsible for theatrical productions, funeral decor and catafalques, triumphal arches for royal entries and fireworks displays. His work for the Austrian Imperial family took him to Dresden, Munich, Prague, Venice and Berlin. Since the productions of Bibiena were, by nature, temporary, knowledge of his work must come from his drawings or from contemporary engravings.

COURTYARD SCENE
Ink and wash, 6x8⅛ in., date unknown
No. 152

The Bibiena family was responsible for popularizing a new kind of background for theatrical productions. Instead of a backdrop parallel to the front of the stage, the Bibienas devised the *scena per angolo* in which the spectator looked into the corner of an architectural space. This gave an illusion of greater depth and offered opportunity for more inventive staging. The Bank's drawing, which is attributed to Bibiena, is a study for one of these stage sets.

Daniel Blair

Born 1940 in Fall River, Massachusetts. Blair graduated from the department of sculpture at the School of the Boston Museum of Fine Arts in 1967. The following year he traveled to Japan on a fellowship and spent the next three years in Kyoto working on sculpture. A Fulbright grant made a second trip to Japan possible in 1972. Blair now teaches sculpture at Stonehill College in North Easton, Massachusetts.

UNTITLED NO. 2
Pencil, 23x29 in., 1973
No. 1883

UNTITLED NO. 3
Pencil, 23x29 in., 1973
No. 1884

Two studies of twisted and crumpled paper bags suggest traditional academic renderings of classical drapery folds.

William Brooker (for biography see p. 42)

STUDIO INTERIOR
Pencil, 20½x24½ in., 1966
No. LN2016

A drawing of one of Brooker's favorite themes, the interior of his studio.

George Buehr, *The Great Buddha of Changhua*

George Buehr

Born 1905 in Chicago. Buehr, who studied with his father the painter Karl Buehr, was for many years director of education at the Art Institute of Chicago. In 1959 he left to become chairman of the art department at the American University in Beirut, Lebanon. His love of travel has taken him on sketching tours through numberless countries. His work, usually spontaneous and highly expressionistic, is at its best in watercolor.

THE GREAT BUDDHA OF CHANGHUA (TAIWAN)
Ink and wash, 34x23 in., 1969
No. 398

Alexander Calder (for biography see p. 118)

HEAD AND HAND
Gouache, 29¼x43¼ in., 1966
No. 435

STRIPED MOON FACE
Gouache, 29¼x43¼ in., 1970
No. BS1367

Two gouache drawings suggest the tensile strength of metal coils and show the influence of Calder's jewelry designs.

Martin Carey

Born 1938 in Worcester, Massachusetts. Carey studied at the School of the Worcester Art Museum, at Yale, where he took his BFA in 1960, and at Bowling Green State University in Ohio. In 1962 his work won a Ford Foundation Purchase Award at the Museum of Modern Art. He has written two books in collaboration with his brother: *A Tribal Cookbook* and *Truckin' Through Mexico With the Community Free School*, the latter describing his work with a school he helped to found. Since 1969 he has lived in a community of artists, designers, builders and musicians called the "True Light Beavers" in Willow, New York. His forte is skillful and painstaking draftsmanship in what he has described as "visionary ink drawing." The subject matter is encyclopedic with an emphasis on nature and mysticism.

THE FIRST AMERICAN
Ink, 27x30½ in., 1968
No. BE228

Alexander Calder, *Striped Moon Face*

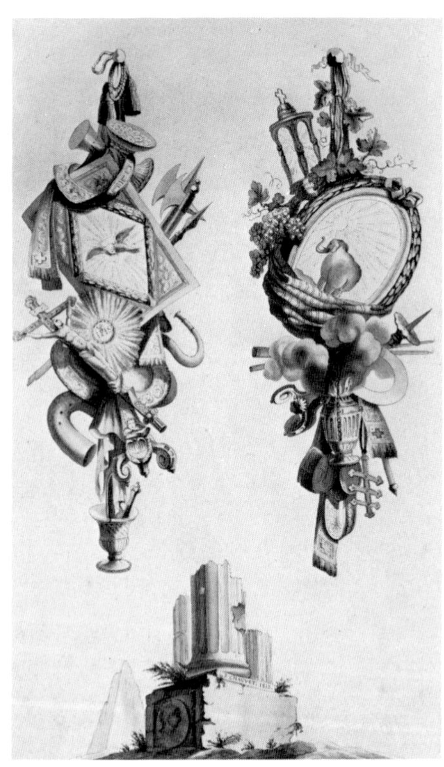

J. Chauvet, *Ornamental Panel with Symbols of the Church*

J. Chauvet

The name J. Chauvet matches no known artist but offers the possibility that the artist may have been the father of Jules Adolphe Chauvet, a French engineer who designed bookplates in the second half of the nineteenth century.

ORNAMENTAL PANEL WITH SYMBOLS OF THE CHURCH
Ink and wash, 14x8½ in., 1813
No. 155

A variety of Christian symbols and artifacts, generally Eucharistic in nature, are here arranged as two vertical trophies. On the left, the Holy Ghost in the form of a dove is surrounded by a crucifix, a monstrance, a paten and chalice, halbards and a broken spear, among other items. All are suspended from a spike on a tasseled cord. On the right, grapes—the symbol of the resurrection—a candelabra, a censer and an elephant in a wreath of laurel leaves are part of a similar arrangement. A ruined column at the bottom of the page shows a female profile in bas-relief carved on one side of its base with Chauvet's signature and a date of 1813 on the opposite side. An obelisk or pyramid is faintly drawn in the distance. The placement of the classical motifs and their crumbling condition may connote a comparison with the decorations above intended as a comment on the triumph of Christianity over pagan beliefs.

Serge Chermayeff (for biography see p. 48)

EQUILIBRIUM NO. 3
Pencil, 10⅝x13½ in., 1963
No. LA1879

This design solves the problem of balancing solids and voids.

Manuel Chong Neto

Born 1927 in Panama City. Chong Neto, who studied at the Academy of Art in Mexico, has been a professor at the Arosemena Institute and the School of Plastic Arts in Panama City. He paints and draws solitary, slightly demented human figures cut off from each other by structural devices or by psychological implication. Birds, black and foreboding, also play a role in his pictures. He lives in Panama City.

UNTITLED
Ink, 16½x14 in., 1971
No. PN1606

Jean Cocteau

Born 1889 in Maisons-Lafitte, France; died 1963 at Milly-la-Forêt, France. Cocteau spent most of his life in and around Paris. His boundless and often bizarre imagination gave birth to novels, films, poems, plays, drawings and murals. In 1917 he, together with Diaghilev, Picasso and Stravinsky, was one of the collaborators on the Ballet Russe production *Parade*. Throughout his life he was associated with other great creative minds, with Apollinaire, Satie, Braque and the composers, "Les Six." His ironic drawings were influenced by Picasso. In 1955 he became an unlikely member of both the Académie Royale Belgique and the Académie Française. An eccentric personality, Cocteau was connected with the surrealist movement. He is also remembered for his flamboyant life style and for his experimental films.

THEATRE FORAIN
Pencil, 10½x8¼ in., ca. 1955–60
No. 184

This drawing may have been a project for one of Cocteau's many short plays which he often illustrated, though the illustrated editions were never published. The drawing depicts an act from the *théâtre forain*, a popular street theatre. Here a blindfolded woman guesses numbers which her partner has previously indicated to the audience.

Jean Cocteau, *Théâtre Forain*

Jon Corbino

Born 1905 in Vittoria, Italy; died 1964 in Sarasota, Florida. Corbino, who came to the United States in 1913, grew up on the Lower East Side of New York. He attended the Pennsylvania Academy of the Fine Arts and the Art Students League where he later taught from 1938 to 1956. He received two Guggenheim Fellowships during 1936–38. Corbino tended toward romantic compositions which usually dealt with action; horses, circuses, earthquakes and floods were all favorite subjects.

HORSES WITH FIGHTING MEN
Charcoal, 18x20 in., 1935
No. 568

Lovis Corinth

Born 1858 in Tapiau, East Prussia (now the U.S.S.R.); died 1925 in Zandvoort, Holland. After studying at the Königsberg Academy, Corinth went to Munich where he worked under Ludwig Loefftz. He also studied under Bouguereau and Fleury at the Académie Julian in Paris. Between 1885 and 1891 he was in Königsberg, Berlin and Paris, finally settling in Munich where he stayed for almost ten years. In 1900 he moved to Berlin and there became associated with the Berlin Secession, a group of anti-academic painters that included Menzel, Leibl, Böcklin and Hodler. Corinth's early work was relatively traditional, but his later paintings and drawings were innovative forerunners of modern northern Expressionism.

DR. ALFRED KUHN
Lithographic crayon, 13½x9¼ in., June, 1923
No. 128

Dr. Kuhn was a German art historian who wrote a book on Corinth which was published in 1925, the same year the artist died. This late drawing, with its penetrating character delineation and energetic draftsmanship, was a study for a portrait painted in 1923. The whereabouts of the canvas is now unknown. The drawing, formerly in the collection of Dr. Kuhn, is signed in the upper left and is dated in the upper right.

Rafael Coronel

Born 1932 in Zacatecas, Mexico. In 1954, after studying architecture for two years at the National Independent University of Mexico, Coronel entered the Esmeralda School of Painting and Sculpture where he turned to painting. In 1965 he was awarded the Cordova prize as best young painter in the São Paulo Biennial. Coronel paints hallucinated personages often recalling the work of early Flemish masters or Goya. The artist lives in Mexico City.

MATEO
Ink and acrylic, 29½x33⅓ in., 1969
No. MC1669

Like most of Coronel's drawings, this one emphasizes delicate, definitive draftsmanship.

Jack Coulthard

Born 1930 at Baildon, Yorkshire, England. From 1945 to 1952 Coulthard studied at Leeds College of Art. During 1960 and 1961 he lived in Italy at Tarquinia and Rome. For the next eight years he taught painting and filmmaking at Somerset College of Art in England. Since then he has been a full-time painter, still living in Somerset. The mood of Coulthard's work is surreal, achieved by the juxtaposition of precisely drawn objects in equally distinct but dreamlike environments.

LAWRENCE AT TARQUINIA
Pencil, 9½x11½ in., 1971
No. PR1621

The drawing is signed and dated.

Lovis Corinth,
Dr. Alfred Kuhn

George Dance Jr.,
Dish'd or
Made Spoon-Meat of

Carlos Cuellar

Born 1943 in Mexico City. Cuellar studied engraving at the National School of Plastic Arts in Mexico City from 1962 to 1967. He is now an assistant professor at the same school, where he teaches sculpture as well as graphics. Cuellar implies monumentality by a visionary handling of architectural volume and space.

PLACE FOR PUNISHMENT
Ink and wash, 18x25 in., 1968
No. MC1670

CITY OF THE FOUR EXPLOSIONS
Ink and wash, 25x18 in., 1968
No. MC1671

José Luis Cuevas

Born 1933 in Mexico City. Self-taught except for one term at the Esmeralda School of Painting and Sculpture in Mexico City, Cuevas is a scathing social satirist. He looks to the streets and to madhouses for his themes, often exploiting haunted, grotesque figures as prototypes of modern life. Watercolor and ink are best suited to his strong graphic style, although he occasionally works in oil. He has published several illustrated books, among them *The Worlds of Kafka and Cuevas* and *Recollections of Childhood*. The artist lives in Mexico City where he teaches at the Spanish-American University.

AMERICAN WAY OF LIFE NO. 1
Ink, 7x10½ in., May 5, 1968
No. 232

During an extended New York stay in 1968 Cuevas created four drawings entitled *American Way of Life* which he conceived as fantastic dreams. The Bank's drawing is the first in the series and is signed and dated in the upper left; the title is at lower left.

George Dance Jr.

Born 1740 in London; died 1825 in London. The fifth and youngest son of an architect, Dance followed his father's profession and after the latter's death in 1768 succeeded him as city surveyor for London. Dance, who studied in Rome, is best known architecturally for the rebuilding of Newgate Prison in 1770. Eventually withdrawing from architecture, he turned to portrait painting. After 1798 he specialized in chalk drawings exclusively. Dance was the last to die of the Royal Academy of Art's original forty founding members.

DISH'D OR MADE SPOON-MEAT OF
Watercolor, 7½x10 in., ca. 1785
No. LN2000

Typically eighteenth-century in treatment, this caricature was dashed off with flowing line and splashes of wash. The duelers bear some resemblance to *commedia dell'arte* players. The title apparently refers to the decisive victory scored by one fencer who has just severed his opponent's head from his body.

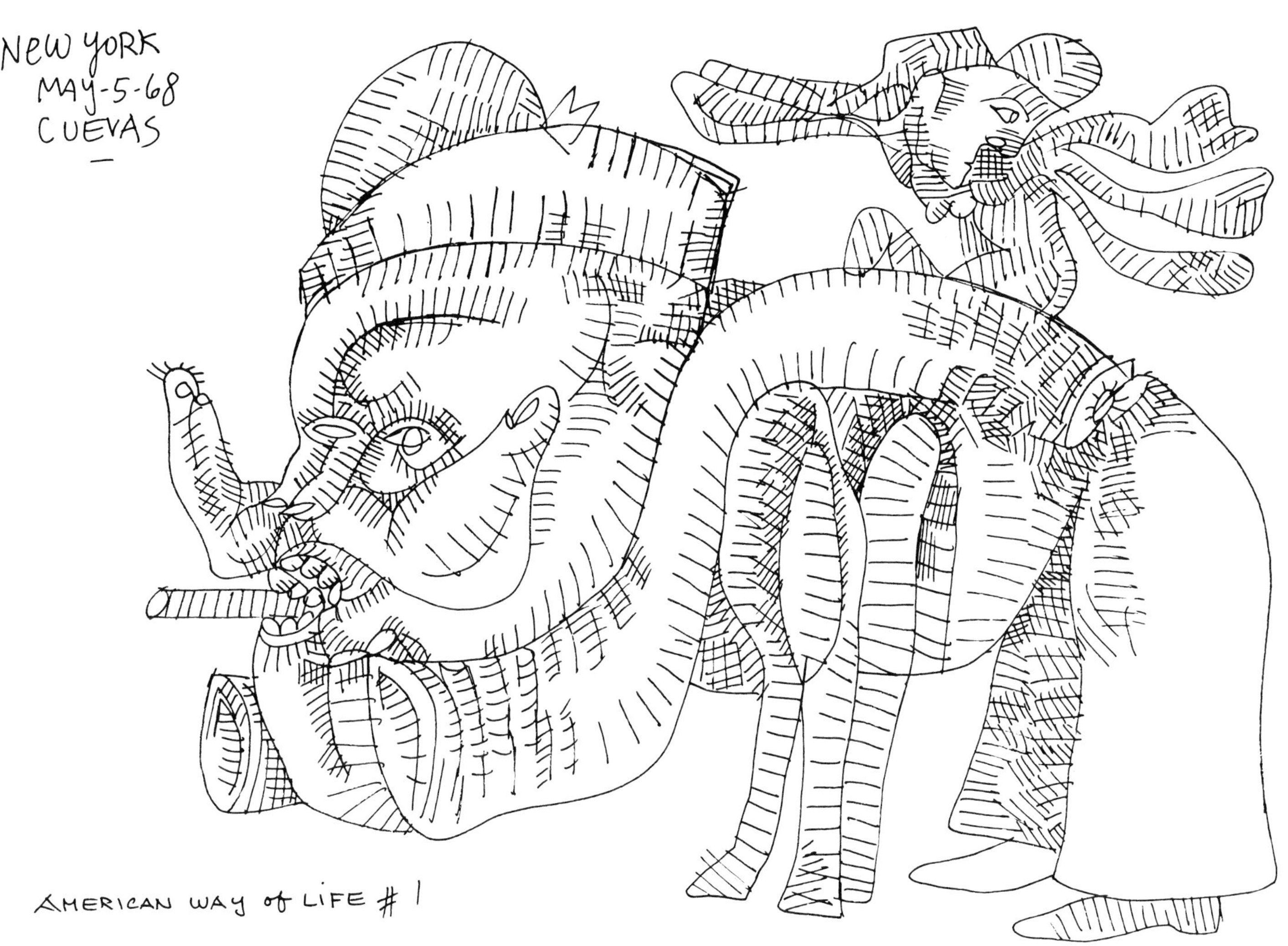
NEW YORK
MAY-5-68
CUEVAS
AMERICAN WAY of LIFE # 1

Dorothy Dehner

Born 1908 in Cleveland, Ohio. After receiving a degree in art from Skidmore College, Dehner attended the Art Students League in New York for three years. She has lived in Greece, Paris, the Virgin Islands and has traveled in Russia, England and Belgium. From 1940 to 1954 while married to David Smith she lived in Bolton Landing, New York. Presently she works in New York. Dehner is an abstract sculptor, also an accomplished printmaker who was awarded a Tamarind Fellowship in 1965. Her drawings, though often finished works in themselves, usually grow out of sculptural forms.

UNTITLED
Pen and ink, 31x22¼ in., 1963
No. 360

This drawing does not relate to any specific sculpture.

Amine Elbacha

Born 1932 in Beirut. Elbacha finished his art studies in 1953 at the Lebanese Academy of Art in Beirut. In 1958 he went to France where he worked for nine years. After returning to Beirut, where he now lives, he became an instructor of painting at the University of Lebanon. He is known both as an abstract painter and an illustrator, working in a wide range of media but specializing in watercolor.

UNTITLED
Watercolor, 26⅓x20 in., ca. 1965–70
No. BE1345

UNTITLED
Watercolor, 20x27 in., ca. 1965–70
No. BE1346

Jacob Epstein

Born 1880 in New York; died 1959 in London. The son of Russian-Polish parents, Epstein studied at the Art Students League and later with the sculptor George Gray Barnard. In 1902 he attended the Ecole des Beaux-Arts and the Académie Julian in Paris. After trips to Italy and England he settled in London in 1905, remaining there for the rest of his life. Epstein worked in both stone and bronze. The most important influences on his stone sculpture derived from African and other primitive carvings which he also collected. His bronze portrait busts were roughly modeled likenesses emphasizing spontaneity. Among his sitters were Winston Churchill, T. S. Eliot, Nehru, Albert Einstein and Princess Margaret of Great Britain. Epstein's major public works, many of them monumental compositions in stone, occasioned bitter controversies, yet now seem relatively conservative.

ILLUSTRATION FOR
"LES FLEURS DU MAL"
Pencil, 22½x17 in., 1938
No. 185

In addition to sculpture, Epstein occasionally made illustrations. When commissioned by the Limited Editions Club to illustrate Baudelaire's *Les Fleurs du Mal* he threw himself into the project with enthusiasm, continually re-reading the poems and visiting Paris to steep himself in its atmosphere. Though asked to do only six or seven drawings, he was so interested he produced sixty. The entire group was exhibited in London at Tooth's Gallery during 1938 and, like so many of Epstein's works, caused a furor. Fifteen of the drawings were sold. Epstein withdrew the exhibition after only two weeks. The Bank's drawing was not among those published in the Limited Editions Club's book.

Jacob Epstein, *Illustration for "Les Fleurs du Mal'*

Philip Evergood

Born 1901 in New York; died 1973 in Connecticut. Evergood, known for his biting social comment, was the product of various schools in England, his mother's home. He graduated from Eton in 1919 and, after entering Trinity College at Cambridge University, decided to transfer to London's Slade School of Art where he received his degree in 1923. Back in New York he attended classes at the Art Students League, which brought him into contact with George Luks, a member of "The Eight." (see p. 53) The anecdotal approach to art which Evergood learned from Luks became a significant influence on his work. Eight years of travel, exhibitions and study preceded the difficult depression years of the thirties. During that period, Evergood worked on the WPA art project making murals for post offices in Richmond Hill, Long Island and Jackson, Georgia. In 1952 he moved to Connecticut. His work, though often filled with symbolic imagery, is frequently characterized by a kind of realistic Expressionism.

GEECHY
Pencil, 13x10 in., 1938
No. 326

Jean Louis Forain

Born 1852 in Rheims, France; died 1931 in Paris. Painter and illustrator, Forain contributed to many of the Parisian satirical journals of his time including *Monde Parisien, Le Courrier Français, Rire* and *Figaro*. He studied at the Ecole des Beaux-Arts in the studio of Gérôme and also worked under the sculptor Carpeaux. However, the greatest influence on his work was Daumier. In addition to satirical drawings Forain also made several separate series of etchings and engravings dealing with problems of social justice. Like Daumier he was fascinated by courts of law. He also dealt with religious subjects. A friend of Manet and Degas, Forain exhibited with the Impressionists in 1879 and 1880.

N'A PAS DINE (HAVEN'T EATEN YET)
Pencil and crayon, 13x9 in., 1888
No. 325

A study for the lithograph *n'a pas diné* which appeared in *Le Courrier Français* on July 29, 1888, Forain's drawing pokes fun at gluttony and the dullness of social life. It is signed to the lower right of center and titled at the bottom to the left of center.

Hermine Ford

Born 1939 in New York. The daughter of painter Jack Tworkov, Hermine Ford began to draw in her father's studio when only a child. After attending Antioch College she pursued graduate studies in art at Yale. Originally a painter, she has recently turned to drawing, concentrating on the use of subtle monochromatic gradations to produce poetic images. She lives in New York.

UNTITLED
Pencil, 18x10½ in., 1971
No. 1880

Shadow and light playing on a factory smokestack are seen through a screen of windowpanes. The drawing is signed and dated.

Russell Forester

Born 1920 in Salmon, Idaho. Forester is an architect who has been a sculptor, painter and photographer. Since 1968 he has confined himself to painting and drawing in pen and ink, at times combining the two media with great expressiveness. His work is nonobjective and often based on modular geometric arrangements. Forester lives in La Jolla, California.

DRAWING
Ink, 23 in. diameter, 1971
No. LA1932

Mary Frank

Born 1933 in London. Presently living in New York, Mary Frank is a sculptor who began as a carver, then changed to modeling in plaster and now frequently works in stoneware. In her sculpture she suggests hidden forces of nature, sometimes allowing small figures to emerge from cavernous settings. The Bank's nine drawings were made as finished works rather than preliminary studies and are not specifically related to her sculpture.

UNTITLED DRAWINGS
Ink wash, 18x24 in., 1968, No. 353

Ink wash, 24x36 in., 1969, No. 351

Ink wash, 24x18 in., 1969, No. 352

Ink wash, 18x24 in., 1970, No. 823

Ink wash, 18x24 in., 1970, No. 824

Ink wash, 18x24 in., 1970, No. 825

Ink wash, 24x18 in., 1970, No. MC1673

Ink wash, 18x24 in., 1971, No. AT1325

Ink wash, 18x24 in., 1971, No. AT1326

Top, Jean Louis Forain, *N'a Pas Diné* (*Haven't Eaten Yet*)

Right, Philip Evergood, *Geechy*

Left, Mary Frank, *Untitled*

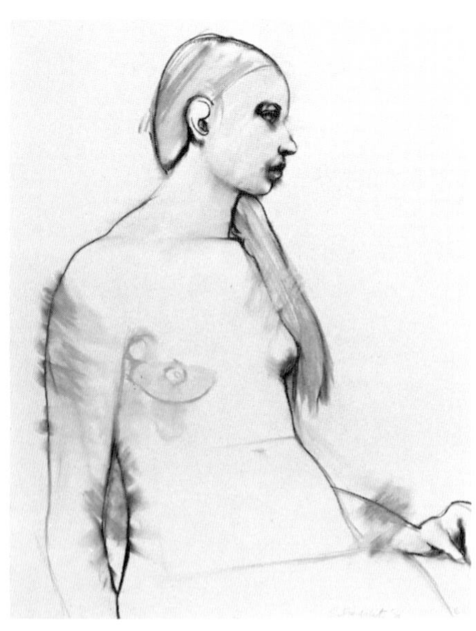

Sideo Fromboluti, *Woman*

Judith Roston Freilich

Born 1948 in Chicago. Freilich graduated from Washington University in 1969 and then studied under Misch Kohn at the Illinois Institute of Design, followed by courses at the School of the Art Institute of Chicago. She often creates sculpture by stuffing cloth shapes and sewing them together. Like all of her work these pieces are filled with biological references. She lives in Chicago.

UNTITLED
Graphite, 31¾x25 in., 1972
No. 1833

Sideo Fromboluti

Born 1921 in Hershey, Pennsylvania. Fromboluti lives in New York and Wellfleet, Massachusetts. His landscapes, usually painted in Wellfleet, are lyrical compositions that shimmer in shifting light and atmosphere; the Bank's two drawings of sailboats were done there. In his New York studio he works with large compositions of human figures.

SAILBOAT
Charcoal, 24x18 in., 1969
No. 410

SAILBOAT
Charcoal, 24x18 in., 1969
No. 668

WOMAN
Pastel, 30x24 in., 1971
No. 1291

This is a sketch from life.

Jacques Ange Gabriel

Born 1698 in Paris; died 1782, Paris. Gabriel, the descendant of a well established line of engineers and architects, followed his father Jean Jacques Gabriel in service to the royal house of France, becoming chief architect to Louis XV. Gabriel won fame by creating the Place de la Concorde as a monument honoring his king and was assigned the formidable task of unifying and completing Versailles, begun under Louis XIII.

ARCHITECTURAL PROJECT FOR A PALACE
attributed to Jacques Ange Gabriel
Pen, ink, pencil and bistre wash
22¾x25¼ in., 18th c.
No. 156

The interlaced monogram of two "L's," presumably for Louis XV, appears prominently on this drawing of a palace façade. The building shown is three floors high; monumental columns punctuate a series of arched windows and doors beneath a classical entablature in the projected central bay. Sculpture in the classical style has been sketched in niches and on the pediment. Two sheets of paper have been joined to accommodate an alternate design for a mansard roof and high gable above the completed neoclassical building. The paper bears a watermark showing a crowned escutcheon with *fleur-de-lys*. At the bottom of the drawing the scale is indicated in pencil. The tentative attribution to Jacques Ange Gabriel is based on his position at the court of Louis XV for whom this plan seems to have been designed. The Bank's drawing has many similarities in common with the façade of the Opera at Versailles, designed by Gabriel.

Jacques Ange Gabriel, *Architectural Project for a Palace*

Gavarni, *Mon Adoré, Dis-Moi ton Petit Nom* (*Darling, Tell Me Your Name*)

Right, *Lithograph from "Mon Adoré . . ."*

Gavarni (Sulpice Guillaume Chevallier)

Born 1804 in Paris; died 1866 in Paris. Sulpice Guillaume Chevallier, better known as Gavarni, was a gifted draftsman whose early training was as an architect and engineer. He later specialized in mathematics. When he was only fourteen he had already begun to study at the Conservatory of Arts and Crafts. Despite his original inclination to tie his artistic talents to some form of technical work, Gavarni's insight into the life and customs of contemporary Parisian society persuaded him to become a full-time artist. He contributed regularly to such illustrated French journals as *La Mode, L'Artiste* and *Le Charivari*. In 1847 he went to England where his work was exhibited at the Royal Academy in 1850.

MON ADORE, DIS-MOI TON PETIT NOM
(DARLING, TELL ME YOUR NAME)
Pencil, 12x10 in., 1841
No. 522

This is probably a preparatory drawing for one of the lithographs in Gavarni's *Les Lorettes,* a series of seventy-nine prints which appeared in *Le Charivari* beginning in June, 1841. The title of the series takes its name from the courtesans who lived in the parish of Nôtre Dame de Lorette in Paris. The print was published in *Le Charivari* on September 30, 1841 and was the sixth in the series. A frieze of small figures in costume at the top of the page may refer to the ball held on Ash Wednesday and attended by the "Lorettes."

Pier Leone Ghezzi

Born 1674 in Rome; died 1755 in Rome. Although Ghezzi was both painter and engraver, his major altarpieces and frescoes have, until recently, been overshadowed by the popular group of caricatures he produced in pen and ink. He differed from many baroque satirists in avoiding dehumanizing exaggerations. Both he and his father, Giuseppe Ghezzi, with whom he studied, were honored members of the Roman court. Pier Leone was a versatile man who, in addition to holding important papal offices, was an archeologist, an amateur musician and the owner of a fine drawing collection.

LE COMTE DIETRISTEIN
Ink, 10¾x7¼ in., ca. 1720
No. 1822

Sketched in broad pen strokes, this figure has the witty individuality that typifies Ghezzi's caricatures. An inscription identifies the subject of the portrait as "Le Comte Dietristein," probably the Austrian aristocrat, Karl Moritz Philipp Franz Xavier Dietrichstein, who could easily have been in Rome on an official mission during this period, and would have been in his mid-thirties at the time.

Pier Leone Ghezzi, *Le Comte Dietristein*

Domenico Gnoli

Born 1933 in Rome; died 1970 in New York. A self-taught artist, Gnoli worked in many fields—portraiture, printmaking, stage design, magazine illustration—and also wrote and illustrated a children's book. However, he is best remembered as a painter and occasional sculptor. Toward the end of his brief career he specialized in close-up views of commonplace details. The knot in a necktie, the part in a man's hair, or even a section of a bedspread, each greatly enlarged, were transformed into curiously new images. In his earlier work Gnoli was more romantic but no less meticulous.

CENTRAL PARK ON SUNDAY
Ink and watercolor, 24½x19 in., 1963
No. 255

The drawing belongs to a series depicting New York on Sundays. Some were published in *Show* magazine in August, 1964; the Bank's drawing was not among those published.

HOROSCOPE
Ink and watercolor, 11x16 in., ca. 1960–65
No. 427

Astrological signs of the zodiac provide the theme for this drawing, which is featured in a film about Gnoli made by friends after his death.

Leon Goldin

Born 1923 in Chicago. Goldin graduated in 1948 from the School of the Art Institute of Chicago and in 1950 earned an MFA from the State University of Iowa. After a brief teaching period at the California College of Arts and Crafts in Oakland he spent 1952 in France as a Fulbright Fellow. Other major grants followed, among them a *Prix de Rome* which made him a fellow of the American Academy in Rome from 1955 to 1958. Since then he has taught painting and printmaking at Queens College in New York and is now on the faculty at Columbia University. Goldin's work displays a confident draftsmanship and a preference for nature as subject matter.

LARGE OAK
Charcoal, 29½x22 in., 1968
No. 173

Jack Gregory

Born 1938 in Fall River, Massachusetts. From 1958 to 1964 Gregory studied at the School of the Boston Museum of Fine Arts and later taught graphics and life drawing there. He has recently been working in Provincetown, Massachusetts. The drawings owned by the Bank are based on the geometry of the circle and suggest the relations of bodies within a planetary system.

UNTITLED No. 29
Pencil, 22x28½ in., 1967
No. 399

AFTER GAUGUIN'S LA LUTTE DE JACOB AVEC L'ANGE
Pencil, 22½x18 in., ca. 1967
No. 400

The title here refers to a Gauguin painting of Jacob wrestling with the angel in the National Gallery of Scotland entitled, "Vision After the Sermon." The arrangement of circles and ellipses in Gregory's drawing bears a spatial relation to Gauguin's composition.

Domenico Gnoli, *Central Park on Sunday*

George Grosz,
The President

George Grosz

Born 1893 in Berlin; died 1959 in Berlin. Although he was both painter and draftsman, Grosz is best remembered for his vitriolic drawings satirizing German society after World War I. He served in the German army where he gathered material which he later used in his drawings. Returning to Berlin in 1919, deeply disillusioned by the war, he produced nihilistic dada works. His books and portfolios, among them *The Face of the Ruling Class* (1919), *Ecce Homo* (1922) and *Love Above All* (1931), brought him fame and also several lawsuits for libel. In 1932 he began teaching in New York at the Art Students League. Except for occasional trips to Europe he remained in the United States until shortly before his death when he returned to Germany. During his American years his anger cooled and his work became more orthodox.

THE PRESIDENT
Ink, 18x12 in., 1926
No. 159

Grosz's *President* is an elegantly dressed fat pig. Characteristic of the artist's German period, the drawing satirizes officialdom.

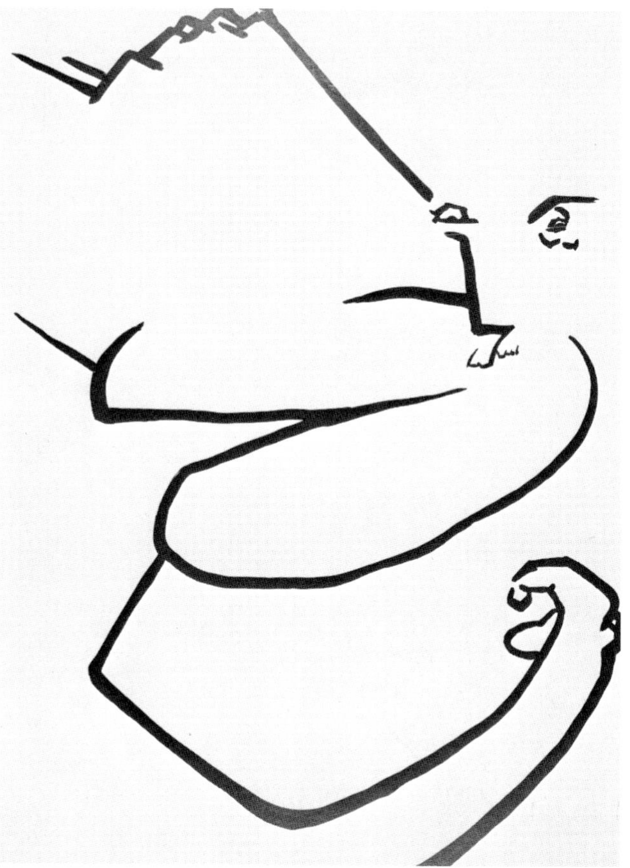

David Hare, *Cronus Growing*

Thomas Hansen

Born 1939 in Joliet, Illinois. After attending the University of Chicago and Roosevelt University, Hansen received a degree in English literature from Drake University in 1960. He limits himself to satirical drawings, some of which have appeared in *Harper's* and *World* magazines. Hansen lives in Chicago.

CLOCK
Ink and acrylic, 12x15 in., 1967
No. 417

NUN
Ink and acrylic, 20x13 in., 1968
No. 418

JUDGE
Ink and acrylic, 30x20 in., 1968
No. 419

BLIND MAN
Ink and acrylic, 30x20 in., 1967
No. 420

David Hare (for biography see p. 124)

CRONUS GROWING
Ink on masonite, 35½x26 in., 1967
No. 549

This work is from a series of drawings, sculpture and paintings on the myth of Cronus, father of Zeus. Cronus, told that one of his twelve children would kill him, ate all of them except Zeus who escaped and became his father's murderer. Here the artist's emphasis is on the symbolic rather than the narrative. The dislocated and fragmented body conjures up the idea of self-destruction.

MOUNTAIN LAND
Pencil, 30¼x40 in., 1968
No. 550

This drawing was made during one of Hare's annual stays in the West. He writes, "I was fascinated by the way the earth and the sky seem at times to exchange places . . . one loses a sense of up and down in the high mountains."

David Hayes (for biography see p. 126)

UNTITLED
Gouache, 19¼x25½ in., 1968
No. GU359

This brightly colored drawing relates to a series of ceramic plates and plaques that Hayes made in the late sixties.

FIGURES
Watercolor, 15½x19¾ in., 1965
No. 358

In the early sixties Hayes made several sculptures of torsos. Though not specifically related to any of the finished pieces, *Figures* is possibly a preliminary study.

Jean Hélion

Born 1904 in Couterne, France. In 1921 Hélion became an architect's apprentice in Paris where he studied architecture at the School of Decorative Arts. At that time he was impressed by the disciplined clarity of two seventeenth-century French artists, Nicholas Poussin and Philippe de Champagne, both of whom subsequently influenced him. In 1925 he gave up architecture and turned to figurative painting, but by the late twenties his work had become totally abstract. In the early thirties he was connected with the group known as Abstraction-Création that included among others Arp, Herbin, Delaunay, Kupka and Gleizes. The group published a review and provided a forum for artists and writers who were involved with experimental nonobjective art. Hélion came to the United States in 1936 where he remained until he returned to France in 1940 to join the French army. Six months later he was taken prisoner but in February, 1942 escaped from a German prison camp. He settled once more in America, returning to Paris when the war was over. He never again painted abstract compositions, for after prison life he became more directly involved with human problems. During the forties his works were influenced by Léger's mechanized figures and eventually by Existentialism. He usually paints in series.

JOURNALIST
Charcoal on paper mounted on canvas,
51x32 in., Nov. 24, 1947
No. 227

During 1947–48 Hélion created a series of paintings dealing with men reading newspapers. Each figure is isolated and is a replica of its neighbor. This large drawing was a study for the painting *Scène journalière* (1947–48) which is in the artist's collection. The vigorous draftsmanship is characteristic of Hélion.

STILL LIFE WITH UMBRELLA
Charcoal on paper mounted on canvas,
30¼x23 in., March 9, 1948
No. PR1622

A sketch for the painting *Chapellerie à l'oeillet* (1948), now in a private Parisian collection, combines commonplace objects in a strong design.

José Hernandez

Born 1944 in Tangier, North Africa. A self-taught artist, Hernandez is involved with macabre and surreal scenes. In 1964 he painted a mural at the Goya Theatre in Madrid based on Strindberg's play, *Spook Sonata*, which typifies Hernandez's preoccupation with other-worldly themes. The artist lives in Madrid.

UNTITLED
Ink, 20x16 in., 1971
No. 1827

UNTITLED
Ink, 20x16 in., 1971
No. KI1210

Jean Hélion,
Journalist

Selwyn Image, *Girl Playing Cymbals*

Selwyn Image

Born 1849 in Bodiam, Sussex, England; died 1930 in Oxford. Image, son of an English vicar, was ordained a deacon after completing his BA at Oxford in 1872, and became a priest the following year. He took his MA at Oxford in 1875 while he was curate at All Hallows, Tottenham. Image's desire to be an artist began at Oxford where he was an enthusiastic disciple of John Ruskin, but it was not until 1883 that he relinquished his orders and became a professional designer. Although best known for his stained glass windows, Image also designed books, made illustrations and even produced a fine Greek type for Macmillan Publishers. He did a great deal of work for Arthur Mackmurdo's design firm, The Century Guild, and his drawings appeared on the cover and pages of Mackmurdo's magazine, *The Hobby Horse*. His stylistic manner followed the English Arts and Crafts Movement with its trend toward linear patterns derived from naturalistic sources. In 1916 Image, a much sought after lecturer, became Slade Professor at Oxford. His avocation was entomology and his butterfly collection, beautifully mounted, is at Oxford.

GIRL PLAYING CYMBALS
Wash, chalk and ink, 41x17 in., date unknown
No. LN2003

This strong design with its heavy contours was made for a stained glass window in a residence at 15 Stratton St., London.

Eugène Isabey (for biography see p. 66)

PORTRAIT
Ink wash, 9x7¼ in., date unknown
No. 158

Following in his father's footsteps (see entry for next artist) Isabey made caricature drawings, often portraits of known people. The monogram of the artist appears at the bottom of the drawing to the left of center. The sitter for this drawing is unidentified.

PORTRAIT OF M. DE COURCELLES
Ink, 9¼x7¼ in., 1835
No. 1835

A swiftly drawn, incisive caricature, probably of the noted nineteenth-century genealogist, Chevalier J. B. de Courcelles. The initials E. I. appear in pencil on the drawing.

Eugène Isabey, *Portrait of M. de Courcelles*

Jean Baptiste Isabey

Born 1767 in Nancy, France; died 1855 in Paris. After first studying art in his native city, Isabey moved to Paris in 1786 where he worked with François Dumont and Jacques Louis David. Well known as a miniaturist, Isabey was also one of the first painters to practice lithography. His work appeared in official French exhibitions from 1793 until the 1840's. A favorite of the ruling class, he numbered among his patrons Marie-Antoinette, Napoleon, Louis XVIII, Charles X and Louis-Philippe. In 1805 he was named *Premier Peintre* to the Empress Josephine.

THE PINCE-NEZ
Ink and watercolor, 6½x7 in., 1818
No. 187

A preparatory drawing for one of twelve lithographs in the series, *Caricatures de J.J.*, published by Isabey in 1818. In it he lampooned powerful Parisians, the very people whose portraits he painted. The drawing is signed in the lower right corner.

Juliet Kepes

Born in London. Juliet Kepes studied art at Goldsmith College, London, the Brighton School of Art in Sussex and the Illinois Institute of Design in Chicago. She is the wife of Gyorgy Kepes with whom she has collaborated on a number of architectural murals and interior designs. She is, however, chiefly engaged in writing and illustrating children's books, particularly on themes dealing with animals and birds. Her major interest is drawing. She lives in Cambridge, Massachusetts.

HIGH NOTE ON A LOW BOUGH
Ink wash, 13½x10½ in., 1973
No. 1881

PENGUINS
Ink wash, 13½x10½ in., 1973
No. AM1882

These works have the spontaneity and rapid brushwork associated with Japanese Sumi painting.

Danny Kreeuseler

Born 1952 in Oudenbosch, the Netherlands. Kreeuseler attends the Free Academy of the Hague, where he lives.

MILK ORDER CARDS II
Pencil, 25¾x20 in., 1973
No. AM2044

Two forms for ordering milk are shown. One awaits the milkman's arrival with instructions for delivery; the other has been canceled after his departure. The drawing is strongly *trompe l'oeil*.

Ellen Lanyon, *Circus Riders*

Ellen Lanyon (for biography see p. 72)

CIRCUS RIDERS
Pencil and crayon, 19¾x25¾ in., 1967
No. 1300

Seven figures crowded on the back of a horse suggest a circus act, but the identity of the riders and the meaning of their performance is shrouded in uncertainty.

Joseph Lasker

Born 1919 in New York. Following graduation from Cooper Union in 1939, Lasker entered the army for the duration of World War II. In 1947 he won the Edwin Austin Abbey Memorial Scholarship for Mural Painting which took him to Mexico where he learned fresco techniques at the School of Fine Arts in San Miguel de Allende. Murals by Lasker are in post offices in Calumet, Michigan and Millbury, Massachusetts and at the Henry Street Settlement Playhouse in New York. He has taught at the University of Illinois and City College of New York. Since 1954 he has been associated with the Institute of Famous Artists School in Westport, Connecticut near his home in South Norwalk.

STILL LIFE
Charcoal, 23½x35½ in., ca. 1960–65
No. 175

James Lechay, *Head*

Charles K. Lassiter

Born 1926 in New York. Lassiter, who graduated from Yale in 1948, received an MA in Art Education from New York University in 1956. He also studied painting at the New School for Social Research, the Skowhegan School of Painting and Sculpture and the Brooklyn Museum School of Art. Using patches of color, he fragments images of human beings and animals. He lives in New York.

MAN AND HIS DOG
Watercolor, pen and ink, 24x18 in., 1967
No. 415

SILT WOMAN
Watercolor, pen and ink, 22½x30½ in., 1968
No. 284

ENGLAND SPEAKS
Watercolor, pen and ink, 25½x18½ in., 1968
No. 285

VINCENT VAN GOGH
Watercolor, pen and ink, 25½x19½ in., 1968
No. 414

JONES BEACH
Ink on rice paper, 25x35 in., 1969
No. 413

HORSE PARADE
Watercolor, pen and ink, 14x36 in., 1969
No. 416

James Lechay

Born 1907 in New York. Lechay, who originally studied with his father, Myron Lechay, has taught art at Iowa State University for many years. He lives in Iowa City and spends his summers at Wellfleet on Cape Cod. Lechay creates simplified figurative compositions that depend on lyrical color surprises.

HEAD
Pencil and ink wash, 10x12½ in., 1965
No. 1317

A large head, lying horizontally against a dark background, is sketched in rapid but controlled arabesques. The artist has achieved monumentality with linear freedom and a reduction of form which recalls Matisse.

HEAD
Ink wash, 10x12½ in., 1973
No. SP1885

HEAD
Ink wash, 12½x10 in., 1973
No. AM1886

These drawings are intended as artistic exercises and not as preliminary studies for paintings.

David Levine

Born 1926 in Brooklyn, New York. Levine studied painting at the Tyler School of Art in Philadelphia and early in the 1950's with Hans Hofmann in New York. He began as a watercolorist and only by accident embarked in the direction for which he is most widely known—caricature. In 1960 an editor of *Esquire* saw some of his humorous sketches and commissioned him to do more. His satirical drawings have appeared on the covers of *Newsweek* and *Time* and are seen regularly in *Esquire* and the *New York Review of Books*. Not only a caricaturist, he also devotes himself to watercolors of daily life and of realistic portraits unrelated to caricature. The artist lives in New York.

VIGNETTES OF FAMOUS MEN
Ink, 13x19 in., 1962
No. 448

Nine caricatures of world leaders, including Nehru, Nasser, De Gaulle, and Mao-tse-tung, the latter seen as a Chinese dragon, plus Khrushchev as a threatening cloud, make up this sheet of ink studies.

CASANOVA
Ink, 13½x10½ in., 1967
No. 225

Casanova, the famous seducer in eighteenth-century literature, is shown by Levine in disdainful profile with a reclining female draped about his neck like the folds of a gentleman's stock.

Mon Levinson

Born 1926 in New York. A graduate of the University of Pennsylvania, Levinson never attended art school but was influenced by the Abstract Expressionists when he first began painting; later he became interested in Constructivism as well. The artist, who taught sculpture for two years at C. W. Post College in New York, often works with plexiglas in order to explore the problems of light. Recently he has concentrated on drawings that reveal the structure of paper.

UNTITLED
Graphite, 22x30 in., 1973
No. NA1926

Obsessive repetitions are here modified by almost imperceptible variations. This is a Levinson drawing that results from his interest in the physical properties of paper.

David Levine, *Vignettes of Famous Men*

Seymour Lipton, *Clairvoyant*

Seymour Lipton

Born 1903 in New York. Lipton received a degree in dentistry from Columbia University in 1927. Essentially self-taught as an artist he supported himself as a dentist, but spent every free moment making sculpture. His first works in plaster and wood were closely based on nature. Later in the 1940's he began working directly with metal and since then has devoted himself exclusively to this material, usually monel metal that he brazes, welds and carefully refinishes. His forms are at once symbolic and abstract, but his titles, usually only one emotive word, are always based on familiar experiences. A number of his monumental pieces have been commissioned for public institutions. The artist lives in New York.

STUDIES FOR SCULPTURE

Before starting a sculpture, Lipton makes preliminary sketches on paper. His next step is to execute small metal models. Finally he carries out the finished piece. All nine of the Bank's drawings are signed and dated by the artist.

UNTITLED
Charcoal, 8½x11 in., 1963, No. 189

UNTITLED
Charcoal, 11x8½ in., 1963, No. 190

UNTITLED
Charcoal, 11x8½ in., 1966, No. ML1529

UNTITLED
Charcoal, 8½x11 in., 1968, No. ML1530

UNTITLED
Charcoal, 8½x11 in., 1969–70, No. ML1531

UNTITLED
Crayon, 8½x11 in., 1972, No. 1867

UNTITLED
Crayon, 8½x11 in., 1961, No. NA1868

CLAIRVOYANT
Crayon, 8½x11 in., 1969, No. 1869

A study for the sculpture *Clairvoyant* which is in the artist's collection.

ALTAR
Crayon, 8½x11 in., 1965, No. NA1870

A sketch for the sculpture of the same name in the artist's collection.

Carlo Lorenzetti

Born 1934 in Rome. Lorenzetti studied at both the State Institute of Art and the National Academy of France in Rome. The artist is known for his sculpture, ranging from monumental steel works to smaller pieces in plastic; he also creates jewelry, drawings and graphics. His work is abstract and influenced by the purity of Constructivism.

DESIGN
Pencil, 27¼x39 in., 1972
No. RO2021

DESIGN
Pencil, 27¼x39 in., 1972
No. RO2022

Richard Loving

Born 1924 in Vienna, Austria. Loving, whose parents were free-lance writers, grew up in Austria, France and New York. Although predominantly self-taught, he attended the Art Students League in New York for a short time in 1952. A friend's interest in enameling led him to study the process which he first used in jewelry and later in painting. He has been teaching at the School of the Art Institute of Chicago since 1962 and is chairman of the painting department there. Loving has created several murals and large enameled works for industrial buildings in the Chicago area and in New Jersey.

ORANGE AND RED SPAGHETTI
Ink and tinted wash, 38x25 in., 1968
No. 425

In a series of drawings concerned with the machine, Loving has produced landscapes of electronic and mechanical objects. The forms are familiar, though never definitively identifiable, and are linked together with tangles of tubular wire.

LARGE DRAWING
Ink and tinted wash, 42x77 in., 1969
No. 430

UNTITLED
Felt tip pen and acrylic, 38x25 in., 1969
No. 680

Robert Malaval, *Duel*

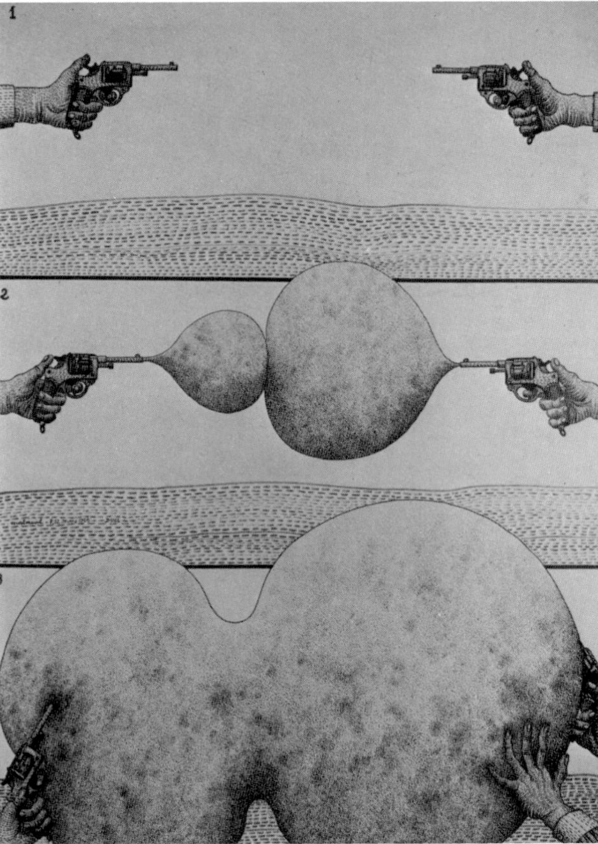

Sebastian Antonio Matta Echaurren

Born 1911 in Santiago, Chile. After architectural studies in Santiago, Matta worked in Paris with the French architect Le Corbusier but soon gave up architecture for painting. On a trip to Spain in 1936 he met Garcia Lorca and through him Salvador Dali and André Breton and was thus attracted to the surrealist movement which had been strong in Paris since the late twenties. During World War II he, like many other artists including his friends Marcel Duchamp and Yves Tanguy, fled to the United States. He returned to Europe in 1948 after building strong bonds with both artists and collectors in America. During 1950–54 he lived in Rome and thereafter in Paris. Matta's surrealist creatures, part human, part machine, part sheer invention, seem to rush through space with tremendous energy. In certain works, whole armies are projected into an extraterrestrial zone. The immediacy of Matta's early paintings had considerable influence on Abstract Expressionism.

SPATIAL COMPOSITION
Black crayon, 14¼x18¼ in., ca. 1950
No. 182

Schilli Maier

Born 1923 in Leipzig, Germany. Maier, with his family, came to the United States in 1929 and settled in New York. Beginning his education at City College, he received his BFA in 1953 from Columbia University. He studied with and assisted Amedée Ozenfant at his art school in New York, and has taught at Ithaca College and Temple University School of Fine Arts. For the last five years Maier has been art director for a frame designing firm in New York where he lives.

PROTOGENEA
Acrylic, gilt and crayon, 50x39½ in., 1969
No. 340

The embryo in the center of this composition represents the first female child born after the great biblical flood. She was named Protogenea, according to apocryphal literature. Although Maier feels that Ozenfant's influence was strong in his development, there are no signs of Purism in this work.

Robert Malaval

Born 1937 in Nice, France. Rock and roll music, noises heard at carnivals, on subway trains and in crowded streets are among the sources that have triggered Malaval's paintings, sculpture and ensembles. A certain wry quality is characteristic of his art. Malaval lives in Paris.

DUEL
Ink, 26x20⅛ in., 1965
No. PR1625

A cartoon strip format and drawing style borrowed from nineteenth-century commercial illustration emphasize the humor of this drawing. The amusing notion of balloons replacing bullets is also a device drawn from the comics. But the playfulness fades in the final panel when the balloons increase in size and viscosity until they threaten to encroach fatally upon the duelers.

Fernando Maza (for biography see p. 77)

UNTITLED NO. 1
Ink, 13⅝x26 in., 1967
No. 506

UNTITLED NO. 4
Ink and gouache on green paper, 20x26 in., 1968
No. 507

UNTITLED NO. 10
Ink and crayon, 22½x28½ in., 1969
No. 508

UNTITLED NO. 11
Ink, 23⅛x35 in., 1968
No. 509

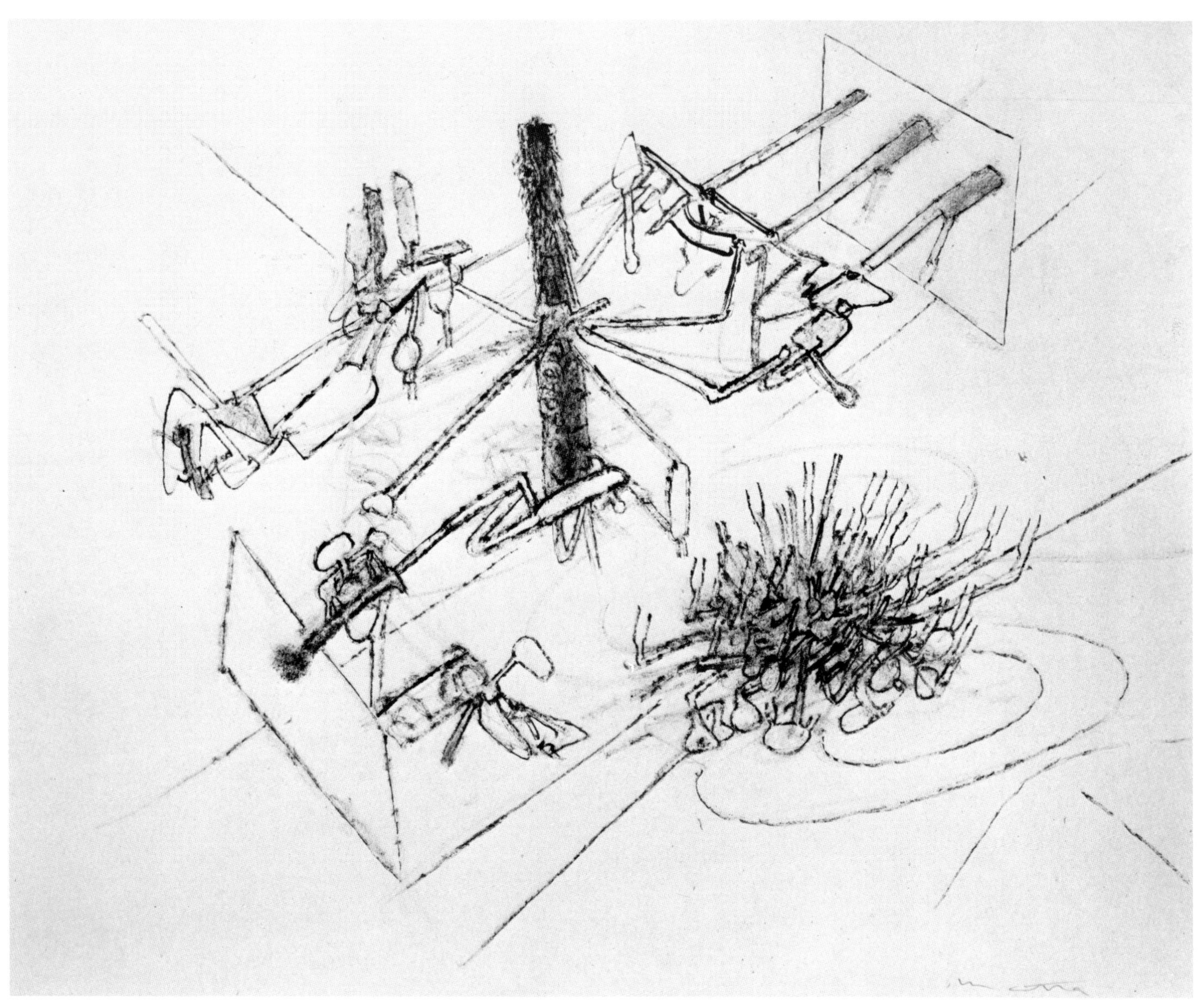

Matta, *Spatial Composition*

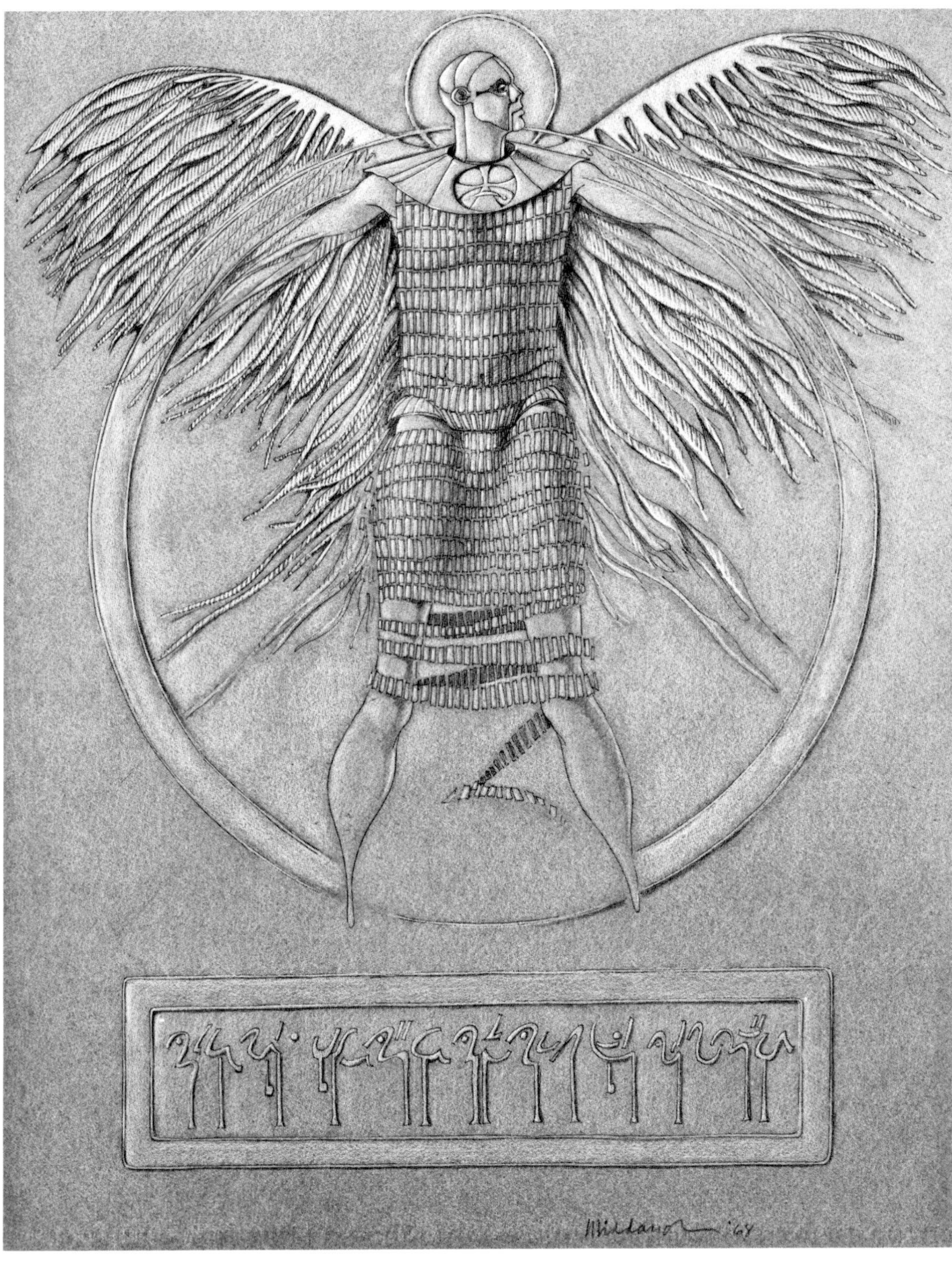

Robert Middaugh,
Virtuous Doubter

Jerome Myers,
The Train

Denis McCarthy

Born 1935 in New York. McCarthy studied at Cooper Union until 1963 when he enrolled at Yale where he received a BFA in 1964 and an MFA in 1966. He began teaching in New York at the School of Visual Arts in 1967 and became a member of the Hunter College faculty in 1970. A minimalist, this artist is essentially a painter involved more with form and space than with color. Some of his "paintings" are actually unpainted canvas rectangles bolted together to form large assemblages with irregular contours. The artist lives in New York.

UNTITLED
Airbrush, 40x30 in., 1969
No. 652

UNTITLED
Airbrush, 40x30 in., 1969
No. 739

Both drawings are pure geometric abstractions concerned with space.

Robert Middaugh (for biography see p. 79)

FREE FLIGHT
Ink, 20x26 in., 1966
No. 429

Inspired by the exploration of space, Middaugh improvised on the theme in a series of drawings and paintings made during 1966–67.

VIRTUOUS DOUBTER
Pencil and crayon, 26x20 in., 1968
No. 428

A figure from one of Middaugh's mythological series.

Jerome Myers

Born 1867 in Petersburg, Virginia; died 1940 in New York. Myers arrived in New York in 1886 with very little training in art. He first worked as a theatrical scene painter while attending Cooper Union and later the Art Students League. Though not a member of "The Eight," Myers concerned himself, as they did, with the street life of New York, in his case chiefly the Lower East Side. Various ethnic groups newly arrived in America especially interested him. The people he depicted were poor but their lives were colorful. He emphasized group scenes such as park concerts, religious festivals or children in playgrounds.

THE TRAIN
Crayon, 7¼x10 in., ca. 1925
No. 172

A study of people riding in a railroad coach.

Thomas Nast, *Mikado in the White House*

Thomas Nast

Born 1840 in Landau, Germany; died 1902 in Guayaquil, Ecuador. Nast's family moved to New York in 1846. There he studied with a German artist, Theodore Kaufmann, and later at the Academy of Design. When only fifteen he was hired as an illustrator for *Leslie's Weekly*. This marked the beginning of his career as an illustrator and cartoonist for the most important periodicals of the day. In 1860 and 1861 he traveled with the armies of Garibaldi in Italy, sending back drawings to the *London News* and to the *New York Illustrated News*. He returned to the United States in 1861 and a year later began his long association with *Harper's Weekly*. Nast's virulent cartoons attacking Boss Tweed and Tammany Hall helped bring about the defeat of both in the 1871 elections. President Theodore Roosevelt appointed Nast to a diplomatic post in Ecuador where he died soon after his arrival. He is considered America's greatest nineteenth-century cartoonist.

MIKADO IN THE WHITE HOUSE
Ink, 7½x9½ in., 1885
No. 327

This drawing, dated 1885 on the front, is inscribed on the reverse, "Rehearsing the Mikado at the White House. Cleveland as Pooh-Bah, 'Mind, I will not kiss them. How de do, how de do, little ones?'" Gilbert and Sullivan's popular *Mikado* was first performed in March 1885 at the same time Grover Cleveland began his initial presidential term. Although the operetta was loosely connected with political events of the nineteenth century which restored communication between Japan and the rest of the world, the reference here to Cleveland as a character from the *Mikado* probably relates to the scandal of the 1884 campaign which revealed that he was the father of an illegitimate daughter. In the cartoon a woman's profile seen in shadow on the wall may be intended to represent Maria Holpin, the baby's mother, while the three children in the foreground, who are Gilbert and Sullivan's "three little maids from school," could also be Mrs. Holpin's two elder daughters and the illegitimate child fathered by Cleveland. In spite of being staunch Republicans, both Nast and his publisher at *Harper's Weekly* (where the artist's cartoons appeared) supported the candidacy of Cleveland who was a Democrat. This drawing was never published in *Harper's*, perhaps rejected as too unsympathetic.

The Netherlands/Anonymous

SHIPS IN THE HARBOR AT LIVORNO
Ink and wash, 7x11¼ in., 18th c.
No. 154

This drawing by an anonymous artist, showing merchant ships armed with cannon and lying in a fortified port, belongs to a tradition of marine art which originated in the seventeenth century in the Netherlands and England. An inscription on the back of the picture, apparently copied from an old label, reads: "Kauffahrtschiffe im Hafen von Livorno. Feder Zeichnung, 18 Jahrhd." ("Merchant ships in the port of Leghorn. Pen drawing, 18th century."). Tricorn hats, knee breeches and long coats with puffed sleeves worn by the small foreground figures bear out the date and probable Italian setting. Livorno is famous for the numerous fortifications which ring its port, although none of them is accurately represented here. Two ships clearly fly the Union Jack of Great Britain, while one shows a horizontal tricolor which could be Dutch.

Anthony Padovano, *Study for a Sculpture*

Anthony Padovano
(for biography see p. 139)

STUDY FOR A SCULPTURE
Smoke and pencil, 15½x21½ in., 1963
No. 280

Experimenting with an idea for a new sculpture, Padovano placed the projected form in an imaginary landscape. The drawing is signed and dated in the lower right corner.

STUDY FOR MAJA
Sepia ink, 18½x24 in., 1966
No. 279

This drawing was made in preparation for Padovano's sculpture, *Maja*, which is now in the collection of St. Lawrence University, Canton, New York. Padovano's sculpture is not often related to natural objects; however, a reclining female figure is intimated here.

STUDY FOR SCULPTURE NO. 7
Ink, 26x20 in., 1967
No. 554

Beverly Pepper

Born 1924 in Brooklyn, New York. Pepper studied at Pratt Institute and at the Art Students League before going to Paris where she worked under Fernand Léger and André Lhote. She began as a figurative painter, later turning to abstraction and finally specializing in sculpture. She lives in Rome where she has been working in light-reflecting metals such as aluminum and stainless steel. Pepper has carried out several large architectural commissions in the United States and abroad, often in the simple reduction of form she prefers.

UNTITLED
Acrylic on paper, 38½x27⅓ in., 1972
No. RO2017

A somber, highly simplified tonal composition that suggests the artist's more recent sculpture.

Vita Petersen

Born 1915 in Berlin. Vita Petersen studied with Carl Hofer at the Berlin Academy of Art and later attended the Munich Art School. In 1938 she came to New York where she still lives. She was a student of Hans Hofmann in 1947–48 and has been teaching drawing and painting in New York secondary schools for ten years. Her work depends on a careful manipulation of color and tone.

APPLES
Crayon, 30x22 in., 1969
No. 662

CROWDS ASSEMBLING NO. 1
Crayon, 24x19 in., 1969
No. 663

Both drawings are based on staccato, rhythmic line.

Joseph Piccillo

Born 1937 in Buffalo, New York. In 1964 Piccillo received his MA from the State University College at Buffalo where he is now on the staff of the art department. Two of his drawings have been reproduced on covers of *Time*. Essentially a draftsman, he has recently been producing large drawings on canvas which, like much of his work, are concerned with ironic social comment.

UNTITLED
Pencil, 40x30 in., 1973
No. 1933

This strange figure, raging but mute behind the ambiguous bonds that gag him, has been set up as a target—literally—for Picillo's sardonic sense of humor.

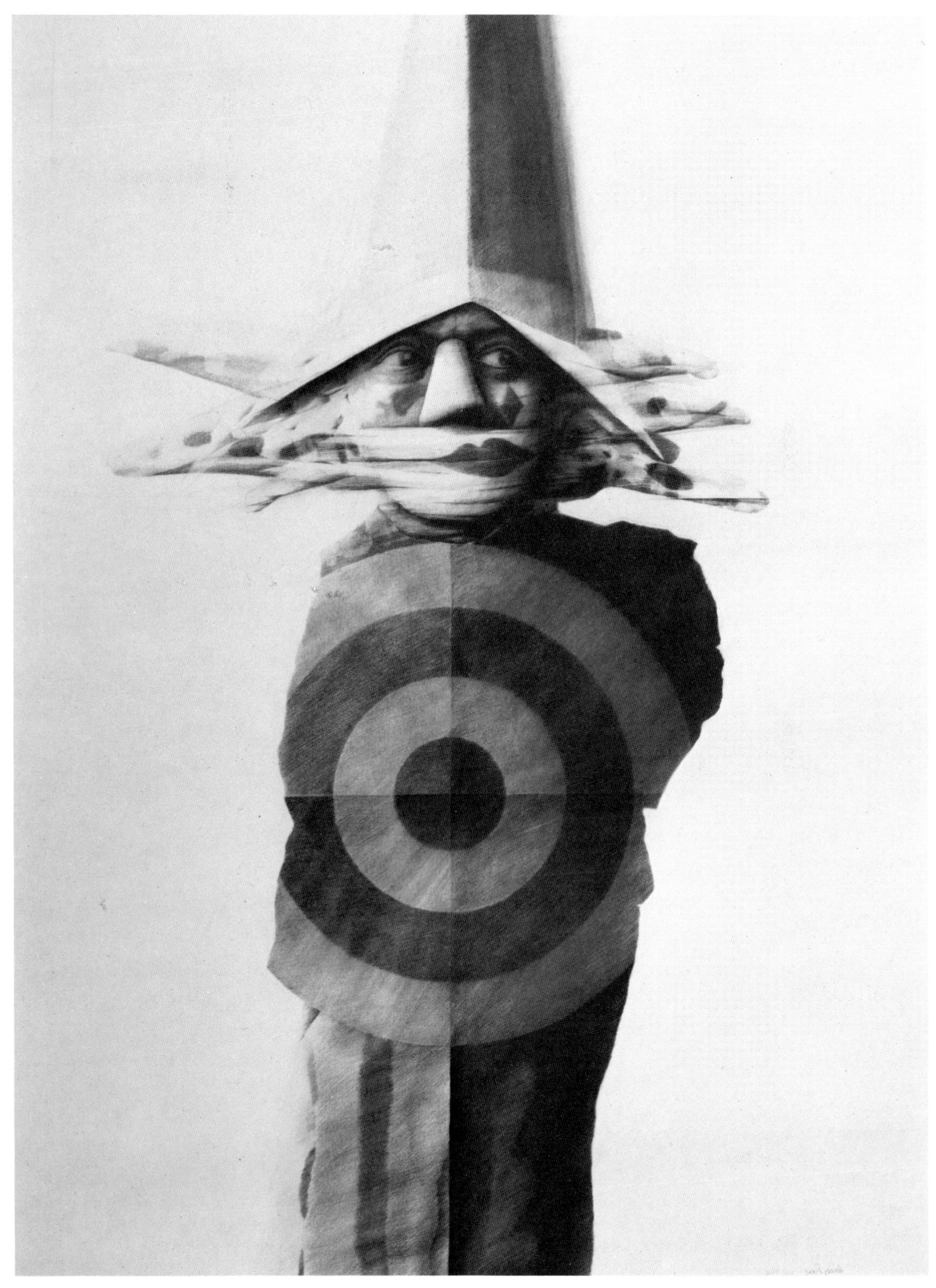

Joseph Piccillo, *Untitled*

Fairfield Porter, *Breakfast Table*

Arnaldo Pomodoro

Born 1926 in Morciano di Romagna, Italy. Pomodoro has worked both as theatre designer and jewelry maker, but is primarily a sculptor. His bronzes with their gleaming surfaces opposed to areas of eroded and intricate detail often share qualities of the goldsmith's craft. For his large-scale works many preparatory drawings and models are made before the final sculpture is cast. As a rule Pomodoro depends on a few basic forms, chiefly columns and spheres. The artist has lived in Milan since 1954.

UNTITLED
Charcoal, 17¾x15⅝ in., 1957
No. ML1534

A delicate, early, slightly surrealist drawing.

Fairfield Porter

Born 1907 in Winnetka, Illinois. Porter, who graduated from Harvard in 1928, studied painting at the Art Students League in New York with Boardman Robinson and Thomas Benton. He took on a many-sided career when he became the editorial assistant for *Art News* and art critic for *The Nation*. He has also written for *Art in America* and *Evergreen Review* and is the author of a book on Thomas Eakins. Porter has taught both journalistic criticism and painting on the faculties of Southampton College at Long Island University, Queens College and Amherst College. A painter who has shunned the high-powered movements of nonrepresentational art, he produces simple interiors and understated landscapes flooded with light. He lives in Southampton, Long Island.

BREAKFAST TABLE
Ink, 13¾x16¹¹⁄₁₆ in., ca. 1965–70
No. 1826

This economical study for a painting is typical of Porter's country-house scenes where a room, though empty, projects the personalities ordinarily occupying it. Colors to be used in the final work are noted on the sketch.

Larry Rivers

Born 1923 in New York. Growing up in the Bronx, Rivers started out as a jazz saxophonist. After receiving a medical discharge from the army in 1943, he attended the Juilliard School of Music. Encouragement by artist friends led him to Hans Hofmann's school in 1947 and also to New York University where he studied under William Baziotes, finally receiving a degree in 1951. An accomplished draftsman, sculptor and painter, he has specialized in unexpected historical subjects, realistic nudes and ironic juxtapositions of allusive themes drawn from his own life. He often shocks with his frankly unorthodox subjects and his equally unorthodox methods.

PORTRAIT OF COMPLETE SELF-DEDICATION
Pencil, 16x14½ in., ca. 1960–65
No. 183

Here Rivers produced an ambiguous drawing with an equally ambiguous inscription: "Portrait of complete self-dedication & those who hate pay Larry."

GIRL AND LION
Pencil, crayon and collage, 13⅝x15 in., 1966
No. 186

The head of a girl is superimposed over a familiar Rivers motif, a lion. He used a similar lion, borrowed from an advertisement, in 1964 for a series of paintings he called *The Dreyfus Fund*. In 1968 Rivers again made lion paintings that recalled a trip he took to Africa.

Larry Rivers,
Portrait of Complete Self-Dedication

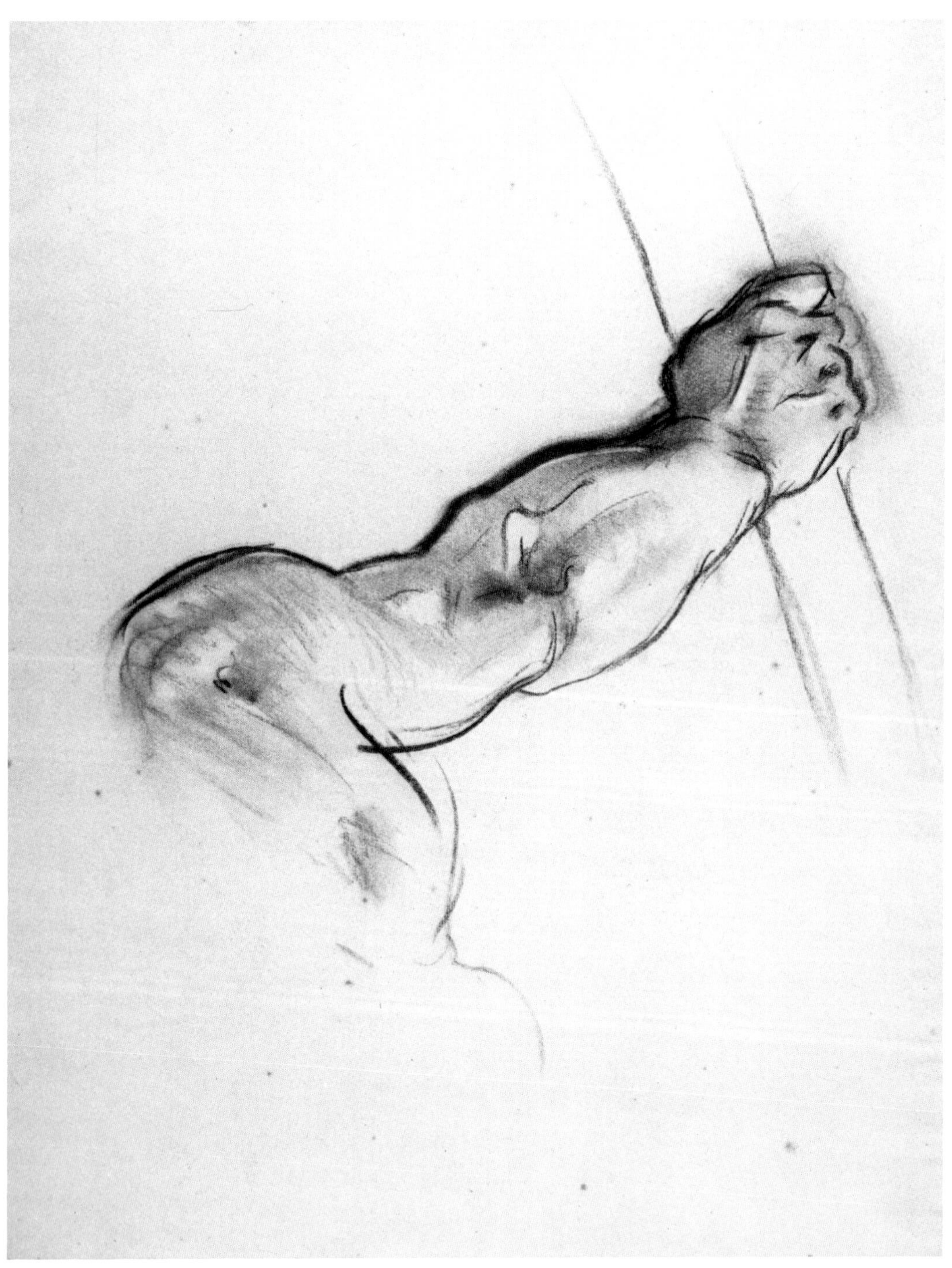

John Singer Sargent,
Study for
the Figure of Time

John Singer Sargent

Born 1856 in Florence, Italy; died 1925 in London. Born of American parents living in Europe, Sargent began his studies at the Academy of Fine Arts in Florence and later worked in Paris with Carolus Duran at the Ecole des Beaux-Arts. At the age of twenty-one he was already exhibiting in Paris at the Salon. His deft, rapid handling of pigment, inspired by Velàsquez and Hals, plus his sometimes probing, sometimes fashionable portraits brought acclaim from both sides of the Atlantic. Sargent's fluent watercolors, usually done on the spot, show the influence of Impressionism. He executed two important mural cycles, one for the Boston Public Library (1892–1916) and the other for the Boston Museum of Fine Arts (1916–1925). Over the years he divided his time between England and the United States.

STUDY FOR THE FIGURE OF TIME
Charcoal, 23x18 in., ca. 1916–21
No. 256

An oval composition in the rotunda of the Boston Museum of Fine Arts contains an allegorical painting by Sargent entitled *Architecture, Painting and Sculpture Protected from the Ravages of Time*. This drawing of an arm is a study for the figure of Time, represented with a scythe.

STUDY OF FEET AND DRAPERY
Charcoal, 18x23 in., ca. 1916–25
No. 181

A sketch probably belonging to the large body of study material for the decorations of the Boston Museum rotunda.

John Singer Sargent,
Rotunda Decoration
Courtesy Museum of Fine Arts, Boston

STUDY FOR A MALE NUDE
Black chalk, 24x17½ in., ca. 1916–1925
No. 1821

In the rotunda of the Boston Museum of Fine Arts a mural in lunette form depicts Classical and Romantic Art. The physical proportions of the figure in the Bank's drawing suggest that it might be a sketch of the model who posed for the youth personifying Romantic Art.

Anne Schlanger

Born 1941 in New York. The artist studied at Sarah Lawrence College and briefly in Paris. She stayed in Florence, Italy from 1969 to 1971, spending part of the time there in a cooperative studio working on several large, collaborative painting projects. Influenced by both Expressionism and Surrealism, she is presently living in New Rochelle, New York.

UNTITLED
Charcoal, 23x29 in., 1973
No. 1925

In an unexplained confrontation, a man and whale meet in the shallows of the sea.

Antonio Segui (for biography see p. 89)

UNTITLED
Pencil and gouache, 20x25½ in., 1970
No. 1288

During 1970–71 Segui, in an abrupt departure from his more brutal style of the sixties, employed a deceptive serenity. His irrational *fin de siècle* seascapes carry a sense of uneasy anxiety.

Antonio Segui, *Untitled*

Shelby Shackleford

Born 1899 in Halifax, Virginia. Educated at the Maryland Institute of Art, Shackleford went on to study with Othon Friesz, William Zorach and Fernand Léger. She was chairman of the art department at St. Timothy's School in Maryland from 1944 to 1962 and was an instructor in painting at the Baltimore Museum of Art from 1950 to 1965. Her paintings and drawings are sensitive understatements of experiences related to the landscape of Cape Cod, in particular to shifting aspects of sky and water. The artist divides her time between Baltimore and Wellfleet, Massachusetts.

SMALL SUN CAUGHT IN A THICKET
Soot, 29x36 in., 1968
No. 569

A Cape Cod drawing, made of soot extricated from an oil stove, is characteristic of this artist. She applies the fine black powder to paper, shaking it on lightly and rubbing gently until general forms are defined; then with a kneaded eraser she carefully removes all superfluous soot to produce detailed refinements.

VESSEL
Soot, 22x15 in., 1973
No. LN1922

The drawing was inspired by microscopic photography of biological organisms.

ASCENT
Soot, 22x15 in., 1973
No. 1921

Everett Shinn

Born 1876 in Woodstown, New Jersey; died 1953 in New York. Shinn went to Philadelphia in 1891 to pursue mechanical training at the Spring Garden Institute but later switched to the Pennsylvania Academy of the Fine Arts. The young painter met John Sloan in the art department of the *Philadelphia Press* where both were working as reporter-illustrators. Shinn later claimed that capturing the essence of a news event was better training than years at an art school. He moved to New York in 1897 where he was associated with the *Herald* and the *World*. In 1908 he and John Sloan joined "The Eight" (see p. 53). One of Shinn's favorite subjects was the theatre with special emphasis on burlesque and vaudeville scenes.

HANDS
Charcoal, 7¼x6¼ in., 1910
No. 129

BURLESQUE QUEENS, OLYMPIA THEATRE
Pencil and charcoal, 5x2⅜ in.; 5x2⅞ in.; 5x2⅜ in., 1920–30
Nos. 130a, 130b, 130c

These three drawings framed together were probably done on the spot by Shinn. In the center drawing he jotted down color notations for the costume. The drawing on the left is signed by the artist.

John Sloan

Born 1871 in Lock Haven, Pennsylvania; died 1951 in Hanover, New Hampshire. As a draftsman and printmaker Sloan was chiefly self-taught. At sixteen he worked for a print seller and book dealer in Philadelphia. Here he taught himself to etch, aided by Hammerton's *The Etcher's Handbook*. From 1890 to 1891 he attended night drawing classes at the Spring Garden Institute and worked as a commercial artist. In 1892 he joined the staff of the *Philadelphia Inquirer* as an artist and also enrolled in night drawing classes at the Pennsylvania Academy of the Fine Arts where he met Robert Henri under whose guidance he began to paint. In 1895 he moved from the *Inquirer* to the *Philadelphia Press*. With the increasing use of halftones in newspapers, the need for artist-journalists decreased, causing Sloan to leave Philadelphia for New York in 1904. There he supported himself by doing illustrations for magazine and book publishers. He was one of "The Eight" (see p. 53). Throughout his career, Sloan's work dealt with the realities of city life, with both its humorous and seamy sides.

ILLUSTRATION FOR "EGGS A LA CASEY"
Crayon and ink on cardboard, 18x13½ in., 1908
No. 174

After Sloan moved to New York in 1904, he worked as a freelance illustrator, often for *Collier's* and *The Century*. "Eggs à la Casey," a short story by L. H. Bickford with five illustrations by Sloan, appeared in *Collier's*, June 27, 1908. The drawing is signed and dated lower right.

John Sloan, *Illustration for "Eggs à la Casey"*

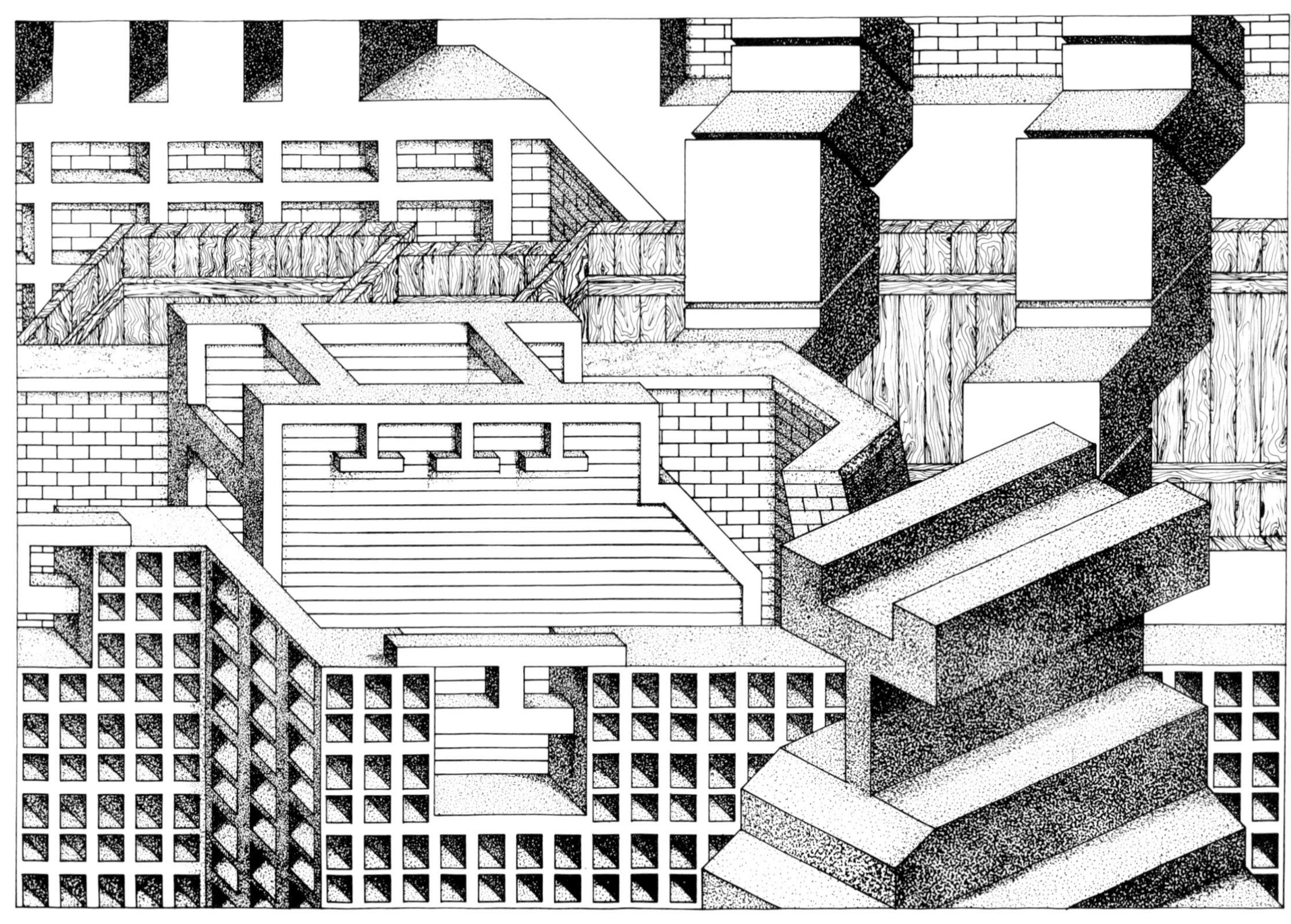

David Smyth, *Untitled*

David Smyth

Born 1943 in Washington, D.C. Smyth graduated with a BFA from the School of the Art Institute of Chicago in 1967 where he also earned an MFA in 1969. In 1968–69 he was an instructor at the Chicago Academy of Fine Arts and the following year taught at Indiana University. He spent 1972 working at the Tamarind Institute of Lithography and now lives in New York. Smyth is a sculptor, painter and printmaker who sometimes shows a preference for architectural forms.

UNTITLED
Ink, 24x36 in., 1970
No. 649

A maze of walls in brick, wood and concrete make up an architectural fantasy of impossible structures.

Leonello Spada

Born 1576 in Bologna, Italy; died 1622 in Italy. In spite of his nickname, "scimmia del Caravaggio" (Caravaggio's ape), Spada belonged to the academic circle of the Caracci family in Bologna. The influence of Lodovico Caracci is especially felt in some of his large frescos. Malvasia, writing in his seventeenth-century history of Bolognese artists, says that Spada accompanied Caravaggio on his trip to Malta, and also recounts that toward the end of his career the artist worked in both Reggio and Parma where contact with Correggio's work mellowed his style.

UNTITLED
Sanguine chalk, 10x12 in., 17th c.
No. 308

Two drawings, apparently alternate designs for an ornamental escutcheon, have been mounted side by side with a covering center strip. The arrangement gives the appearance, at first glance, of a single design, but closer observation shows a lack of precise continuity between the two halves. In each case, vegetation and putti weave a tangled border around an organic form.

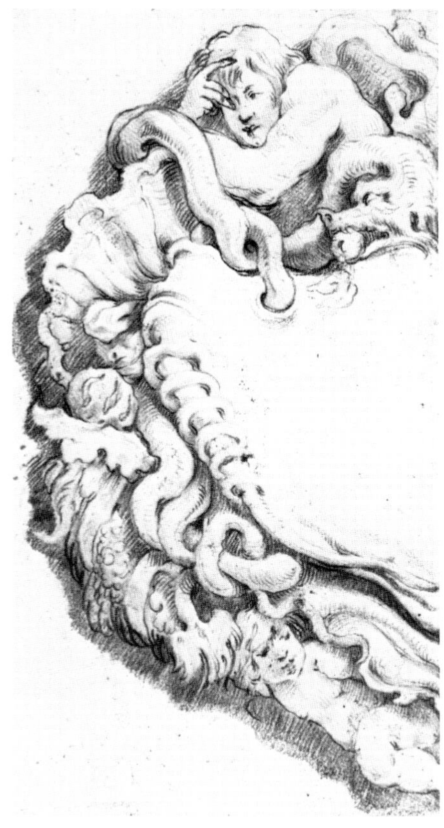

Leonello Spada, *Untitled*

Nora Speyer

Born 1923 in Pittsburgh. Speyer, who divides her time between studios on Cape Cod and in New York, works in different styles according to her environment. In the country she paints directly from nature with sonorous color and heavy pigment; in the city she handles large figure compositions. The flower drawings in the Bank's collection were done in the garden of her home in Wellfleet, Massachusetts.

FLOWERS
Charcoal, 18x23½ in., 1969
No. BE408

FLOWERS
Charcoal, 18x23½ in., 1969
No. BE409

TIGER LILIES
Charcoal, 23x29 in., 1973
No. 1910

Saul Steinberg,
Nebraska

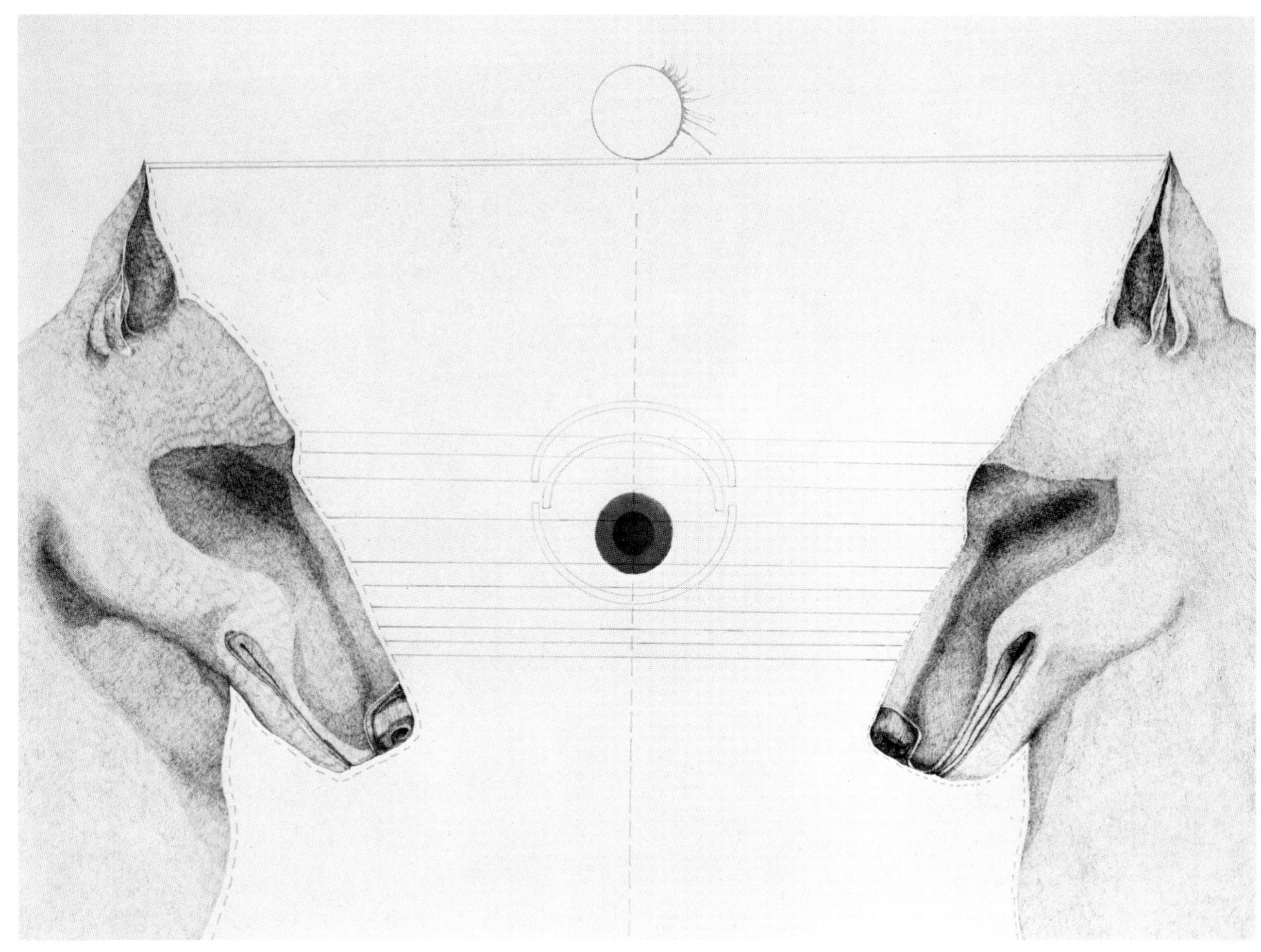

Pat Steir, *Dog Days*

Saul Steinberg

Born 1914 in Romanic-Sarat, Rumania. After studying architecture at the University of Milan from 1932 to 1940 Steinberg came to the United States in 1942 and settled in New York. He is best known for his drawings, many of which appear regularly in *The New Yorker*. A potent social commentator, he is also a consummate draftsman.

NEBRASKA
Ink and gouache, 28½x22½ in., 1969
No. 547

This composition is entirely predicated on rubber stamps specially designed by the artist, a technique he developed in the late sixties. *Nebraska* lampoons bureaucratic symbols and the stamp-like conformity of present-day life. The work is signed and dated in the lower right.

DOGS
Crayon and pencil, 19¾x24 in., 1969
No. AT548

Upon close examination the viewer finds that one dog has only two legs. The question is: Which is more human, the dogs or the human being? The drawing is signed and dated in the lower right.

Pat Steir

Born 1938 in Newark, New Jersey. Steir began her education at Boston University in 1958 but left after two years to enter Pratt Institute where she earned her BFA in 1962. She divides her time between New York and California, where she teaches art. Her work shows an indebtedness to New York art of the sixties.

DOG DAYS
Ink, 30½x22½ in., 1969
No. 674

This drawing belongs to a series in which animal heads, particularly those of dogs, were predominant.

Hedda Sterne (for biography see p. 92)

LADY IN THE SUBWAY
Ink, 14x11 in., 1969
No. 339

A study of old age, resulting from a face the artist saw by chance on the New York subway.

PROFILE STUDIES

During 1970–71 Sterne made innumerable profile drawings which often suggested portraits of people she knew, although she insists the likenesses were not deliberate and were only recognized by her after the work was completed. The six sketches in the Bank's collection are all from this series.

Ink, 14x11 in., 1971
No. BE1348

Ink, 14x11 in., 1971
No. BE1349

Ink, 14x11 in., 1970
No. ML1537

Ink, 14x11 in., 1970
No. ML1538

Ink, 14x11 in., 1970
No. FR1728

Ink, 14x11 in., 1970
No. FR1729

Emilio Tadini

Born 1927 in Milan, Italy. Tadini received his training at the Academy of the Brera in Milan. The impact of industry, transportation and mass society is strong in his work. He floats familiar consumer objects in improbable spatial relations. His technique is reminiscent of photomechanical advertising layouts. The artist lives in Milan.

UNTITLED
Watercolor and pencil, 16½x22 in., 1968
No. ML1539

UNTITLED
Watercolor and pencil, 16½x22 in., 1968
No. ML1540

John Tenniel

Born 1820 in London; died 1914 in London. Tenniel was the son of a well-known dancing master and instructor in arms. The father's profession prompted his son's long interest in arms and armor, but the latter made his name as caricaturist and chief political cartoonist for *Punch*, the British satirical journal. Starting his art studies at the Royal Academy School and the Clipstone Street Life Academy, he sold his first oil painting when only sixteen at an exhibition of the Society of British Artists. In 1845 he won a competition to design a fresco in the House of Lords and in preparation visited Munich to study fresco techniques there. Joining the staff of *Punch* in 1851, he began to publish a weekly cartoon in 1862. Tenniel drew over two thousand cartoons for this magazine. He was well-known, too, for his book illustrations, the most famous of which were the original drawings for Lewis Carroll's *Alice in Wonderland* and *Alice Through the Looking Glass*. He also illustrated Dickens' novels.

ALL THE WORLD'S A STAGE
Black and white chalk, 9x7 in., ca. 1890
No. LN2002

Shakespeare's famous description of the ages of man from *As You Like It* has been interpreted whimsically by Tenniel in a sketch representing the final stage of life. Old age, personified in Elizabethan costume resembling that worn by a court fool, totters past the shop of a watchmaker, a reference to the inevitable passage of time. A sign bearing the enigmatic phrase, "Going One," is seen on the shop's façade just above the legs and feet of a body disappearing upside down inside the shop window, all of which may indicate the demise of the old man. A puckish figure, sprouting fairy antennae from his head, stands to the left observing the activity in the shop window. The drawing is signed with Tenniel's monogram at the lower right.

John Tenniel, *All the World's a Stage*

Jean Thomas Thibaut

Born 1757 at Montiér-en-Der, Haute Marne, France; died 1826 in Paris. Thibaut was a painter, architect and professor of perspective at the School of Architecture in Paris. He was the author of a treatise, *Application de la perspective linéaire aux arts du dessin*, published after his death in 1827. He held the post of King's Pensioner to the Academy of Arts in Rome, during which time he studied classical antiquity.

ARCHITECTURAL INTERIOR WITH A STAIRCASE
Ink and wash, 4⁵⁄₁₆x5⅝ in., ca. 1800
No. 153

The artist has invented a neoclassical building of palatial scale, employing a variety of architectural devices to demonstrate the pictorial use of linear perspective. An interior courtyard with a central staircase is surrounded by an arched loggia, beyond which the building continues in an enormous hall supported on columns and arches. The deliberate patterns of interlacing arch and column emphasize an optical illusion of three-dimensional space projected on a two-dimensional surface.

Anna Ticho

Born 1890 in Brunn, Austria. Ticho grew up in Vienna and received her first training in drawing and painting there. Since 1913 she has lived in Jerusalem where she finds her subject matter in the ancient city and surrounding countryside. She is particularly known for her weblike, topographical drawings of the Judean landscape.

SUMMER HEAT
Pencil, 23x28 in., ca. 1960–68
No. NA1588

In this panoramic view of the hills near Jerusalem, the artist conveys the feeling of a summer day with waves of heat rising from rocks and shrubs. A masterful draftsman, Ticho works in both pencil and charcoal.

Raymond Toloczko

Born 1925 in Chicago; died 1972 in Chicago. In 1951 Toloczko received simultaneously his BA from De Paul University and his BFA from the School of the Art Institute of Chicago. During the following year he was at the Skowhegan School of Painting and Sculpture and then studied at the School of Fine Arts in San Miguel de Allende, Mexico. He toured Europe, studying art in Venice during 1956, and returning to work in Texas in 1957. In 1962 he was a visiting fellow at the Huntington Hartford Foundation in California and the next year a resident at Yaddo, the artist colony in Saratoga Springs, New York. In 1964–65 Toloczko painted murals for the Tiffany Blake library at the Skowhegan School. Best known for his watercolors and aniline dye works, Toloczko's essential trademark was the complicated pattern of dot and line he developed.

JOLIET GRADUATION
Ink on rice paper, 24x18 in., 1961
No. 450

A bitter subject is emphasized by the harshness of its execution and the jagged contour of the composition. Joliet is a maximum security prison in Illinois.

SEPTEMBER DAYS
Ink, 37x25 in., 1962
No. 449

The artist's technique of using dotted lines emphasizes the old-fashioned quality of almanac-type sun faces that make up the composition.

Raymond Toloczko, *Joliet Graduation*

Jack Tworkov, *Untitled*

Guillermo Trujillo

Born 1927 in Horconcitos, Panama. Trujillo became a licensed architect from the University of Panama in 1953, after having spent a year in Madrid on a scholarship to the Academy of San Fernando where he studied painting. In 1954 he returned to Spain for two years to study ceramics and take a special course in landscape architecture. His work is varied; he is a craftsman who uses materals ranging from fabric to tile and also paints and draws both on a large scale and an intimate one. At times his pictures are filled with fantasy, at times they are abstract. He is one of the best known artists in Panama City where he lives.

UNTITLED
Ink, 14x16 in., 1971
No. PN1607

A strange bird's head sprouts human arms while a naked baby sits on the lap of one of two grotesque figures.

UNTITLED
Ink, 14x16 in., 1971
No. PN1608

Malformed creatures frolic in an anthropomorphic jungle. Both drawings are influenced by Surrealism.

Jack Tworkov

Born 1900 in Biala, Poland. Tworkov came to the United States in 1913 and later studied at Columbia University, the National Academy of Design and the Art Students League. His early paintings were naturalistic, but during the 1950's he became associated with the abstract expressionist movement. During the late sixties Tworkov was head of the Yale University art department. Always an expert draftsman, his paintings from the late sixties and early seventies are based on his drawings. They are understated, meticulously designed and subdued in color. Tworkov lives in New York and Provincetown, Massachusetts.

UNTITLED
Charcoal, $23\frac{3}{16}$x$19\frac{1}{8}$ in., 1969
No. 681

This drawing, with its carefully arranged parallel strokes, shows the same development as Tworkov's paintings during the late sixties and early seventies. Vast sweeping areas of paint applied with great dramatic force characterized his canvases of the early sixties. The change to more disciplined compositions with subtle shifts of color typifies his later work, of which this drawing is a fine example.

Vladimir Velickovic

Born 1935 in Belgrade, Yugoslavia. Velickovic studied architecture in Belgrade but later turned to painting. In 1963 he moved to Paris where he still lives. His work is usually related to grotesque, hostile images. Decaying heads with bulging eyes, often recalling the excesses of German Expressionism, are unexpectedly juxtaposed with geometric elements painted or drawn with precision.

UNTITLED
Ink, $42\frac{7}{8}$x$28\frac{3}{8}$ in., August 14, 1966
No. BS1372

A large screaming head characteristic of Velickovic's emphasis on violence.

Antonio Visentini, *An Architectural Drawing of the Grimani Palace*

Antonio Visentini

Born 1680 in Venice; died 1782 in Venice. Visentini, trained as engineer and architect, was a relatively minor painter in eighteenth-century Venice. He is remembered for his graphic work, especially the engraved suites which he produced after Canaletto's celebrated Venetian *vedute*.

AN ARCHITECTURAL DRAWING OF THE GRIMANI PALACE
attributed to Antonio Visentini
Ink and wash, 18⅞x14 in., 18th c.
No. 309

The Italian inscription on this architectural drawing is written in a style peculiar to the Veneto. It reads: "Palazo del Grimani a S. Lucca di Michel S. Michel." The palace depicted here still stands and has sometimes been considered the crowning achievement of the High Renaissance architect, Michele Sanmichele. It was built at the end of his life, around 1550. Unfortunately a third story was added after his death which destroys the beauty of Sanmichele's original proportions. The Bank's drawing shows the palace façade, its ground plan and scale. The dry, precise quality of the draftsmanship is close to known works by Visentini.

Frederick J. Wardy

Born 1937 in Los Angeles. After receiving his BA in 1960 from the University of the City of Los Angeles, Wardy formed a corporation for the design and manufacture of surfboards, catamarans and aquatic equipment. In 1965 he began to study art, first at UCLA and then for two years at Chouinard in Los Angeles. To get experience in steelworking techniques he wanted to use for large sculpture, Wardy worked in a foundry for a year. In 1969 he moved to New York where he became a playground and park designer for a city planning firm, and since 1970 has been at the Whitney Museum as an assistant on the exhibitions staff. Wardy's drawings are constructed of finely drawn parallel lines which produce both form and light.

NEW YORK NO. 15
Ink, 30¾x22½ in., 1973
No. 1907

NEW YORK NO. 14
Ink, 30¾x22½ in., 1973
No. NA1920

Hugo Weber

Born 1918 in Basel, Switzerland; died 1971 in New York. From 1937 to 1939 Weber studied in Basel with the sculptor Ernst Suter and later with Aristide Maillol in Paris. Both a painter and sculptor, Weber worked in Paris during 1945 with Jean (Hans) Arp who was the most important early influence on his art. At the invitation of Laszlo Moholy-Nagy, Weber came to Chicago in the late forties where he taught at the Illinois Institute of Design (now part of the Illinois Institute of Technology). Weber lived in Paris from 1950 to 1960, subsequently settling in New York. In his later years his work was related to Action Painting. At the same time he made several expressionistic portraits in bronze of Mies van der Rohe, the renowned architect.

FRED ASTAIRE AND GINGER ROGERS
Ink, 20x25½ in., 1958
No. NA1589

Abstract brushstrokes suggest weightless dancers. The drawing, signed and dated in the lower right, was influenced by the dynamics of Abstract Expressionism.

Jeffry Wyatville, *Cottage at Chatsworth*

Jan Yoors, *Untitled*

Jeffry Wyatville

Born 1766 in Burton on Trent, England; died 1840 in London. Son and nephew of important architects, Wyatville served an apprenticeship with his uncles, Samuel and James Wyatt. He established an independent office in 1799 and in the 1820's became a member of the Royal Academy where he had exhibited since 1786. He was a fashionable architect who counted the most important members of the British aristocracy as his patrons. One of his commissions was the remodeling of Windsor Castle for George IV. The appearance of this British royal residence as we know it today is largely the work of Wyatville. He began the project in 1824 and was involved with it for almost fifteen years. During the remodeling George IV and Wyatville became such good friends that the King commissioned a portrait of the architect to be painted by Thomas Lawrence. The painting still remains at Windsor Castle.

COTTAGE AT CHATSWORTH
Watercolor and ink, 14½x20½ in., ca. 1820–30
No. 247

During the 1820s Jeffry Wyatville, who was employed by the Duke of Devonshire in the expansion of his estate at Chatsworth, designed a new wing and tower for the main building, two entrance gates and several smaller structures. Probably the "cottage" in this drawing is one of the latter. Across the bottom of the sheet is written, "The East Front of the . . . Cottage—facing the road from Chatsworth House."

Jan Yoors

Born 1922 in Antwerp. At the age of twelve, Yoors joined a band of gypsies with whom he lived until he was eighteen. Wandering through Europe, he acted as a saboteur behind the German lines during World War II, an experience so fascinating that he has written two books about it and about his life with the gypsies. From 1944 to 1948 he studied international law at London University but in 1950 he and his wife bought a loom and began producing large tapestries. Although Lurçat and Gromaire were reviving interest in tapestries simultaneously, Yoors disliked their use of *hachure* (effects of painterliness achieved through short parallel lines of color). He chose instead to weave his abstract patterns in the classic tradition of Aubusson and Gobelin, a method he and his family of craftsmen continue to follow in the New York studio where they live. Yoors also makes sculpture and drawings from time to time.

UNTITLED
Charcoal, 30x26 in., 1968
No. 540

UNTITLED
Charcoal, 30x26 in., 1968
No. 541

Both nude figure studies are signed and dated.

Mahonri Young, *Buffalo*

Mahonri Young (for biography see p. 148)

HIPPOPOTAMUS
Ink and wash, 6½x8¾ in., date unknown
No. 440

BUFFALO
Ink and wash, 6½x8¾ in., date unknown
No. 441

Young often worked at the zoo where undoubtedly the *Hippopotamus* was made. A conbination of realism and humor, the drawing is characteristic of the artist's sketchy draftsmanship. The *Buffalo* may also have resulted from a visit to the zoo or from one of Young's trips to the West. Both drawings are signed with the artist's initials.

Zush

Born 1946 in Barcelona. Zush, who lives on Ibiza in the Balearic Islands, did not attend art school. He seems most interested in nude forms as starting points for his compositions, but he constantly fragments and reorders his figures, covering them with symbols which show his strong interest in the occult.

HAND
Ink and watercolor, 19½x19½ in., 1973
No. MA2030

A hand and forearm are covered with mystical signs, possibly of astrological or Tantric inspiration.

WALL HANGINGS

This section has been arranged alphabetically except for the first seven entries.

Marie Cuttoli and Twentieth-Century Tapestries

In the early thirties a French woman, Marie Cuttoli, introduced twentieth-century design into the ancient art of tapestry weaving. In Paris she persuaded some of the outstanding painters of her time to make designs suitable for reproduction in fiber; she also used some of their existing works as the basis for her tapestries. These were executed on the looms of Algerian craftsmen, thereby reviving the collaboration of artist and artisan in tapestry making. Mme. Cuttoli's work with European artists has inspired the creation of an American collection of tapestries as well. Both sets are represented in the Bank. The following seven tapestries by Arp, Ernst, Miró and Picasso were initiated by Mme. Cuttoli.

Jean (Hans) Arp (for biography see p. 110)

RED CIRCLE
Wool, 78x57 in., ca. 1960–65
No. 1855

This tapestry in delicate grays and blues enlivened by sharp areas of black and white and a single bright red circle was woven from a design specifically made for the purpose.

Max Ernst, *Comet*

Max Ernst

Born 1891 in Brühl, Germany. Ernst studied philosophy, psychiatry and art history at the University of Bonn from 1909 to 1912. After serving in the German army, he founded the Cologne Dada group in 1919. He moved to Paris in 1922 where he joined with Arp, André Breton, Paul Eluard, Man Ray and Francis Picabia to become one of the founding artists of the surrealist movement. During the second world war Ernst lived in New York and Arizona until 1949 when he returned briefly to Europe. He came back to the United States in 1950, and, after teaching at the University of Hawaii in 1952, returned to Paris the following year. Presently he lives in Seillans, France. An artist of inventive irony, he is known for his collages, *frottages* (rubbings), sculpture, paintings and costume designs. He explores disturbing themes, often handled in meticulous detail, and constantly shocks with the unexpected.

COMET
Wool, 63x82 in., ca. 1960–65
No. 234

With broken white lines, Ernst suggests cosmic rays and a flashing comet against a deep black background accentuated by a red sun. This tapestry was woven from a design specially made for the purpose by Ernst.

Joan Miró

Born 1893 in Montroig, Spain. After studying in Barcelona at the School of Fine Arts and at the Academy Gali, Miró left for Paris in 1919. There he associated himself with the Paris Dada movement, also becoming friendly with his fellow Catalan, Picasso, whose family he had known in Barcelona. Starting in the twenties, Miró divided his time between Paris and Spain, a pattern he continues to this day. The artist's first paintings were somewhat realistic, yet so vigorously drawn and richly colored as to reflect the influence of Matisse and Fauvism. Later he turned to more abstract images, but always organic ones such as human and animal figures plus stars, moons and suns. Miró has worked as painter, printmaker, sculptor, set designer and book illustrator. His compositions have boundless humor and a sense of rhythmic space. During the thirties under the influence of Surrealism, he worked with found objects. In the forties Miró began a long association with the Spanish master potter Artigas, at first only decorating works made by Artigas, but later creating and decorating his own ceramic sculpture.

DREAM
Wool, 75x61 in., ca. 1960–65
No. 235

The design for this tapestry originated as an illustration which Miró made for Tristan Tzara's volume of poetry, *Parler seul*, published in 1950. The brightly colored shapes, reminiscent of Chinese calligraphy, represent human figures.

SPANISH DANCER
Wool, 80x58 in., ca. 1960
No. RO238

The inspiration for this tapestry came from a collage of 1928, also entitled *Spanish Dancer*, now in a private collection in Chicago.

MONGOOSE
Wool, 75x60 in., ca. 1960
No. 1856

Pablo Picasso

Born 1881 in Malaga, Spain; died 1973 in Mougins, France. Picasso, the son of a painter and art teacher, became a child prodigy under his father's training. After studying in Barcelona, he went to Paris in 1900 where he fell under the influence of bohemian life and the paintings of Lautrec as well as the discoveries of the Impressionists and other contemporary artists. Picasso absorbed innovations quickly and just as quickly began to create new styles of his own. His many changes of style are too numerous and too well known to list here, but his part in the foundation of Cubism is perhaps the single achievement for which the twentieth century owes him the greatest debt. In designing tapestries, he again absorbed and broke with tradition, allowing himself great freedom in theme and composition.

JACQUELINE
Wool, 72x89 in., 1964
No. TK236

Named for his last wife, the tapestry shows her profile at the left overlooking a building resembling one of the many villas Picasso occupied in the South of France. A man stands silhouetted on the balcony. The tapestry is limited to tones of blue and white.

SHADOWS
Wool, 72x88 in., 1964
No. 239

Picasso designed the maquette for this tapestry at the same time as that for *Jacqueline* but here the forms are less explicit. The weaving is conceived entirely in blue and white.

Giacomo Balla, *Design*

Arcadio Blasco Pastor, *Tapestry*

Richard Anuszkiewicz
(for biography see p. 110)

BANNER NO. 2
Felt 2/20, 60x60 in., 1968
No. 292

Typical of Anuszkiewicz's work, the lines in this banner seem to move and bend as the colors interact.

Giacomo Balla

Born 1871 in Turin, Italy; died 1958 in Rome. Balla, who studied at the Albertina Academy in Turin, became a painter, sculptor and interior decorator. In 1895 he moved from Turin to Rome where he lived for the rest of his life. A trip to Paris in 1900 brought him in contact with the French Neo-Impressionists whose experiments in color relationships inspired Balla and his pupils, Umberto Boccioni and Gino Severini, to work with color in an abstract way. Balla signed both futurist manifestos of 1910. His most famous painting, *Dynamism of a Dog on a Leash* (*Leash in Motion*), was based on the idea of a single form shown in multiple movement with an obvious debt to film animation.

DESIGN
Printed linen, 56x56 in., ca. 1920
No. RO2037

This tapestry, silk-screened on linen in blue, green and yellow abstract floral patterns, is the original of an edition printed later and limited to 200.

Herbert Bayer

Born 1900 in Haag, Austria. In 1921 Bayer entered the Bauhaus at Weimar to study with Kandinsky. From 1925 to 1928 he taught at the Bauhaus in Dessau where he worked with Gropius, Moholy-Nagy and Breuer. Later he went to Berlin as a graphic designer and painter, remaining there until 1938 when he came to the United States. Bayer, who spent several years in New York, now lives in Aspen, Colorado. He has experimented with architecture, photography, city planning and advertising; he has also been chairman of the design department at Container Corporation of America. His work is usually based on clean abstract motifs.

CHROMATIC A
Wool, 10 ft.x69 ft. 8 in., 1968
No. 1090

CHROMATIC B
Wool, 10ft.x69 ft. 8 in., 1968
No. 1091

Two immense abstract tapestries, commissioned for the employee's dining area at the Bank, fill the walls with vibrant blocks of color. In *Chromatic A* the entire color spectrum moves from its lightest values in the middle to the deepest hues at either end; in *Chromatic B* the arrangement is reversed. Both tapestries serve to deaden sound in an otherwise noisy area. *See end-sheets for colorplate.*

Arcadio Blasco Pastor

Born 1928 in Muchamiel, Alicante, Spain. Blasco studied at art schools in both Madrid and Valencia, and has since devoted himself to crafts and design. He is especially known for his ceramic murals and large tapestries which are usually variants of geometric abstractions. Blasco is a resident of the Spanish Academy in Rome.

TAPESTRY
Wool embroidered on natural linen,
36x72 in., 1972
No. MA2018

Herbert Bayer, *Chromatic A*

Peter Collingwood,
Macrogauze No. 83

Georges Braque

Born 1882 in Argenteuil-sur-Seine, France; died 1963 in Paris. Braque, whose father and grandfather were both amateur painters, began his art studies in Le Havre where his family moved when he was eight. He also worked there for one year as an apprentice to a house painter-decorator before moving to Paris and entering the atelier of Léon Bonnat. The Impressionists and Cézanne were both early influences on Braque, who subsequently became a leading Fauve. From 1907 until the first world war Picasso and Braque worked interdependently to bring about the evolution of Cubism. They also shared in the initiation of collage as an important art form and made still life their principal theme. When Braque resumed painting after recovering from wounds received in the war, he concentrated more and more on developing monumental compositions of tabletop arrangements and classical nudes; later he turned to interiors. His work was always enriched by subtle textures and sensuous color. He is also remembered for his sculpture and graphics.

BIRD
Wool, 48x85½ in., 1968
No. 1938

The design for this tapestry was taken from a color lithograph, *Bird Passing Through a Cloud*, which Braque made in 1957. The tapestry, of which there are only five, was woven in 1968.

Alexander Calder (for biography see p. 118)

SPIDER
Wool, 60x78 in., 1955
No. 237

Calder's design was made specially for this tapestry.

Peter Collingwood

Born 1922 in London. Trained as a physician, Collingwood first became interested in weaving after he spent nine months with the Red Cross in Jordan. His spare time there was devoted to the study of this craft. Returning to England, he worked with several weavers, among them Ethel Mairet, Barbara Sawyer and Alistaire Morton. Collingwood now lives in Essex and teaches at the Central School of Arts and Crafts. Rug-making occupied his early career and he wrote a book, *The Technique of Rug Weaving*, which was published in 1968. In the late fifties Collingwood began his "macrogauze" wall hangings which consist of coarse fiber and steel rods combined to create transparent geometric forms.

MACROGAUZE NO. 63
Fiber and steel rods, 69x25 in., 1970
No. 1092

MACROGAUZE NO. 70
Fiber and steel rods, 60x41 in., 1970
No. AT1094

MACROGAUZE NO. 83
Fiber and steel rods, 70x24 in., 1970
No. 1093

Allan D'Arcangelo

Born in 1930 in Buffalo, New York. D'Arcangelo, who in 1953 received a degree in history and government from the University of Buffalo, began to paint two years later without having formal art training. Hitchhiking trips around the United States provided him with pop themes. His imagery derives from sights and signs of the highway. He has taught at the School for Visual Arts in New York and has been a visiting critic at Cornell and visiting artist at Yale. He lives in New York.

UNTITLED
Felt 3/20, 74½x72 in., 1968
No. 334

Highway barrier, road sign and sky are combined in this banner with billboard directness.

Jim Dine

Born 1935 in Cincinnati, Ohio. Dine studied painting at the Cincinnati Art Academy and at the Boston Museum school. Starting as an Abstract Expressionist, he soon became interested in reproducing functional objects and articles of clothing, especially neckties, bathrobes and boots. As one of the first pop artists, he painted these images realistically and with humor, at times attaching actual objects to his canvases.

PALM
Felt 2/30, 94x71 in., 1970
No. 821

In 1966 Dine designed costumes and sets for a production of Shakespeare's *Midsummer Night's Dream* which was presented at the San Francisco Actor's Workshop and later in Pittsburgh and New York. *Palm* is a larger version of the glove for Oberon's costume. The five colors used in this banner recur in the costumes and sets for the play.

TWO RED BOOTS ON A BLACK GROUND
Felt 7/20, 59x61 in., 1965
No. 291

Title, signature and date inscribed along the contour of one boot are integral parts of this banner's composition.

VALENTINE
Wool, 60x84 in., 1967
No. 317

The valentine, a frequent theme with Dine, varies within his work from an iron sculpture six feet high to a straw image large enough to fill a room. This tapestry was woven from a collage made in the form of a valentine.

MIDSUMMER
Wool, 84x60 in., 1967
No. 650

A watercolor by Dine was the inspiration for this tapestry. It includes many of his favorite motifs such as lips, a heart and a man's hat.

Robert Goodnough

Born 1917 in Cortland, New York. Goodnough, who attended Syracuse University, received his MA from New York University in 1949. He later attended the Ozenfant School of Fine Arts and the Hans Hofmann School. While a graduate student at New York University, he attended meetings of "The Club" at the Cedar Bar where he came to know such artists of the New York School as Franz Kline, Jackson Pollock and Mark Rothko. Though his early work showed the influence of Cubism, his current paintings are based on interacting two-dimensional color areas that have the spontaneity of Action Painting. Goodnough has taught at New York University and Cornell University. He lives in New York.

UNTITLED
Felt 10/20, 66x64 in., 1965
No. 293

An abstract design based on flat color areas and jagged outlines is the basis for this banner.

Robert Indiana

Born 1928 in New Castle, Indiana. Indiana, who adopted this name, was one of the originators of Pop. He attended John Herron Art Institute in Indianapolis during 1945–46 and, while in the army, the Munson-Williams-Proctor Institute in Utica during 1947–48. He graduated from the School of the Art Institute of Chicago in 1953. While in Chicago, Indiana worked intermittently for a steel company, a department store and a printing firm. His compositions derive from familiar images—flags, letters, numbers—arranged in designs of flat color. Words such as "love," "eat," "die" have become his trademarks. The artist has lived in New York since 1954.

NEW GLORY
Felt 14/20, 85x53 in., 1963
No. LN335

The banner takes its motif from the American flag.

Nicholas Krushenick

Born 1929 in New York. Krushenick studied at the Art Students League and the Hans Hofmann School. From 1951 to 1957 he designed displays for the Museum of Modern Art and later operated the Brata Gallery with his brother, John. He has taught at the New York School of Visual Arts, at Cooper Union and the University of Wisconsin. He has been artist-in-residence at both Dartmouth and Cornell, also visiting critic at Yale. Krushenick feels that Matisse and Léger have been two important influences on his work which, characterized by bold abstract color areas often defined by thick black lines, is also related to Pop. The artist lives in Ridgefield, Connecticut.

BANNER NO. 2
Felt 3/20, 77x55 in., 1968
No. SI336

Here an unidentified object speeds toward the viewer from a cloud of smoke. Krushenick often uses distorted, disturbing perspectives.

Richard Lindner

Born 1901 in Hamburg, Germany. Lindner studied at the School of Fine and Applied Arts in Nuremberg from 1922 to 1924 and at the Academy of Fine Arts in Munich from 1925 to 1927. He worked as a commercial artist for a publishing firm in Munich, later leaving Nazi Germany for Paris in 1933. After a period of political activity, confinement as an enemy alien and service in both the French and British armies, he moved to the United States in 1941 where he became a citizen in 1948. During his first decade in New York he was a successful illustrator whose work appeared in *Fortune, Vogue, Harper's Bazaar* and *Seventeen*. From 1952 to 1965 the artist taught at Pratt Institute. In his paintings he deals with sadistic characters in a dehumanized urban environment. Images from Lindner's past are omnipresent as are also certain pop motifs. The artist lives in Paris and New York.

BANNER NO. 2
Felt 9/20, 86x46½ in., 1966
No. 337

In an arrangement resembling a weathervane, two favorite motifs of Lindner—an aggressive woman and a lecherous man—join with arrows and a target, also familiar objects in his work. The date of the banner and the artist's initials are incorporated in the design.

George Ortman

Born 1926 in Oakland, California. After attending the California College of Arts and Crafts in Oakland, Ortman studied in Paris at Atelier 17 with Stanley William Hayter and at the Atelier André Lhote. Returning to New York in 1950 he attended the Hans Hofmann School. Ortman has held numerous teaching positions and is currently chairman of the painting department at the Cranbrook Academy of Art. In his paintings and constructions he stresses geometric shapes emphasized by strong color. His work in recent years has used famous Old Master compositions as a frame of reference. Designs for banners are an important part of Ortman's work. In 1966 he completed a series of twelve *Banners of the Cross* for the Christian Theological Seminary in Indianapolis. The artist lives in Bloomfield Hills, Michigan and Castine, Maine.

BANNER NO. 2
Felt 15/20, 73x56 in., 1968
No. 294

The design for *Banner No. 2* was later used by Ortman for a 1971 construction, *The Village*.

Henry Pearson

Born 1917 in Kinston, North Carolina. Pearson attended the University of North Carolina and received his MFA in scenic design from Yale. He later studied at the Art Students League. During ten years in the army he continued working as an artist and even found time to study painting in Japan. One of his army jobs was to interpret topographical maps, the linear designs of which influenced him. He has taught at the Art Students League, the School of the Boston Museum of Fine Arts and at the New School in New York. In 1964 he received a grant to the Tamarind Lithography Workshop in Los Angeles. Pearson's paintings usually consist of wavy striations of color that resemble the patterns of greatly enlarged fingerprints. As one of the fathers of op art, he produces subtly vibrating linear compositions. Pearson lives in New York.

UNTITLED
Felt 7/20, 72x72 in., 1966
No. 290

The topographical maps which Pearson interpreted in the army influenced the design of this banner. Undulating lines suggest hills and valleys seen from above.

Michel Seuphor,
Siren and Triton

Michel Seuphor

Born 1901 in Antwerp, Belgium. Seuphor, who was educated in the classical humanities, at the age of twenty became publisher of *Het Overzicht*, an international review of modern art and poetry which numbered many of the avant-garde among its contributors, including Moholy-Nagy, Tzara, Léger and Prokofieff. In 1922 Seuphor went to Berlin to write for *Der Sturm*, and in 1925 he settled in Paris where he became intimately connected with contemporary art. At that time he organized a group and magazine both called *Cercle et Carré*, in which over eighty painters and sculptors participated. In 1930 he spear-headed the first international exhibition of abstract art in Paris. A deep religious experience caused him to leave the city and live in a mountain village for the next fourteen years during which he wrote poems, essays and novels. In 1948 he returned to Paris, published a history of abstract art and also set up a second exhibition of abstract painting. Seuphor was in New York in 1950–51 but has made his home in Paris ever since where he continues to write books and critical articles and also has made drawings and collages. Tapestries from some of his designs have been woven in Holland and Belgium, showing the abstract style he prefers.

SIREN AND TRITON
Wool, 60x48 in., 1962
No. LA2039

A nonobjective flat-woven tapestry in black, white and gray forms that recall the abstract dislocations of Cubism. This unique piece was woven by Elisabeth de Saedeleer in Brussels.

Lenore Tawney

Born 1921 in Lorain, Ohio. Tawney began her studies at the University of Illinois in 1943 and completed her work at the Illinois Institute of Design in 1947. Planning to become a sculptor, she worked with Archipenko while at school in Chicago but finally turned to weaving and began to work in fiber instead of clay, bronze or marble. The artist studied in Finland with Martta Taipale and later herself became a pioneer craftsman in modern weaving. At times influenced by American Indian art, her weavings are worked out in a full range of natural earth colors, although black is a favorite with her. Playing on the variations between gossamer thin threads and coarse substances, Tawney creates a sense of weight, light, tension and space. In addition to weaving, she makes small box constructions, collages and assemblages, often from found objects. She lives in New York.

THE FOUR-PETALED FLOWER
Linen thread, 84x84 in., 1973
No. NA1887

This woven hanging is a cruciform, each of the arms symbolizing one of the four directions of the compass. In the center, a square of open weaving has for its center another cruciform made by still smaller divisions of threads. The center encompasses light and light gives it form. The effect of the all-black fabric, thinly lanced with brightness, is at once austere and mysterious.

Guillermo Trujillo (for biography see p. 209)

MOLA
Appliquéd fabric, 62x70 in., 1970
No. PN1761

Concentric circles in bold colors are set against other geometric forms. This hanging is made of appliquéd cloth, cut and arranged in a composition influenced by optical art and by the molas of the Cuna Indians from the San Blas Islands of Panama.

Victor Vasarely

Born 1908 in Pécs, Hungary. Vasarely first took up medicine but in 1927 transferred to art which he studied at the Poldini-Volkmann Academy in Budapest. In 1929 he attended the Muhely Academy in Budapest where his teacher was Laszlo Moholy-Nagy. A year later he moved permanently to Paris. Throughout his career he has been concerned with optical theories and has been a prime influence in the development of Op. In conjunction with the 1955 "Movement" exhibition at the Paris Galerie Denise René, Vasarely published his *Yellow Manifesto* dealing with theories of perception and color. He is a proponent of multiple art, believing that emphasis should no longer be centered on unique original paintings and sculpture. Lithographs, serigraphs and other multiples which reproduce the hard-edge precision of his paintings are, he feels, as valid esthetically as unique works. He suspends his abstract forms in an undulating space that produces strong three-dimensional illusions.

NOVAE
Wool 7/50, 99x99 in., 1970
No. FR959

In keeping with his attitude toward multiple art, Vasarely created this abstract tapestry design, allowing the purchaser to choose within a preselected group of colors. The Bank's *Novae* is limited to black and white and was hand-woven in Portugal.

William Walton

Born 1909 in Jacksonville, Illinois. Walton graduated from the School of Journalism at the University of Wisconsin in 1931 and became a staff writer on a succession of magazines and newspapers. In 1949, after spending the war years as a correspondent in Paris, Vienna and Prague, he turned to painting. One college art course and a one-month critique with artist Karl Knaths constituted Walton's entire formal art training. In 1963 President Kennedy appointed him chairman of the United States Commission on Fine Arts, the body which has jurisdiction over art and architecture in all federal buildings. Walton resigned from the post in 1972 but still resides in Washington, D.C. From the beginning, his work has shown a tendency toward abstraction based on familiar objects or landscape, often fragmented by panels of color. Flags and heraldic devices are motifs he often uses.

UNTITLED
Felt 2/20, 71½x60 in., 1968
No. 675

Blue and purple arrows converge to form a star on a red background.

Victor Vasarely, *Novae*

Jack Youngerman

Born 1936 in Louisville, Kentucky. After attending the University of North Carolina and the University of Missouri, Youngerman studied at the Ecole des Beaux-Arts in Paris. He remained in Europe until he settled in New York in 1956. His work shows the influence of both Matisse and Arp. Bold interlocking shapes suggesting flower and leaf forms are often defined by striking color contrasts. In addition to painting and print-making, Youngerman has also done stage design.

ARGOSY
Felt 19/20, 85x60 in., 1965
No. 295

A large black plant form with a brilliant yellow center fills this banner designed by Youngerman in 1963 and executed in felt in 1965.

BANNER NO. 3
Vinyl 6/20, 84x66 in., 1969
No. 822

The shiny material of this banner accentuates Youngerman's explosive style.

Claire Zeisler

Born 1903 in Cincinnati, Ohio. Claire Zeisler, who has lived in Chicago since early in the twenties, became seriously involved with weaving when she was over fifty. Regarding her work as three-dimensional sculptures made from fiber, she relies heavily on the knotting technique known as macramé, a craft practiced in ancient Peru. Her weavings are often conceived on a large scale. As a rule she makes preliminary designs which are frequently carried out in fiber by assistants working under her supervision. Of late she has been creating smaller pieces on her own. She has also become interested in working with leather.

RED FOREST
Red jute in five panels, 98x88x24 in. overall; each panel 17 in. wide, 1969
No. 100

Five large-scale panels of red yarn falling from knotted cores create an environment and give an architectural quality to this work, despite the suppleness of the material.

BLACK WALL HANGING
Black jute, 72x24x9 in., 1969
No. BS598

Claire Zeisler, *Red Forest*

Larry Zox

Born 1936 in Des Moines, Iowa. Zox studied at the University of Oklahoma, Drake University and at the Des Moines Art Center under George Grosz. Since 1958 he has lived in New York. He usually divides his paintings into interrelated geometric shapes often separated by bands of unpainted canvas. His hard-edge color is evenly and smoothly applied with a silk-screen squeegee. The artist first plans his paintings on graph paper and then transfers the designs to canvas. He received a Guggenheim Fellowship in 1967 and has been artist-in-residence at Cornell University and Dartmouth College.

UNTITLED
Felt 2/20, 80½x64 in., 1969
No. LN338

In 1967 Zox painted his so-called *Diamond Drill Series*. The design for one of these canvases, *Fifield*, is here transferred to a banner.

ANCIENT ORIENTAL AND PRIMITIVE ART

This section, divided under three headings, is arranged chronologically according to country of origin.

Coptic Art

Coptic art, the art of Christian Egypt, reached its high point in the fifth and sixth centuries. The culture of Egypt at this time blended Greco-Roman, Byzantine and indigenous Egyptian influences. Art centers were usually located in monasteries which included libraries, churches, living quarters and burial grounds. The population of Egypt during the Coptic period was far from homogeneous, its colonies of Greeks and Romans mingling with native Egyptians. Art of the period fused elements from these cultures and from nearby Byzantium.

FUNERARY STELE
Limestone, 21½x10x5½ in.,
late 4th or early 5th c.
No. 564

Carved stone reliefs such as this were used as grave markers. Because of the stylized nature of Coptic art, it is difficult at times to determine the age and sex of the person represented. However the figure here would appear to be that of a young boy holding a bunch of grapes in one hand and a wreath in the other. These symbols were important in both Greek and Christian iconography. The sculpture was originally painted.

TWO FIGURES HOLDING
WREATHED CROSS
Limestone, 10½x14¾x3¼ in., 5th c.
No. 563

This relief, probably part of the architectural decoration of a monastery or, less likely, of a sarcophagus, shows an intermingling of elements from different cultures. The two figures, presumably angels, derive from classical Roman Victory figures. The wreathed cross and the communion table beneath it are clearly Christian motifs.

HELMET
Bronze, 11⅜x8½x12 in., 6th c. B.C.
No. 766

An Italian variant of a Corinthian helmet comes from southern Italy, once a part of Greece (Magna Graecia). The helmet was originally topped by a plumed crest. Three studs for the crest remain. An ancient green patina covers the bronze.

HEAD OF A WOMAN
Marble, 15½x12½x11½ in., 3rd or 2nd c. B.C.
No. RO2038

In this larger-than-life size female head the sensuous handling of the carving recalls sculpture from Pergamon in Asia Minor. The Bank's head, which was probably part of an architectural figure, shows facial features borrowed from Hellenistic art. At this time the Romans were deeply influenced by the Greeks. Ropy waves of hair, resilient fleshiness, deep-set eyes and slightly parted, full lips are all characteristics of late Greek art.

PORTRAIT BUST OF A MAN
Marble, 14x8¾x10 in., ca. 70 A.D.
No. 980

Roman portrait sculpture, like this unusually well preserved bust of an unknown man, is noted for its emphasis on realism. The Roman religious custom of making wax or terra-cotta death masks as a form of ancestor worship combined with an interest in naturalism inherited from late Greek and Etruscan sculpture was influential. The uncompromising reality of portraits in the Republican style was tempered by idealism in the first century A.D. but with no loss of strength or expressiveness. The noble features of this man's face were probably once embellished with painted details, such as the irises of his eyes and the texture of his eyebrows, but age and wear have removed the pigment.

Rome, *Head of a Woman*

Rome, *Portrait Bust of a Man*

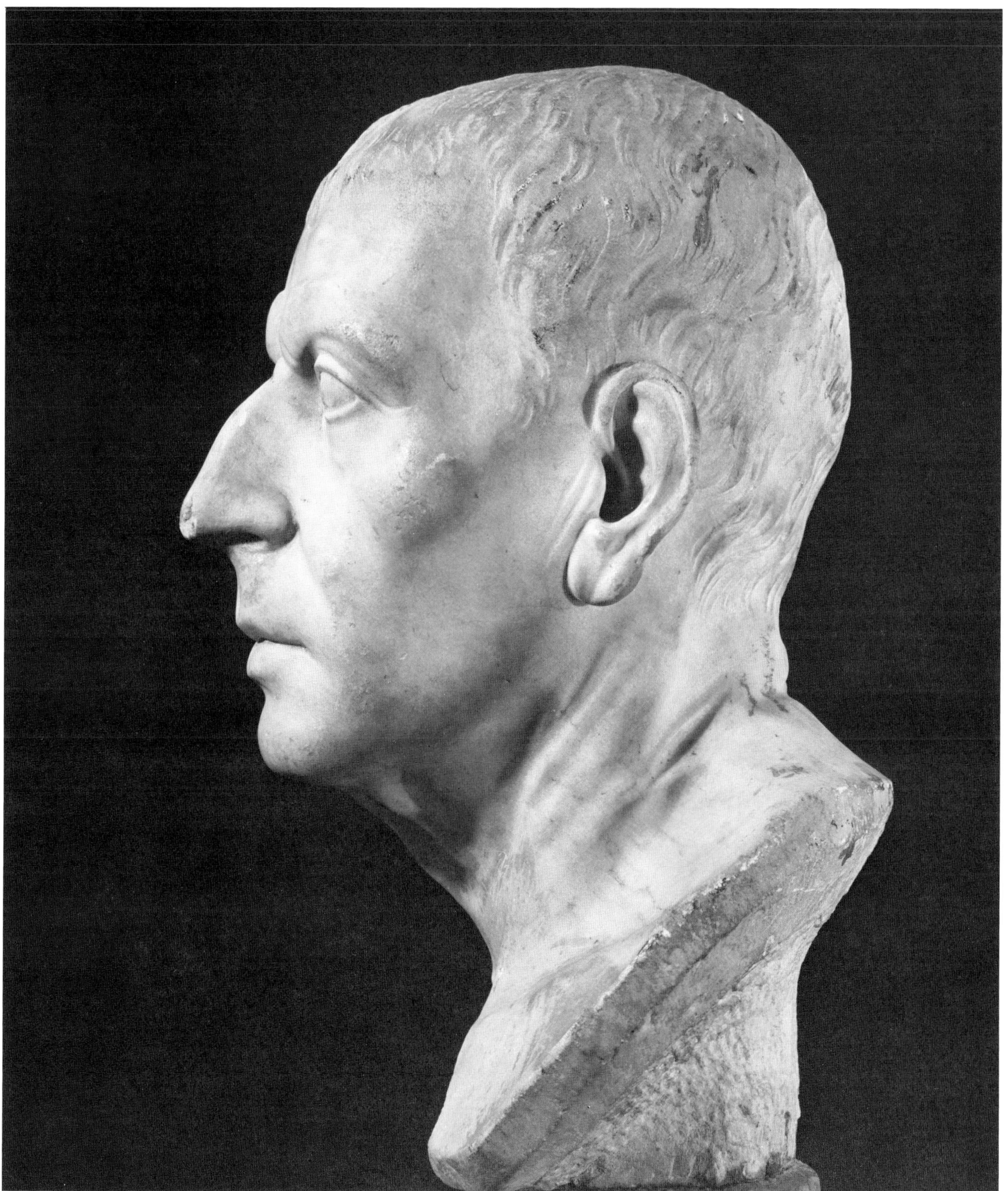

Rome, *Head of a Horse*

Ancient Art / Rome

HEAD OF A HORSE
Marble, 25x10x25 in., 2nd c.
No. 1874

This life-size horses's head was possibly part of a *quadriga* (team of four) drawing the chariot of a triumphant Roman and mounted on a monument or public building. Although the bit in the horse's mouth has been carved in the marble, the remainder of the bridle must have been fashioned from metal in the usual manner for classical sculpture of horses. Flaring nostrils and wind tossed forelock give the animal an appearance of racing forward.

SCULPTURE FRAGMENT
Marble, 11x9⅓x3 in., 3rd c.
No. BE1351

This marble fragment shows part of a warrior's figure carved in low relief with emphasis on linear description rather than on earlier classical interest in plasticity. The sculpture, excavated near Tyre on the coast of Lebanon, probably belonged to a battle scene from the side of a sarcophagus—perhaps of the Sidamara type.

Funerary Portrait Busts from Palmyra

During the early centuries of Christianity, Palmyra in the Roman province of Syria was one of the important Hellenized cities of the Middle East. Here cultures commingled as the oriental schematizations of Palmyran art from the Parthian Empire mixed with idealized Greco-Roman traditions. Funerary sculptures from this area were the endpieces of sarcophagi containing mummified bodies.

FUNERARY BUST OF A MAN
Limestone, 21½x17½x7½ in., ca. 160
No. 390

This bust, which retains the typical classical pose with one hand resting in the sling of the toga, has been orientalized by the Eastern method of reducing facial features to a decorative formula. It is particularly evident in the eyebrows, which seem like the braided filaments of a border design, and also in the schematized folds of the eyelids. An inscription in Aramaic dialect identifies both the deceased and his line of descent, reading: "Ogga Ma'an, Son of Ogga, Alas!"

FUNERARY BUST OF A BOY
Limestone, 21½x15½x11¼ in., 3rd c.
No. 684

Linear abstraction of facial features, hair and clothing indicates the Eastern hallmarks common to funerary sculpture from Palmyra. Although it is somewhat damaged and obscured by restoration, the inscription in Aramaic on the sculpture has been translated: "Woe! Demas (son of) Buthainu (son of) Rushesa."

Palmyra, *Funerary Bust of a Man*

Syria,
Boy Gathering Grapes

BOY GATHERING GRAPES
Mosaic, 45½x33½ in., 5th c.
No. 658

In the early centuries of Christianity, new religious ideals were often expressed through themes borrowed from late antique art. This mosaic fragment depends on a popular pagan motif, the idyll of grape harvesting to symbolize the Christian hope for life in the hereafter. The harvest, representing a change in nature, signifies resurrection, and the grapes contain the juice which even today represents the blood of Christ in the Eucharistic sacrament. In the lower left quadrant are remnants of peacock feathers; the peacock meant eternal life in classical mythology and became an Early Christian motif. In Roman times mosaics were frequently employed as paving, but a decline in the use of human figures and religious themes for floor decorations took place in the late fourth and early fifth centuries. This piece, however, has been identified as a section from the floor of a church located in northern Syria, near Antioch. The same stylization of basket, grapes and peacock feathers appears in another mosaic from the site, now in the collection of the Cleveland Museum of Art. Inscriptions in the church where the mosaics were found give dates for the decoration of the building ranging from 415 to 516 A.D. The relatively coarse stone tesserae of a nearly uniform size and the subdued colors of the mosaic mark it as a provincial work of the first Byzantine period. It has been reset in a mixture of mortar and chalk in its present oval form.

HEAD OF A KING
Marble with traces of polychrome,
11x7x6½ in., ca. 13th c.
No. LN1493

The discovery of this marble sculpture near Izmir, Turkey, and its Gothic appearance suggest that the head was once part of the decoration for a Crusader church of the thirteenth century. Some Byzantine influence may be seen in the ornamentation of the crown. The eyes are recessed for inlay. A rounded contour and sweetness of facial expression make the identification as a male somewhat tenuous. Four similar but larger heads are in the Byzantine Museum, Athens.

Head of a King, found in Turkey

India, *Atlas*

HEAD
Terra-cotta, 4½x4½x2½ in., ca. 3rd or 4th c.
No. 958

This small head is similar to those found in areas where both the later Andhra dynasty and the Gupta style of art flourished. Although worn by time and the elements, the characteristically Indian facial features—elongated oval eyes and pronounced hooked nose—remain strongly in evidence.

ATLAS
Blue-gray schist, 7½x8x3 in., ca. 4th c.
No. 983

In the ancient world the region around modern Peshawar, known as Gandhara, was a crossroad between East and West for several hundred years. This area produced an art style that fused Buddhist spiritualism with classical motifs. The brief reign of Alexander the Great in the fourth century B.C. had already brought Hellenism to India but it was the rise of Buddhism under the Kushan dynasty in the first century B.C. that saw craftsmen emigrating to Gandhara from the eastern part of the Roman Empire. This small stone sculpture of a winged male figure has the Romanized form associated with Gandharan art. It is similar to several examples in the Victoria and Albert Museum, all remnants from architectural friezes.

SHIVA BHAIRAVA
Gray schist, 39x20x8 in., 10th–11th c.
No. 571

In the trinity of Hindu gods, Brahma is the center of the universe, Vishnu is its saviour and Shiva is its destroyer. But Shiva is also the god of regeneration, the source of renewal. Aspects of Hinduism are so varied that each of its gods appears in many—often mutually antagonistic—manifestations. Shiva alone is credited with 1008 roles. Most familiar is his posture as the Conquering Dancer, known best in the Natajara form of south Indian bronzes. He is also the Lord who is Half-Woman and, in that sense, protector and preserver. He can be benign, fierce, ascetic and cosmic. In this stone carving, possibly from a temple niche in Bengal, Shiva appears in his "terrible" incarnation as Bhairava. He stands on a double-lotus pedestal signifying his godliness, in a double *tribhanga* pose which bends the body in three directions as in a dance. Shiva is shown here with four arms, each hand holding an attribute; the shield and sword equate with his destructive powers; the bowl with his role as a holy mendicant; the trident symbolizes his supremacy in the three-fold scheme of the universe. Around his body Shiva wears a garland of heads and skulls, each signifying the sin he committed by destroying one of Brahma's four heads and also representing Brahma's reincarnations in the future. His jewelry consists of serpents on each wrist and ankle and around his chest, ornate arm bands and a necklace which seems to be made of animal teeth. Shiva's hair is traditionally long, matted and piled high on his head, the unshorn locks representing—as they do in the Christian story of Samson—his unrestrained might. The third eye of wisdom appears on his forehead. Clouds, garlands and *apsaras* (celestial nymphs) float above Shiva's head. On the receding planes of the sculpture's base, a pair of female attendants with fly whisks, called *chowry* bearers, stand ready to serve their god; beneath them a male and a female donor kneel in attitudes of supplication beside containers of gifts.

India, *Nandi*

NANDI
Stone, 22x21x10 in., 13th c.
No. 1857

Each Hindu god is supported by his or her own particular "vehicle," manifested in the form of an animal. This seated bull, Nandi, from Benares was probably originally intended for a temple porch dedicated especially to him as Shiva's attribute. Thus Nandi actually represents Shiva's energy on an animal plane. The trappings which adorn Nandi are suited to his high position and the small figures of bull and rider on his flanks are motifs describing the god and his vehicle poised for flight. On Nandi's back, *nagas* (serpents), a *lingam* and *yoni* (abstract representations of male and female reproductive organs) represent the fertility of Lord Shiva.

SADHU
Polychrome wood, 37x12x6 in., 18th c.
No. 1863

This bearded beggar, a religious mendicant, holds a lute and raises his hand in one of the ritual *mudras* (position expressing some action or power) of the gods. Intricate carving forms his clothing, jewelry and a fantastic hair arrangement. The pedestal on which the figure stands and the columnar form of the sculpture suggest that it was originally an architectural bracket. This carving comes from Kerala.

DANCING KRISHNA
Polychrome fabric over wood, 17x6x4 in., 19th c.
No. 1861

Krishna is the "dark" *avatar* (incarnation) of Vishnu and battle hero of the Hindu epic, *The Mahabharata*, but in later legend he is best known for his boyhood escapades among the cowherds who raised him. These simple people were totally charmed by the blue-skinned, beautiful boy. Small statues representing Krishna often show him as a boy dancing with glee because he has successfully stolen a butter ball from his mother's kitchen. This figure from Orissa might represent that incident and, if so, would be known as a *Navanita-Krishna*.

VENUGOPALA (KRISHNA PLAYING THE FLUTE)
Polychrome fabric over wood, 18x10x4 in., 19th c.
No. 1862

Krishna was so enchanting that all the *gopis* (cowherd girls) fell in love with him, but his special love was Radha, for whom he played his flute in amorous joy. Here the flute has been lost, but the body in the *abhanga* pose (the upper portion thrust slightly to one side) has a gay, springy quality which expresses Krishna's mood. The figure comes from Orissa.

DANCING FIGURE
Wood, 16x6x5 in., 19th c.
No. 956

MUSICIAN
Wood, 17x5½x4 in., 19th c.
No. 957

These two folk-art figurines resemble the wooden carvings found in Gujerat in western India. They are probably a pair of bracket figures used in either a religious or domestic setting. The dancer carries a ring of bells and a rattle, while the musician is holding a stringed instrument. Both figures are female.

Temple Car Sculpture

The term *rath*, or temple car, is used to designate processional wooden vehicles which transport religious idols to the temple on special festival days. It also applies to a certain type of temple itself, which as a sanctuary is intended to reproduce the actual celestial chariots of the deities. Konarak is the most famous example of such a temple. As a rule, the carts are intricately carved and become extraordinary works of art themselves.

MALE GUARDIAN FROM A TEMPLE CAR
Polychrome wood, 45x15x5 in., 19th c.
No. 1864

An exaggerated physical form with wildly animated features—fangs, protruding tongue and grotesque elongated fingers—is matched by the exuberant ornamentation of the costume which this guardian figure wears. His frightening appearance is intended to ward off evil spirits. The sculpture comes from Kerala.

FEMALE GUARDIAN FROM A TEMPLE CAR
Polychrome wood, 35x10x4 in., 19th c.
No. 1865

Carved in high relief, this creature from Kerala also protects a specific deity.

YALI BRACKET
Wood, 36x5x10 in., 19th c.
No. 1859

The *yali* is a fantastic animal, part lion, part elephant and part horse, each of which has its own religious significance in Hindu mythology. The shape of this carving suggests that it might have been used as a decorative bracket on a temple car.

FEMALE DRUMMER
Polychrome wood, 45x14x13 in., 19th c.
No. 1871

This figure's posture suggests that it may once have adorned a temple car or building as a bracket ornament.

LAKSHMI
Painted wood, 29½x9x11 in., 19th c.
No. 362

This wooden carving is in the form of Laksmi, Goddess of Prosperity and Beauty, and wife of Vishnu. Her outstretched hands are intended to hold garlands of flowers on holy festival days. This sculpture was used as a household deity.

HEAD OF A BULL
Polychrome wood, 30x9x9 in.,
late 19th or early 20th c.
No. 1860

The religious importance of the bull in India can be traced to the Indus Valley civilization in the third millenium B.C., when it was worshipped as a fertility symbol. In Hindu mythology Shiva's vehicle is the bull (Nandi) and in some villages, bull-headed male figures form a protective ring around a statue of the local deity. This head was probably used in a rural religious ceremony and belongs to the wide-ranging examples of Hindu folk art.

— India, *Male Guardian from a Temple Car*

JAGANNATHA PILGRIM PAINTING
Varnished gouache on fabric, 37 in. diameter, 19th c.
No. 361

In the twelfth-century temple at Puri in the state of Orissa, Krishna, one of Vishnu's *avatars* (incarnations), is worshipped in the form of Jagannath, Lord of the World. Pilgrims have been known to throw themselves beneath the wheels of the Jagannatha temple cars in a frenzy of devotion, thereby providing us with the word "juggernaut," defined as "a massive inexorable force which crushes everything in its path." For many centuries Puri artisans have made religious objects—paintings, boxes, small figures or miniature shrines—which the devout keep in memory of their pilgrimage. Generous use of red color and tiny dots are special signs of the religious importance with which this Puri painting is endowed; more specific are the multitude of scenes relating to Vishnu-Krishna-Jagannath. In the band of arches at the top of the circle are Vishnu's ten *avatars*, in which he has already manifested himself as boar, man-lion, Rama, Buddha, Krishna, etc. and at the end, the horse-man incarnation of the future. The central motif is, of course, the temple itself with the sacred images of Krishna as the black-faced Jagannath enshrined beside his older brother, Balaram, and his sister, Subhadra. Their bodies are mere columns with u-shaped "arms" which are uplifted, the whole outline forming a sacred trident. The rude simplicity of the images is explained by the legend of the carpenter who was ordered to carve a figure of the god from a log found floating in the sea. He became angry when the king interrupted his work and went away without finishing it. Because the carpenter was discovered later to be the god himself, the incomplete holy work was placed in the temple, a simple wood cylinder with enormous painted eyes. On each side of the shrine in the Puri painting, Shiva wearing a *naga* (snake) and Brahma with four heads are shown paying homage, while three priests guard the temple below with the aid of two lions flanking a Jagannath figure. One of the tales relating to Jagannath is shown mid-left center, where Jagannath, dark-skinned and on a white horse, with Balaram, who is pale and riding a dark horse, meet the milkmaid Manika and give her a ring as a symbol of their promise to aid the Raja of Orissa. Opposite and one level lower, two boats carrying statues of Krishna represent the festival of Chandana Jatra, when the images are carried to a small island temple for worship. Each niche is filled with further representations of Jagannath, other Hindu deities and a variety of decorative emblems, all produced in the flowing Orissan manner which remains bright and lively despite the years of repetitious tradition behind it.
For colorplate see page 31.

India, *Pabuji-Ki-Phard*, detail

PABUJI-KI-PHARD
Block-printed and hand-painted fabric,
51x94 in., 19th c.
No. 682

Block-printed and hand-painted fabric,
48x120 in., 19th c.
No. 1858

These cloths are used by itinerant bards in India. Their design follows a traditional, unvarying arrangement that tells the complicated story of Pabu, a pastoral hero of the militant Rathor tribe in the province of Rajasthan. The storyteller spreads his *kavya* (story cloth) on the ground and narrates the tale in song, dance and mime. Neither of the two cloths in the Bank's collection is complete but together they show some two-thirds of the story.

JAMBUDVIPA (TANTRIC COSMOGRAM)
Tempera on canvas, 34x35 in., late 19th c.
No. RO2042

Tantra contains the seeds of both Hindu and Buddhist teaching. Magic, meditation, *mantras* (incantation) and *yantras* (diagrams) play a large part in the Tantric experience. The word *Tantra* means literally "expansion tool" and with its aid the *sadhaka* (religious devotee) is led upwards, through higher and higher levels of religious experience to final cosmic bliss. The cosmogram, a kind of space-time chart for the universe, can be used in *puja* (worship), although it is not exclusively Tantric in origin and is more closely related to Jainism. Like the cosmogram, many themes flowing through Indian art lend themselves to Tantric practice and theory. This painting of the *Jambudvipa* (cosmic structure) from Rajasthan shows an expanding universe in progressive layers of density containing continents, planets, seas and rivers surrounding the mythical world mountain, Meru. Since astrology influences the selection of proper times to perform certain ceremonies, Tantric diagrams are often criss-crossed with elaborate patterns of calculation. In addition, the motif of the world tree shown here on mountain sides at the four corners of the diagram, as well as within it, and the enthroned, self-procreating Goddess repeated eight times in the scheme are meant to infuse this *mandala* (magic cosmic shape) with symbolic psychic energy. Swastikas, ancient Sanskrit emblems of good luck, are joined with each crescent moon and fish swim in the seven magical streams of water.
For colorplate see page 32.

Brass Sculpture

In Bihar, Bengal and Madhya Pradesh metalsmiths practice the craft of casting small sculpture in a special technique of the lost wax process. Wax "wires," one-tenth of an inch thick, are placed next to one another over the modeled figure, thus giving the final hollow metal form a curious ribbed surface which imparts a sense of nervous energy to the pieces.

ELEPHANT AND RIDERS ON WHEELS
Brass, 23½x8x10 in., 20th c.
No. 1923

An elephant on wheels with a driver on its back bears a canopied *houdah* and an occupant. Attendants on foot accompany the group. The sculpture is made in demountable sections and is in the Hindu folk art tradition.

HORSE AND RIDER
Brass, 17x3x10 in., 20th c.
No. 1924

Both of these pieces came from a village in Madhya Pradesh.

GRANARY DOOR
Wood, 34½x22½ in., 19th c.
No. AM2048

The Batak People of the northeastern coast of Sumatra have a history immersed in magic and cult practices. Ritualistic objects like this carving are generally the work of the Datu, or priest-magician, who also makes such important decisions as when the tribe should plant or harvest. This granary door, which guarded precious grain, is decorated with a lizard, symbol of fertility.

MASK OF A BOAR'S HEAD
Polychrome wood, 9x8¼x17 in., 19th c.
No. LN2001

Animal heads with hinged jaws are used as masks during ritualistic celebrations in many Asian countries. A cloth to cover the person wearing the mask was often attached to the wooden head. This mask comes from Bali.

CARVED POST
Wood, 70½x9½x6 in., ca. 1900
No. JA2015

Posts of this type are found among the Kayan and Kenyah People of Kalimantan, the southeast section of Borneo belonging to Indonesia. They stand in front of private dwellings where they guard food offerings to patron gods. The wild animal heads carved on the poles are regarded as messengers of the gods.

ACTOR'S MASK
Polychrome wood, 9x7½x5 in., 20th c.
No. JA2013

One of the most important Javanese dramas is based on legends related to the ancient Indian epic, *The Mahabharata*. A series of adventures encountered by a Javanese prince and his friend, the magical Panji, have been adapted for the popular theatre. A number of creatures appear on stage: giants, demons, clowns and buffoons, identifiable to the audience by their special masks. All of Panji's retainers and friends have narrow eyes, while their opponents have round eyes. This mask is for the actor who portrays Gunung Sari, Prince of Kediri and hero of the drama.

Batik

The typical garment in Java is a sarong, the wraparound skirt worn by both men and women and made of batik. This cloth is dyed with colors taken from trees and plants. In Java, the designs and colors vary considerably depending on the locale. Some patterns were once limited to nobility. The unique method for dying batik consists of tracing the design on a well-washed white cloth in ribbons of hot, liquid wax which is poured from a tiny copper vessel with a long, thin spout. All areas intended to remain white are waxed and then the cloth is put into the dye. The process is repeated with different areas being waxed to retain a lighter color or to receive a different shade of pigment in subsequent dyeing steps. In recent years many artists from the area have begun to create paintings in the batik method.

THREE BATIK CHOPS
Copper, 6½x6½x2 in., 20th c.
No. JA2014

Relatively inexpensive batik work is sometimes produced by dipping metal stamps, such as these, into hot wax and transferring the design to cloth.

GARUDA
Polychrome wood, 46½x26½x24 in., 20th c.
No. SI1789

Garuda is the vehicle of Vishnu, one of the three major Hindu gods. The fantastic half-man, half-bird is associated with the sun and heavens over which Vishnu reigns. In this carving from Bali the bizarre figure is highly stylized, encrusted with ornamentation and stands on a decorative abstraction of clouds. The Garuda is Indonesia's national seal.

SHIELD
Wood, 46x10x2 in., 20th c.
No. JA2012

This shield originates with either the Nias or Batak Peoples of Sumatra. Their shields are used to deflect, rather than stop, spears thrown by the enemy, or sometimes to parry blows of the opponent's knife. The form always has the same fish-shaped contour with horizontal cords of twisted palm frond attached at intervals, plus a central circular protuberance. Some shields have pyrographic decoration while the most elaborate are overlaid with beaten metal sheathing at the apex.

Bali, *Garuda*

Japan, *Buddhist Guardian Figure*

BUDDHIST GUARDIAN FIGURE
Wood with traces of polychrome
42x20x11 in., 11th c. (Heian Period)
No. 1808

The figure may represent Bishamonten, the Buddhist guardian of the North. From the position of the statue's arms, it is possible to imagine that the now-missing hands once held a spear and miniature *stupa* (temple), the attributes of this minor god. In any case, the scowling face, bulging eyes and aggressive stance indicate that this is a protective deity from the Buddhist pantheon. Originally, it was probably stationed beside a small shrine or temple. The characteristic vertical splitting of the heartwood used for the *ichiboku* (single-block) method of carving seen here is often associated with Early Heian sculpture of the ninth century, though this piece suggests a provincial sculptor at work in the late eleventh century. Some of the original polychrome is visible around the head, but on most of the surface it has worn away, revealing the grain of the wood carefully integrated with the figure's contours.
For colorplate see page 30.

ANIMAL HEAD FESTIVAL MASK
Polychrome and lacquered wood
10½x12½x11 in., 17th c.
No. 1811

This mask, part of a costume worn during Japanese village festivals of the harvest in October, belongs to the tradition of ritual dance-drama celebrations. The fierce but comical animal head has a hinged jaw which opens to show rows of teeth and a large tongue.

Japan, *Animal Head Festival Mask*

Niten (Myamoto Musashi)

Born 1584 in Harima, Japan; died 1645 in Higo (Kumamoto), Kyushu, Japan. Niten's lifetime saw the beginning of a military dictatorship in Japan which lasted 300 years. Under this regime, culture played an important role, making it possible for Niten to be both painter and soldier. He became famous for inventing a method of fencing with two swords simultaneously. He also enthusiastically followed the spirit of Zen, expounding the virtues of simplicity and spontaneity in painting. Niten, under his given name, Musashi, served the Hosokawa family on the island of Kyushu as a samurai. Today many of his paintings remain with the descendants of this family.

WILD GEESE AMONG REEDS
attributed to Niten
Ink wash, 68¾x147 in.
ca. 1625 (Tokugawa Period)
No. 1809

This six-fold screen is in monochrome ink as are all Niten's known works. Although the modeling of the geese suggests an interest in naturalism, the more freely brushed-in reeds and eccentric balance of the composition show a decorative elegance associated with Niten. A minimal background implies vast space.

DARUMA (Anonymous carving)
Wood, 12x12x12 in., ca. 1750–75
No. TK1765

Daruma was the first patriarch of Zen Buddhism, and known for his unwavering faith. He is said to have cut off his eyelids in penitence for falling asleep during meditation on the Buddha. This carving is a wooden mold used for making Daruma images. Wet material, usually paper, was wrapped around the mold and pressed into shape, after which it was dried and lacquered.

Niten, *Wild Geese among Reeds*

Tani Bunchō, *Wild Geese*

Ikeno Taiga

Born 1732 in Kyoto, Japan; died 1776 in Kyoto. From the age of seven, Taiga was noted as a calligrapher and later earned a reputation for his painted fans. Most of his life was spent wandering with bohemian friends, usually students of Zen who were poet-painters and, like himself, amateurs in the original sense of the word. Taiga was an important member of the Nanga School, a group that derived its interests from the southern Chinese "literary men's style," also known in Japan as the *Bunjinga*. This philosophical school produced a style opposed to the inflexible realism then in vogue, but still remained close to nature. Taiga often painted with unusual textural effects, using stippling, spontaneous calligraphic line, multiple feathery strokes and heavy contours. His best known work, painted jointly with another *Bunjin* artist, Yosa Buson, illustrated verses by the Chinese Ch'ing poet, Li Li-weng, and was titled "Ten Conveniences and Ten Enjoyments of Rural Life."

BAMBOO
Ink wash, 87x21½ in., 18th c.
(Tokugawa Period)
No. 1810

A hanging scroll of bamboo branches, alternating strong dark silhouettes with pale shadowy shapes, is similar to a work by Taiga in the Cleveland Museum of Art.

Tani Bunchō

Born ca. 1763 in Edo (Tokyo), Japan; died ca. 1840 in Edo. Bunchō is most often described as an eclectic artist whose greatest power lay in the strength of his brush work. Although commanding attention through his adaptation of numerous historical styles, he was most closely associated with the *Bunjinga* or "literary" artists of the early nineteenth century. Several of these men were at first amateurs—scholars who painted as an intellectual hobby—but eventually the style became a professional one. Bunchō was also influenced by Japanese exposure to Western realism in art. He is known to have written several books on art and art history and to have taught painting to the famous artist, Watanabe Kazan.

WILD GEESE
Ink wash, 63½x68 in. ca. 1800
No. 770

This two-panel screen of wild geese flying among reeds demonstrates the immediacy of Bunchō's brushwork. A strong feeling for nature is evident; at the same time the painting is conceived as a two-dimensional pattern. Characters at the left side of the screen identify it as "from the brush of Bunchō," and several collector's seals have also been stamped on this panel.

MAP OF MURAYAMA
Watercolor and ink, 23x29 in., 1837
No. 1845

Characteristic of old Japanese maps, this plan has neither top nor bottom. The actual direction of north is designated as pointing to the lower edge of the picture, contrary to Western practice. The map is read from border to center and, while the roads are shown in plan, the mountains are shown in elevation. Japanese cartographers tried to give more information than is ordinarily found on a Western map, even to including days auspicious for travel or the credit ratings of innkeepers.

Thailand, *Head of Buddha Image*

HEAD OF BUDDHA IMAGE
Sandstone, 10x6x7 in., 17th–18th c.
No. 1814

Siamese religious art as seen in this head reflects the Hinayana form of Buddhism. Originating in the late Ayudhyā style, it has been carved according to a classic Thai formula recalling earlier Gupta influences, but placing greater emphasis on stylized austerity. Characteristic linear details define the lips, eyes, chin and nose. Strict interpretation of the Hinayana scriptures accounts for descriptive elements in the Buddha's face with its "parrot-beak nose" and curls "like stings of scorpions." The *ushnisha*, a protuberance on top of Buddha's head which proclaims his godhood, has been somewhat eroded and, if there was once a finial (simulating a light-reflecting "jewel" or flame), it has been lost.

DANCING FIGURE
Wood, 23x11x5 in., 19th c.
No. 1813

The costume of this figure, carved in relief, is similar to that of a temple dancer and the sculpture may have ornamented a sanctuary. The full, short legs, culminating in long feet with prehensile toes, and the disproportionately long arms and fingers suggest that the figure might have belonged to a frieze representing Hanuman's followers. Hanuman was the learned monkey king, a character from the popular Hindu epic, the *Ramayana*. This sculpture, the work of a Burmese artist, was found in Thailand.

STANDING FIGURE WITH CONCH SHELL
Wood, 49x12x10 in., 18th c.
No. 1812

Art of the late Ayudhyā period became stylized through repetition. This figure, defined in the linear terms associated with the Ayudhyā style, has taken on an architectural form so that its clothing resembles a temple scalloped with multiple gables and its conical ringed hat the roof of a *stupa*. The conch shell is a symbol of the origin of existence found in the footprints of the Hindu god Vishnu.

Thailand, *Carved Panel*

CARVED PANEL
Polychrome wood, 53x94x3½ in.,
late 18th or early 19th c.
No. 1845

This carved panel served as an architectural decoration, possibly above the entrance of a temple from northern Thailand. The design is formed by entwined dragons, floral motifs inlaid with colored glass and oriental strap-work at the sides. The surface is somewhat eroded, probably due to exposure to the elements.

PAIR OF DANCING MEN
Wood, 31¼x10½x3½ in., 19th c.
No. SI2024

A man wearing ceremonial dress is mounted on the shoulders of a second man more simply clothed. They are probably represented in some ritualistic act. The carving is a nineteenth-century example of folk art influenced by a Burmese tradition.

Bamenda-Tikar Group, Republic of Cameroon

HELMET MASK
Wood with kaolin pigment and patination, 19½x12x9½ in., 20th c.
No. 1866

This mask from the Cameroons, intended to cover the entire head, is carved in the round as a slightly larger-than-life size human head wearing a high headdress. Facial features are broadly but naturalistically depicted. Spider motifs, a characteristic theme for divination practices in Cameroon grasslands art, create the openwork pattern of the headdress. A smooth gray-brown patina covers the entire carving.

Bamum People, Republic of Cameroon

NECKLACE
Bronze, 12½ in. diameter,
late 19th or early 20th c.
No. 1089

The Bamum People are known for their bronze casting. Each cow's head in this ceremonial necklace was cast from a different mold in the *cire perdu* (lost wax) process.

Republic of Cameroon

DOG
Wood, 20½x7¼x9⅛ in., 20th c.
No. ML1544

The tribe of origin is unknown. Probably this dog served as a cult fetish. Unlike much African art where interest centers on surface pattern, the emphasis here is on the sculptural quality alone. The imposing solidity of the figure along with its bared teeth is foreboding. The back of the dog has been restored.

Africa, *Necklace*

Africa, *Helmet Mask*

Africa, *Antelope Headdress*

Bambara People, Republic of Mali

ANTELOPE MASK
Wood and metal, 45¾x6x10½ in., 20th c.
No. 250

The antelope, an insignia of the Bambara People, is found often in its art. Chiefly agricultural, the tribe reveres this animal because, according to mythology, it played an important role in the origins of farming. Dances which feature antelope masks take place before ploughing and cultivating. Here the animal's svelte curves have been deliberately tautened and elongated.

CROCODILE DOOR LATCH
Wood, 6x28½x3 in., 20th c.
No. 979

The Bambara People decorate granary doors with figures from tribal lore. The crocodile, its surface covered with carving, served as a latch for one of these doors.

Dogon People, Republic of Mali

KANAGA DANCE MASK
Wood and pigment, 34x18¼x7 in., 20th c.
No. 1105

Authorities differ as to whether the crosspieces of the Kanaga mask represent the spread wings of a bird or the legs of a crocodile. The mask is used in expiatory and therapeutic rites. Often, hundreds of tribesmen wear these masks at the same time.

SIRIGE DANCE MASK
Wood and pigment, 72x8¼x6 in., 20th c.
No. 1106

The Sirige mask is an exaggerated representation of either the tallest house in the village or a serpent. Worn for sacrifices and funerals, the mask is usually cut from one piece of wood and can reach a height of fifteen feet. This mask was originally taller, but a section is missing from the center of the shaft.

Kurumba People,
Republic of the Upper Volta

ANTELOPE HEADDRESS
Wood, leather and pigment, 52x8x34 in., 20th c.
No. 659

Like the Bambara People, the Kurumba artists also exaggerated and elongated their carvings of antelopes. Here, in an elaborate dance headdress, the neck and head of the animal have been lengthened. The object is made of carved painted wood with leather appliquéd to the back of the neck to make it more flexible for the wearer. Long strips of raffia were threaded through the holes at the base of the neck so that the dancer's body was almost completely covered. The headdress was used in funerary rites. Before 1940 this type of headdress was smaller, usually about two feet in height, but during the last twenty-five years the Kurumba have made it considerably larger.

Senufo People,
Republic of The Ivory Coast

PAINTED TEXTILES

The repetition of animal or human figures painted in black on a white woven background provides a decorative pattern. These textiles from the Korhogo region, the artistic center of the Senufo, are modern folk art made in the twentieth century for export. Most of the twelve hangings in the Bank's collection measure approximately three by four feet. Many of them are in overseas' offices.

Zulu People, Union of South Africa

BOWL
Wood, 8½x27 in. circumference,
19th or 20th c.
No. 978

A Zulu craftsman has decorated this carved wooden bowl on two sides with a pattern of raised knobs.

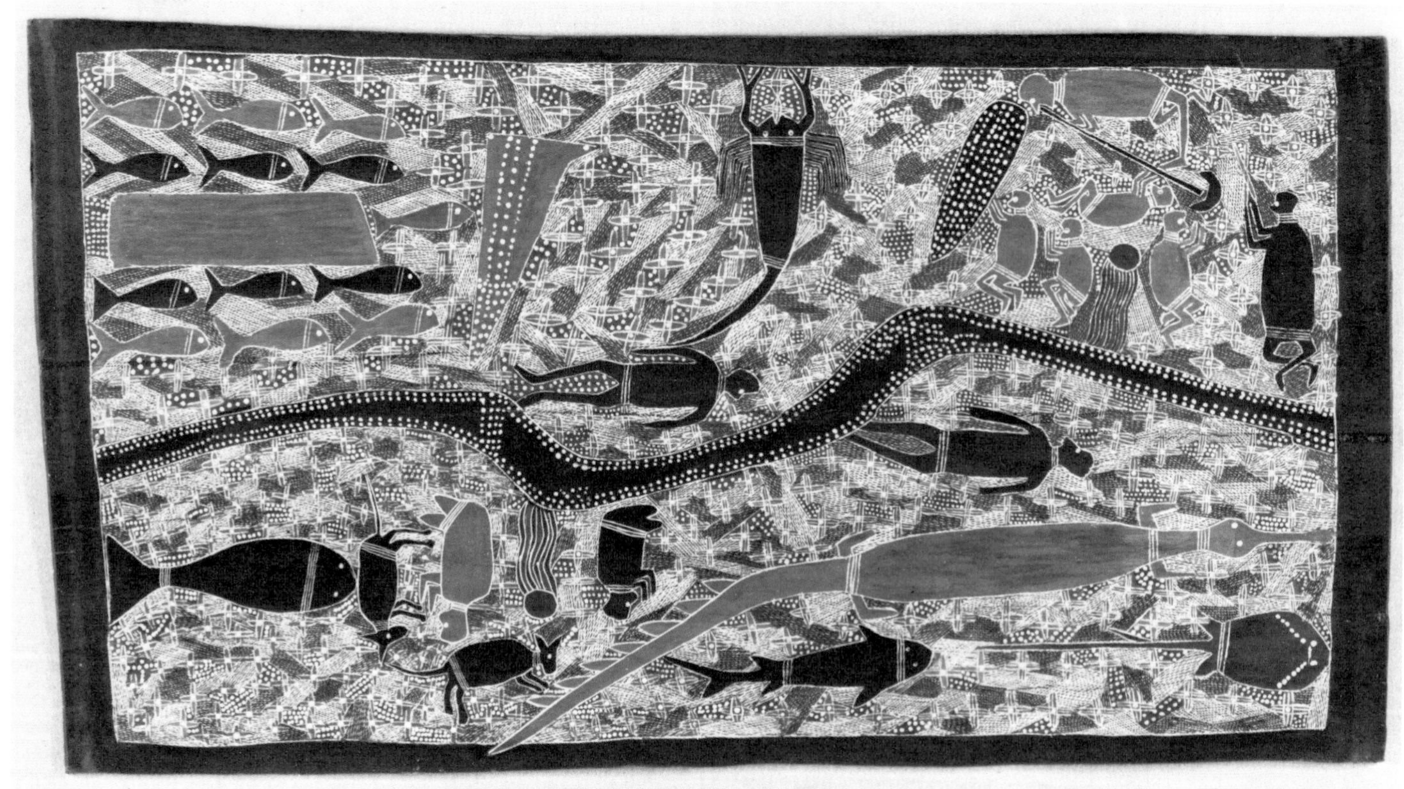

Mawalan

Dates of birth and death unknown. An aborigine of the Reratjingu clan from the Yirrkala Region of Northeast Arnhem Land on the north coast of Australia, Mawalan was a twentieth-century master painter, now deceased. Like other aboriginal artists, he painted on bark from the eucalyptus tree, using a brush made of human hair, feather or chewed twigs. The colors on his stone palette were restricted to white, black, yellow and red earth pigments. Each bark painter learns his craft from an older member of the tribe in a strict and ritualistic tradition. Subject matter is generally limited to tribal myths depicted as sequential events.

BARK PAINTING OF A MADAYIN
(Sacred Myth)
Earth pigments on eucalyptus bark, 23x41 in., 20th c.
No. 1107

In a style characteristic of the Yirrkala Region, where Mawalan worked, this painting is completely filled with fine cross-hatching, broken and solid lines and an overall application of color. The elegantly drawn patterns are probably the exclusive property of the painter's own clan, the Reratjingu. It is thought that this bark tells the sacred story of Djanggawul, a creator ancestor, and his two sisters who wandered across Arnhem Land where they named many animals, created trees and waterholes and gave birth to the ancestors of various clans in the territory.

PRE-COLUMBIAN FEMALE HEAD
Terra-cotta, 11x7¾x7 in., ca. 500 B.C.
No. 955

This head was excavated in the Mixtequilla region of Oaxaca. Probably once part of a complete figure, it resembles in style smaller clay statues of the pre-Classic period found in abundance at grave sites throughout the Valley of Mexico. The technique of modeling and of adding buttons and filets of clay for facial features and decoration is similar to the "pretty lady" figurines found at Tlatilco in Vera Cruz. These clay sculptures of women were nude but decorated with necklaces, ear plugs and elaborate coiffures similar to those seen here.

Mexico, *Mayan Head*

Costa Rica, *Metate*

MAYAN HEAD
Stucco, 13x10x8 in., ca. 400–900
No. 954

This head shows the heavy-lidded eyes and high cheek bones characteristic of the Maya. It still has traces of red and green pigment on its stucco surface. The fragment was found at a ceremonial site in the border area of southern Campeche and northern Peten. Probably one of several sculptures decorating a temple, the head may have been that of a priest or member of royalty as suggested by the remaining details of its ornate headdress.

METATE
Stone, 16x25x20 in., ca. 1000–1250
No. PN1655

Among the oldest artifacts to survive from Pre-Columbian times are *metates*, the stones upon which corn and cacao beans are still ground today. A smaller stone called the *metla-pilli* (*metate's* son) is rubbed over the grain or beans until they have reached the desired consistency. This tripod grinding table is called a "flying-panel *metate*" because of the free-form carving beneath the table. Birds—probably pelicans—and trophy heads surround the legs while a human form with a jaguar mask supports the center. Probably this particular table was employed in ceremonial corn-grinding rites.

MOLAS

Molas are made and worn by Cuna Indian women who live on the San Blas Islands off the coast of Panama. Conceived in layers that are appliquéd and cut in order to allow the material underneath to show through, molas form both the front and back of women's blouses. They are usually composed of brightly colored designs related to birds, fish, animals, Indian lore and occasionally to such modern experiences as the airplane. The numerous molas in the Bank's collection are all approximately one-and-a-half feet square and have been made during the twentieth century.

New Guinea, *Gable Mask*

New Guinea, *Gope*, 19th c.

GABLE MASK
Basketry, clay and pigment, 46x24x16 in., early 20th c.
No. 249

Imposing and aggressive, this large mask from the middle Sepik River region was mounted on the gable of a ceremonial hut. Representing a mythical or recently deceased ancestor, it served as a guardian. The huge staring eyes, emphasized by concentric bands of color which spread over the entire face, show the love of surface decoration which is a hallmark of art in New Guinea.

CEREMONIAL BOARD
Polychrome wood, 73x12½x1½ in., 19th c.
No. PR1629

The Sawos people, who occupy the grasslands north of the middle region of the Sepik River, are known for their intricately carved ceremonial boards. The purpose of the boards is not entirely clear, though possibly they commemorate novices who died during the course of an initiation rite. The Bank's delicately crafted openwork board contains facial characterizations probably representing the deceased novice.

GOPE
Carved wood and pigment, 56½x14x1½ in., 19th c.
No. 551

Carved wood and pigment, 53½x14½x1¾ in., 20th c.
No. 552

The *gope*, a type of ancestral board, is believed to have protective powers and is used by the Kerewa People of the Papuan Gulf region to ward off sickness. These boards also function in initiation rites. The ancestors, whose spirits are represented, were invoked to give assistance in headhunting (a custom no longer practiced). The Bank's nineteenth-century *gope* is stone cut. Both bear traces of paint. Though each board has a different design, interlocking curvilinear forms are common to both. The face of the ancestor, not immediately evident, appears in the upper area.

NAVAJO "EYE DAZZLER" BLANKET
Wool, 52x76¼ in., ca. 1890
No. 1934

During the nineteenth century the Navajo Indians of the American Southwest developed a spectacular group of woven blanket patterns. The first were simple brown and white rectangles but, later, red thread unraveled from a Spanish cloth called *bayeta* was woven into the material. Eventually indigo, black, orange and green found their way into the stripes, diamonds, zigzags and triangles that made up the designs. The style and quality of these blankets began to decline in the early twentieth century after the introduction of commercial yarns, and as increasing demand encouraged large-scale production. This blanket, in red and black with white and yellow zigzags, belongs to a style called the "eye dazzler" because of the flashing motion implied.

Eskimo Art

The themes of Eskimo art are drawn invariably from two sources—religious symbolism and daily life. Eskimos work in materials indigenous to their surroundings, in whalebone, soapstone, ivory and hides. In recent years the highly simplified soapstone carvings and expressive lithographs of Canadian Eskimos show the influence of both their primitive heritage and modern culture.

ORANGE HEAD by ANIRNIK
Crayon, 18½x24½ in., 1971
No. SI1656

WALRUS by KABUBUWAKOTA
Soapstone, 10x16x6 in., 1969
No. 683

A naturalistic form so simplified as to seem almost abstract was made by a native of Cape Dorset, Canada.

SPIRIT NO. 16 by KAROO ASHEVAK
Whalebone, 11½x20x5 in., 1972
No. 1909

Carved from fossilized whalebone, this creature, which represents a "spirit," has a removable mittened hand protruding from one long arm; the other arm is etched on the surface of the bone. Karoo Ashevak was born in 1941 at Spence Bay, Northwest Territory, Canada where he still lives.

THREE DRAWINGS by OONARK

Three drawings by an Eskimo woman from Canada, all revealingly naive representations of familiar sights from her world. In one, three Eskimos and some birds appear to be floating in space while another depicts a fanciful bird and the third shows a child running.

Crayon, 14x17 in., ca. 1970
No. 1911

Ink, 14x17 in., ca. 1970
No. 1912

Crayon on red paper, 11½x18 in., ca. 1970
No. LN 2084

UNTITLED DRAWING by PISTOLAK
Crayon, 11½x18 in., ca. 1970
No. NW1731

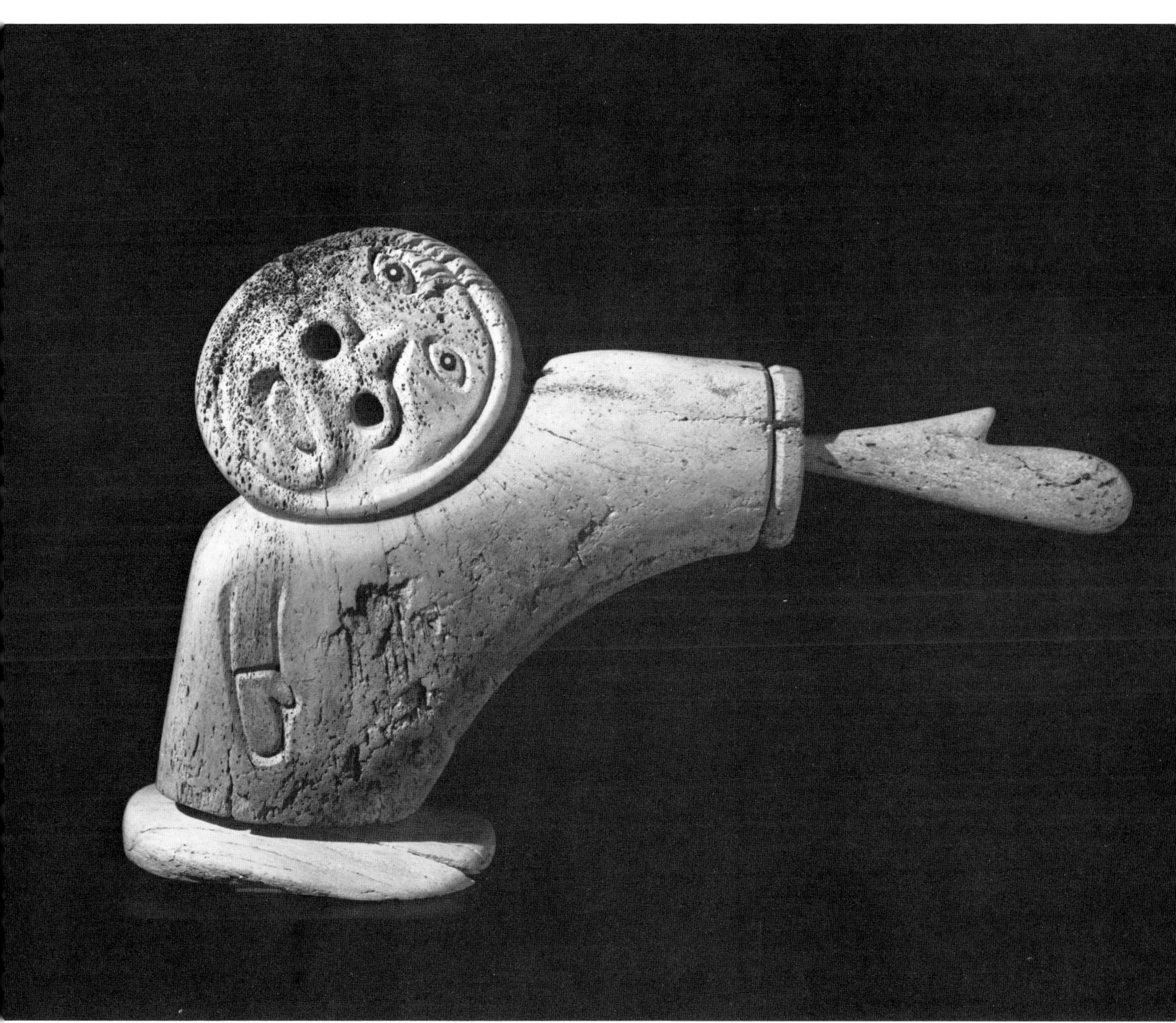

Karoo Ashevak, *Spirit No. 16*

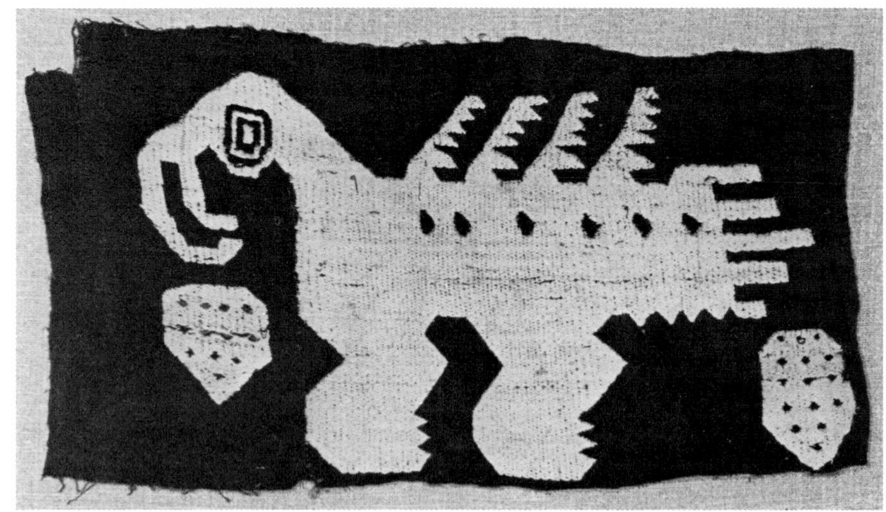

Peru, *Pre-Columbian Textile*

PRE-COLUMBIAN TEXTILE
Wool, 12x22 in., ca. 1000–1500
No. LA2036

A stylized mythical bird is woven in white fibers against a brown background. The vertical sides have selvedges but the horizontal sides were once joined to another piece of material. The work, characteristic of fabric designs associated with people of the Chimu Culture, is unusual for its excellent state of preservation.

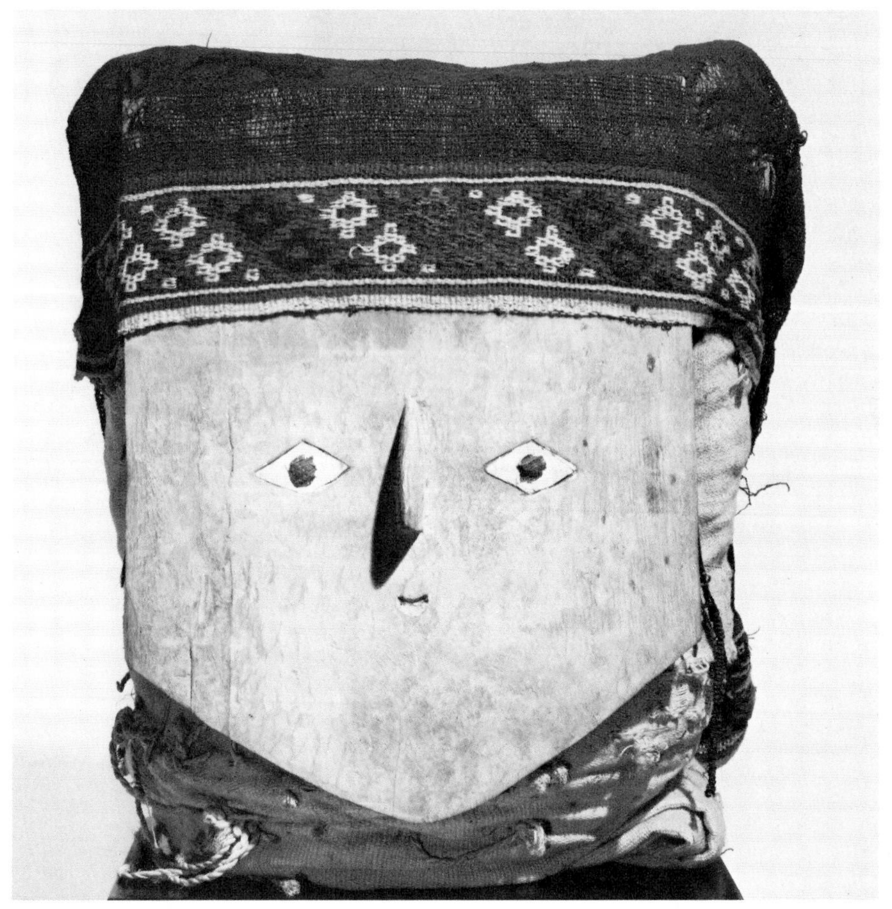

Peru, *Wooden Mummy Mask with Bundle*

WOODEN MUMMY MASK WITH BUNDLE
Painted wood and textiles 16x11x8 in.
ca. 1300–1450
No. 1820

This type of wooden mask, dating from pre-Inca history, is found in Peruvian burial mounds. The dead, propped in fetal position, were swathed in wrappings of wool, cotton wadding and linen together with their favorite possessions. The bundle was then topped with a smaller bundle representing a head. In early examples, faces were suggested by dying the cloth of the head bundle, adding a piece of wood for the nose and either painted or seashell eyes. Later, masks like this one were attached to the front of the head, some even embellished with hair. The Bank's mask, unusual because it still has its original bundle, wears a woven headband over brown gauze suggesting hair. It is painted pink, has eyes with pupils made of clay daubs and a protruding wooden nose. The artifact comes from the central coast of Peru, from the Chancay Culture.